# Forestry Budgets and Accounts

Geoff Bright
*School of Agricultural and Forest Sciences*
*University of Wales Bangor*
*UK*

*with special appendices on the USA and New Zealand/Australia*
*by*

Norman Ellwood
*Department of Forest Resources*
*Oregon State University*
*USA*

*and*

Ted Bilek
*New Zealand School of Forestry*
*University of New Zealand*
*New Zealand*

CABI *Publishing*

**CABI *Publishing* is a division of CAB *International***

CABI Publishing
CAB International
Wallingford
Oxon OX10 8DE
UK

CABI Publishing
10 E 40th Street
Suite 3203
New York, NY 10016
USA

Tel: +44 (0)1491 832111
Fax: +44 (0)1491 833508
Email: cabi@cabi.org
Web site: http://www.cabi.org

Tel: +1 212 481 7018
Fax: +1 212 686 7993
Email: cabi-nao@cabi.org

A catalogue record for this book is available from the British Library, London, UK.

**Library of Congress Cataloging-in-Publication Data**

Bright, Geoff
    Forestry budgets and accounts/Geoff Bright ; with special appendices on USA and
New Zealand/Australia by Norman Ellwood and Ted Bilek
      p.cm.
    Includes bibliographical references (p. ).
    ISBN 0-85199-328-1 (alk. paper)
      1. Forests and forestry--Accounting.  I. Title
SD393 .B74 2001
634.9'068'1--dc21                              2001035116

ISBN 0 85199 328 1

Printed and bound in the UK by Cromwell Press, Trowbridge, from copy supplied by the author.

# Contents

# Preface

The period from conception to the birth of a book can be rather like that of an elephant. In this case it was even longer, for the idea took shape gradually from the time, some years ago, when I was asked to teach budgeting and accounting to the forestry students in Bangor. Not being a forester, this was for me something of an adventure since I was learning about forestry from the students as well as exploring the application of accounting and economics principles within this field. As there did not seem to be a textbook with sufficient coverage and with the students needing a reference source, here was an ideal opportunity to fill a gap.

Even when the decision to write had been made, however, and the project accepted by CABI, more research was required on my part and other demands on my time have meant that the baby really has had a long and traumatic gestation! But finally it has reached the light of day - it is for you, the reader, to decide whether the birth pains have been worthwhile.

Nobody but the author can be criticised for the book's contents, but credit is due to the many people who have provided valuable advice, encouragement and practical help along the way. Successive groups of forestry and other land-use studies undergraduate and MSc students have unknowingly helped to clarify technical issues and provided the spark for further investigation.

Colleagues in Bangor have also provided advice, help, ideas and friendship. John Winterbourne produced the forest model for the example. Graham Mayhead has read and commented on much of the content and Colin Price and Sam Foster have advised on specific chapters. Colin, Tom Jenkins, Shakil Akhter and Jeremy Williams have also provided photographs. Marc Wenmaekers and Gareth Wyn Davies have taken on some of the burden of getting the text into camera ready copy format.

In the industry, comments on some sections and more general advice have come from Robert Rickman of Forestry Investment Management, Roy Lorraine-Smith, Paul Snaith of the Forestry Commission, John Lelliott of the Crown Estate and Bill Fone of Saffery Champness.

Tim Hardwick at the publishers, CABI, has been very patient and given the right amount of cajoling!

The authors of the two special appendices on the US and New Zealand/Australia context, Norman Elwood and Ted Bilek have worked their way through a number of drafts of almost the whole book, giving selflessly of their time and expecting no reward.

Finally, as always, my wife, Rita, has given me support, encouragement and comfort and has made considerable sacrifices to ensure its completion. My children too - Amy, Chloe, Joshua (who drew the cartoons) and Daniel, have encouraged me and waited patiently when their dad was preoccupied.

To all of these, and any others who I might have overlooked, a heartfelt thank-you.

Above all, I am thankful to my God who has continued to meet all my needs according to his glorious riches in Christ Jesus (Philippians 4:19).

# Chapter 1

# Introduction

Many of those studying or working in forestry have to deal, to a greater or lesser extent, with financial planning, control and evaluation. Few would regard it, however, as an area of forestry that is easy to understand or particularly interesting. Yet, a more intimate knowledge via a well-guided exploration of the subject can change that impression: this book aims to do just that. The objective of this exploration is to equip the student and practitioner with an understanding of, and an ability to employ the tools of financial management in a forestry context.

Financial management is just one facet of the general activity of management with which foresters are concerned: other areas of management involve silviculture and technical aspects, marketing and staffing. Yet all are inter-related: what happens to the financial fortunes of the business stems from the decisions that are taken and implemented on the ground with regard to how the land and trees are managed, how the staff are recruited and dealt with, what machines are purchased and used, how, where and in what form the produce is sold and how the business is financed. Thus the following general definition should cover all aspects of **management**:

> "Management is the dynamic activity of making and carrying out decisions concerning the use of the scarce resources of land, labour and capital and the ensuing product, in the light of the objectives of the business."

It is worth spending a few moments looking more carefully at this definition. The key term to consider is the word 'objectives': all that we do in our management role, indeed, all that we do in our lives, should be weighed against our individual or organisational objectives. We need to ask ourselves the questions, "Where are we going? ", "What are we trying to achieve? ", "What are we aiming for?" and then to fit our actions within those objectives. Thus we can 'manage by objectives'. We may have only one or a few overall, or **strategic** objectives, for the whole business, but we are likely also to have **tactical** objectives relating to the daily routine activities. Nevertheless, objectives at all levels and over all time periods need to be in tune with those strategic objectives set for the whole organisation. Such objectives might include maximisation of profit, dividend payments to shareholders, business growth, sales revenue or environmental benefits, or minimisation of risk. The activities of the organisation should therefore take place in the light of its objectives.

The management activities are not once-and-for-all, but ongoing and changing in the light of experience, hence the term 'dynamic'. And those activities involve not only evaluating the situation and then taking decisions, but also putting them into practice; that is, carrying them out.

But what are those decisions about? The definition uses the phrase 'scarce resources... and product'. The economist considers only four categories of resources[1] in the production process, namely: land, by which is meant land and all the God-given natural resources allied to that; labour, the supply of effort, skill and knowledge embodied in workers; capital, anything produced by people and itself used in production (seeds, chemicals, machinery, roads, drains and even the growing stock of trees); and the entrepreneur, the owner-manager of the business. The entrepreneur, which in larger business may be a number of people, decides how to combine those resources and what to produce with them, with decisions ranging from the strategic down to the tactical level. Furthermore, these decisions will be taken at different levels: the major, strategic decisions will be taken at the organisational level - the level of the estate, forest, plantation, company or farm; whereas others may take place closer to the ground and further down the management structure - the level of the compartment, **cost centre**[2], work gang or contractor.

As we saw above, management decision making is a dynamic process: Fig. 1.1 illustrates this process diagramatically. At the centre are the objectives, with what is going on around them focused on them. Decisions follow a circular pattern: the manager evaluates past performance and future expectations, makes plans, then decides upon a course of action which is then implemented. Such planning will take place every year or perhaps six months. Less frequently, however, depending on asset lifetimes, forest structure and market and investment opportunities, longer-term plans will be made. Performance is then checked or monitored and if it deviates from expectations further action may need to be taken to bring it back under control. Periodically, the manager will stand back and, having collected performance data, will evaluate that

---

[1] Bannock *et al.* (1978) give clear definitions of the four 'factors of production'.

[2] In order to be able to plan for, record and evaluate the performance of sections of the business we split it into production units or **cost centres.**

performance and plan for the next period. All this takes place within the 'environment', which is not just the natural environment in which the organisation is situated, but also the socio-cultural, legal, policy, economic and infrastructural environment which surrounds it and within which it must operate. This 'environment' provides limits or constraints and even threats to the organisation, but also opportunities that can be used to its advantage.

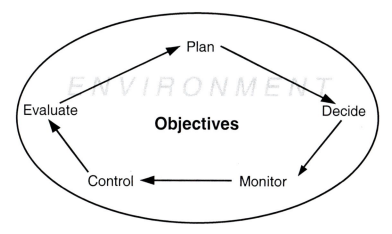

**Fig. 1.1** The management process.

At certain stages in this management cycle the decision-maker will be looking forward (planning ahead), and at others he will be looking back (monitoring and evaluating performance). From the financial point of view this 'looking forward' activity is known as **budgeting**, and 'looking back' is known as **accounting**. In this book we are concerned with equipping the reader with an understanding of and ability to employ the tools or methods of budgeting and accounting.

As objectives are so important, budgeting and accounting must be able to measure the extent to which predicted and actual performance meets those objectives. Whatever our objectives might be, there are three inter-connected aspects of financial performance which need to be measured, commonly referred to as:

**PROFIT**         **CASH**         **CAPITAL**

although these terms are, strictly speaking, misnomers. More correctly, we should use the terms:

PROFITABILITY      LIQUIDITY      STABILITY

Let us consider each of these in turn:

PROFIT or **profitability**: we need to know whether it was, or is expected to be, financially worthwhile doing business over the period. Someone might say, "making profits is not one of our organisation's objectives", but unless there is a limitless supply of money to fund the organisation, a series of losses year after year will eventually mean that the other objectives can no longer be pursued. Therefore, most organisations will have to aim to make at least some profit and consequently this needs to be planned for and monitored. Profit is measured as the surplus or difference between all of the financial benefits and financial costs (not just cash) relating to the business or organisation.

CASH or **liquidity**: for the business to remain in existence in the short term enough cash must be available to meet the day to day requirements - bills must be paid if the business is to be solvent. The business is rather like a machine - if it is to continue turning it must have lubrication - the wheels must be oiled. And like the machine's need for oil, the business needs cash.

In a sense, having cash is a waste of money: it is not tied up in money-making form, such as trees, but it is needed, nevertheless. Otherwise we could go out of business simply because all our money was tied up in other things, leaving us with insufficient money available to pay our bills.

CAPITAL or **stability**: In the longer term we need to know whether the business is growing, shrinking or remaining the same size. More importantly to the owners of the business, is their share or **net worth**[3] changing? Again, a falling net worth cannot be allowed to proceed unabated, otherwise the owners will eventually find that their wealth has diminished to zero! But surely, if the business makes profits then net worth will grow? Only if profits are retained or 'ploughed back' into the business. If too much money and resources are withdrawn from the business for the owner's personal use or to pay taxes, and these exceed the amount of profit and any other injections into the business, net worth will decline.

Profitability, liquidity and financial stability are linked, and we will see this more clearly in subsequent chapters, but they are not the same and need to be separately assessed. This may seem obvious to you, but people do sometimes confuse them and you should therefore be aware of the danger.

Most of this book is taken up with how we construct a financial picture of the profit, cash and capital aspects of the business, from both budgeting and accounting perspectives. In order to give the reader a clear understanding the picture is built up in a series of steps. At each step the 'theory' will be explained in as straightforward a way as possible, followed by a worked case study example to illustrate procedure in practice. At some points the theoretical aspects can become quite complicated or lead onto more complex issues: on these occasions, so as to avoid confusing the reader who does not want to be bothered with the

---

[3] The owner's share of the business, calculated by subtracting the value of all that is owed from the value of all that is owned. A more formal definition comes later.

academic arguments, appendices are provided for those who do want to know more.

The structure of the book is intended to follow the chronological process within the management cycle: we break into the cycle at the planning, or 'looking ahead', stage and so spend the next seven chapters dealing with budgeting and issues related to it, namely valuations and depreciation. In order to be able to check whether the actual results concur with those predicted by the budget we will have to have in place a recording system: this is therefore the subject of Chapter 9. From the records we can 'look back' at performance by constructing a set of accounts then evaluating the results contained in them. Hence Chapters 10 and 11 deal with accounts construction and accounts appraisal respectively. This takes us back round to the planning phase of the cycle.

Nevertheless, there remain some other important topics which will not have been dealt with. During the budgeting process explained in the early chapters we assume, for the sake of simplicity, that the plan has been determined. However, it may be that certain longer-term options need consideration, options such as purchasing another tract of forest or investing in the construction of a road, bridge or car park. How such investments might be appraised is therefore the subject of Chapter 12.

As part of the budgeting process consideration will have to be given to the source of the money to meet the finance needs of the business over the period of the plan. As with periodic longer-term investments, more careful assessment of how the business is to be financed over the longer term needs to be carried out every so often. Consequently, this aspect is given special attention in Chapter 13.

Chapter 14 deals with taxation. Because taxation is a complex area needing to be dealt with by experts (the author is not one), and because tax regimes differ between countries and within any particular country the tax system tends to undergo rapid and frequent change, any discussion of specifics would quickly become out of date. Nevertheless, it is both important and useful to deal with general issues surrounding taxation of forestry and the implications for accounting. It is, therefore, a general approach that is taken here.

Given the IT revolution that has taken place over the past two decades, no book on financial management would be complete without discussion of the part played by computers. Although reference is made to computer software, particularly spreadsheets, throughout the book, the penultimate chapter allows a more thorough discussion to take place on the subject of computers and the programs run on them.

Finally, almost, there are a few concluding remarks. However, this does not spell the final words of the text. Two special appendices have been added at the end to help those who are working and/or interested in forestry accounting in the USA, Canada, Australia and New Zealand. And at the end of the book you will find a table showing discount factors for those who might have problems in calculating them for themselves, and a glossary of the key terms used in the book.

To complete this introduction there are four final points. One, in the text, when a new key word or phrase is introduced, you will see it in **bold**. There will usually be a definition at that point, and you will also find a definition in the glossary of terms at the end of the book. Two, the terms 'he' and 'his' have tended to be used, but except where a person has been named, these words could be substituted by she and her. Three, spreadsheets to support the worked case study and some of the more complex tables can be downloaded from the web site: www.safs.bangor.ac.uk/fba. Four, this book is concerned with the financial information to support the management process. Consequently, we will be looking at the presentation of that information in a way that will best help management, not in a way that will impress the shareholders, or minimise the tax bill. So please do not expect the approach to be otherwise or criticise the methods because they do not fit those other expectations.

We are now ready to get down to business. Although the book is structured to allow you to work through from beginning to end, your experience and interest may lead you to take a different approach, perhaps skimming over some parts, and spending more time on others, perhaps not all at once but when time or need arises. Whichever route you take, the aim of the book will have been achieved if it improves your understanding of forestry budgets and accounts.

# Chapter 2

# Budgeting - Step 1 - The Plan

We saw in Chapter 1 that the part of the management cycle involved with planning ahead is known as **budgeting**. Budgeting can be defined as:

> "A detailed quantitative statement of a ... plan, or a change in a ... plan, and the forecast of its financial result." (Barnard and Nix, 1979, p. 314)

and can be carried out for the business or estate as a whole or the forest as an individual enterprise. For the forest enterprise the budget is sometimes referred to as the **management scheme** which is set out in the form of a **working plan** (Hart, 1991) or woodland management plan (Mayhead, 1990)[1].

Although we dealt earlier with the need to budget as part of the management cycle, it is useful at this point to list the specific reasons for undertaking budgeting. These are to:

- forecast financial performance
- compare options
- estimate cash requirements
- identify and quantify potential financial problems before they occur
- enable monitoring and control
- support loan and grant applications.

These requirements, except the final one, are for the management of the business by ourselves or our colleagues; they are not to convince some other party of our case, or to persuade someone to give us more money or to tax us

---

[1] Although these latter may also be used to refer to the physical outline plan (the first budgeting step) along with more technical information than is covered here.

less. Consequently, it is only ourselves who we deceive if we are not realistic and honest in the figures which we use. On the other hand, we do not have to follow the bank or tax authorities' conventions on valuations and allowances, but it is still wise to follow accounting conventions in order to give our calculations comparability and credibility.

What happens if nothing is likely to change over the next year? Surely last years' plan will do? Even if nothing new is envisaged for the year ahead, change is almost certain to occur: trees will grow, different operations in different compartments will be required, and external forces will have an effect on prices. Therefore, even if not radically altered, a new plan is necessary.

The budgeting process involves a series of steps in order to facilitate accurate estimation and to arrive at forecasts of profit, cash and capital performance. The steps are as follows:

1.    Physical outline plan
2.    Profit budget based on cost centres
3.    Cash flow budget
4.    Budgeted trading and profit and loss statement
5.    Budgeted balance sheet.

Each of these steps will now be considered in detail.

## Physical Outline Plan

Planning ahead over a one-, two- or even five-year period does not necessarily involve the manager in a lot of choice: the resources available and the form of the product may largely have been determined when the longer term investments were made - when the trees were planted, the machines purchased or the sawmill built. Nevertheless, there are likely to be options available even within the short-medium term planning horizon - for instance, what operations to carry out when, when to harvest timber and where to market the produce. In order to plan carefully, it may be helpful to list the following:

**objectives** - what are we trying to achieve? What are our key and subsidiary strategic objectives?

**resources/assets** - what land is available, what have we got growing at present, what labour (numbers and skills) and machinery (types and numbers), and what finance have we available?

**liabilities and constraints** - what do we owe others and what are the limitations on our activities in the form of weather, resources, legal requirements, etc.? What are we able to do, what must we do, what are we unable to do?

It is useful for later calculations to list the value of everything owned by the business (assets) and everything owed by the business (liabilities) at the start of the period. How we value these items will be explained in later chapters.

From these considerations we can put together a **plan of operations** (Hart, 1991). We need to break the business, estate or organisation into sections; this will be particularly useful for cost allocation later. Remember that the divisions are for the benefit of you, your employer, your staff and anyone else who might use the information generated. Therefore, the categories upon which you decide should be those which are most useful to you. Aspects to consider are:

- what are the natural divisions?
- will the extra benefit of detailed division of the business in terms of identification of where strengths and weaknesses of the business lie, outweigh the extra costs of recording involved?

To break the **business**[2] into sections, first of all identify **enterprises**: those areas of the organisation which are involved in producing distinctly different products. It may be that forestry is the only enterprise; on the other hand, an estate might have farming interests, fishing, tourist facilities, forestry and business: each one of these would constitute a separate enterprise within the estate.

**Fig. 2.1** Compartments and sub-compartments will constitute cost centres. Clear - felled and mature stands of sitka spruce in the Forest of Ae, Scotland (photo: Colin Price).

---

[2] The 'business' is the organisation for which a separate set of accounts is provided and with the overall financial performance of which we are concerned.

Next, each enterprise is broken into separate production units or **cost centres**. In forestry these might be compartments and sub-compartments within forest blocks, tracts of agricultural land, a nursery, a sawmill and even a visitor centre, although the last four might usefully be put into enterprise categories of their own. Figure 2.2 shows how a business might be structured and Table 2.1 shows how this structure might be organised into enterprises and cost centres.

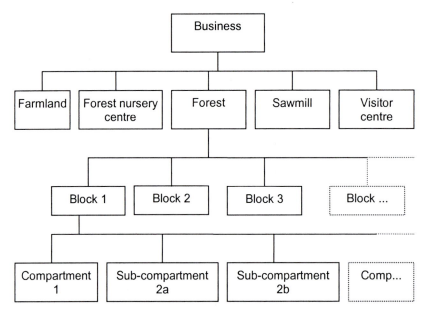

**Fig. 2.2**  Example diagram of business enterprises and cost centres.

Note, then, that where the enterprise is small and not complex, it can also constitute a cost centre. A large and multi-structured forest, on the other hand, may be comprised of blocks, compartments and sub-compartments. Cost centres may then consist of blocks, compartments and sub-compartments.

**Table 2.1**  Example list of business enterprises and cost centres.

| enterprise | | cost centre | |
|---|---|---|---|
| number | title | number | title |
| 1 | Farmland | 1.1 | Farmland |
| 2 | Forest Nursery | 2.1 | Forest Nursery |
| 3 | Forest | 3.1 | Compartment 1 |
| | | 3.2 | Compartment 2a |
| | | 3.3 | Compartment 2b |
| | | 3... | Compartment... |
| 4 | Sawmill | 4.1 | Sawmill |
| 5 | Visitor Centre | 5.1 | Visitor Centre |

Once the enterprise and cost centre structure has been established we can then go on to outline the operations planned to take place over the period as well as the volumes of production.

For longer term planning a period of 10, 20, 50 years or even longer, depending on the crop and the country, is needed in order to cover the lifetime of planned rotations. Price (1989) deals with the appraisal over such periods, although we will also look at the appraisal of medium- and long-term investments in Chapter 12. However, such planning, precisely because of the long life of the investments concerned, only needs to be undertaken every so often. The planning horizon for the regular budgeting process is much shorter (5 or 10 years are common), supported by a less detailed outline for 20 years.

At this point, rather than having one firm plan, we may have a number of different options in mind. This could include options about enterprises and cost centres (invest in a sawmill, what to plant) or about operations (whether to fertilise, what to harvest). We must now appraise and compare these, both in terms of their viability (which is the most profitable?), and their feasibility or practicability (which will work best?). If we wish to assess the financial viability and feasibility of certain options we may wish to run through the whole budgeting procedure which follows, or at least the first three steps; this is where computer spreadsheets prove to be extremely useful - once the budget template has been set up as a spreadsheet it is fairly straightforward to run alternative plans. Otherwise we might discard most of the options after initial appraisal at this first stage. We will not go into how these decisions are made at this point - other texts deal admirably with the technical (Hart, 1991, for instance) and economic issues (Price, 1989), and the appraisal of investments is dealt with in Chapter 12. Suffice it to say, when deciding which option to pursue, we need to compare the pros and cons (financial and otherwise) and decide on that option which, on balance, most closely meets the objectives of the business.

Once we have decided on a specific plan or course of action we can put together a more detailed plan of operations and the **organisation plan**, which shows how the former is to be put into effect. Thus, the resources required can be allocated and the operations scheduled (Hart, 1991).

Because of increased uncertainty about forecasts further into the future and because of the need for more detail over the immediate future to allow closer budgetary control, it is probably best to make the first year's plan the more detailed, with the following years' only as detailed as is felt necessary. Once in place, the five-year plan can be extended annually by a further year, with the new first year detail being filled in each time.

Finally, as part of the planning exercise, and before construction of the plan of operations, the manager will wish to produce a **production forecast**. This will enable more informed decisions to be made with regard to planning operations to handle the volumes of timber predicted and budgeting revenues as well as costs. A 20-year forecast of volumes and areas of thinnings and clear fell probably gives a sufficiently long-term view. How the figures are arrived at will not be discussed here as it is a complex topic more appropriately dealt with in a specialist mensuration text.

## Example

Throughout the book we are going to illustrate the 'theory' material with a case study. At each stage, after discussing the procedure and the rationale behind it, we will move across to the example to show how that procedure is used in practice.

This example has also been set up as a spreadsheet file. So if you have access to a computer you may wish, as you are working through the book, to follow the example on the spreadsheet which is available from the web site, www.safs.bangor.ac.uk/fba. You can then see how the different steps are linked together by viewing the formulae in the relevant cells. Details of how you can obtain the spreadsheet are given in the appendix to Chapter 12.

So let me introduce to you, Mr Douglas Hornbeam who is manager of the Menzies Estate in Caledonia. The estate (which constitutes 'the business') is comprised of 350 hectares of forestry, along with a 3 hectare forest nursery supplying the estate as well as selling to other forest businesses.

Douglas sits down to plan the next five years' operations and to produce a budget. First he sets down the objectives, resources and constraints:

**Fig. 2.3** Douglas and his assistant.

**Objective**:

Maximise annual dividend payments to shareholders, whilst at the same time maintaining, or enhancing the net capital value of the business, subject to short-term solvency and environmental sensitivity.

**Assets/Resources**:

Douglas firstly maps out the 353 ha of the estate's land and forest resources: this map (not to scale) is presented as Fig. 2.4. He also tabulates the information: Table 2.2 provides the details.

**Table 2.2**  Land and forest resources.

| name | description | area (ha) | year planted | spacing (m) | yield class |
|------|-------------|-----------|--------------|-------------|-------------|
| Nursery | tree nursery | 3 | - | - | - |
| Cpt. 1 | Knots pine (*Pinus notbadicus*) | 35 | 1991 | 2 x 2m | 16 |
| Cpt. 2 | *ditto* | 40 | 1996 | *ditto* | *ditto* |
| Cpt. 3 | *ditto* | 40 | clear cut end 2001, to be restocked 2002 | *ditto* | *ditto* |
| Cpt. 4 | *ditto* | 20 | 1959 | *ditto* | *ditto* |
| Cpt. 5 | *ditto* | 35 | 1961 | *ditto* | *ditto* |
| Cpt. 6 | *ditto* | 35 | 1968 | *ditto* | *ditto* |
| Cpt. 7 | *ditto* | 30 | 1956 | *ditto* | *ditto* |
| Cpt. 8 | *ditto* | 45 | 1978 | *ditto* | *ditto* |
| Cpt. 9 | *ditto* | 30 | 1976 | *ditto* | *ditto* |
| Cpt. 10 | *ditto* | 40 | 1970 | *ditto* | *ditto* |

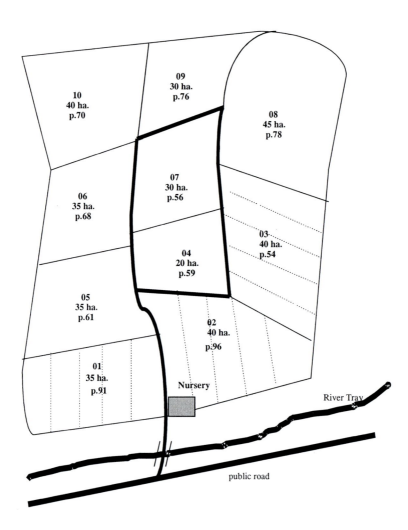

**Fig. 2.4** General plan of the Menzies Estate (not to scale).

The trees and land are not, however, the only resources at Douglas' disposal; he lists other key resources as:

*Labour*: forest manager (Douglas - half-time, contracted from forest management company), forest worker (part-time, shared between forest and nursery), part-time secretary, with casual labour and contractors available.

*Machinery*: 1 four-wheel - drive vehicle, 1 tractor, 1 trailer, tools and equipment.

*Office*: furniture and equipment.

*Buildings*: plant, general store and workshop, office.

*Roading*: well maintained, appropriate for all lorries, with direct access over the River Tray onto the public road.

There are also other resources including cash and stocks of inputs. In Table 2.3 Douglas has listed all of the items of value (assets) owned by the business and has tried to estimate their current value. We will see how some of these values have been arrived at later, but Douglas is likely to have these figures already available as he will have had to make the calculations for the previous year's accounts.

**Table 2.3**  List of opening assets @ 31/12/01.

| Assets | value (£) |
|---|---|
| cash in hand | 50 |
| trade debtors[3] - timber sold, but not yet paid for. | 95,058 |
| fertilisers and pesticides in store | 80 |
| other materials | 100 |
| production equipment | 800 |
| office equipment | 1,500 |
| vehicles, etc. | 9,500 |
| furniture | 560 |
| storage building | 7,680 |
| office building | 25,600 |
| plants in nursery | 49,021 |
| growing crop & land | 3,111,684 |
| **Total** | **3,301,633** |

So the estate manager has resources valued at just over £3.3 million. Against these, however, must be weighed the amounts owed by the business and the constraints facing it.

---

[3] Money owed to the business by other individuals or organisations.

**Liabilities and constraints**

Just as Mr Hornbeam listed the assets or amounts *owned* by the business and their values, so he can list the amounts *owed* by the business - the **liabilities** as accountants call them. These are set out in Table 2.4 below.

**Table 2.4** List of opening liabilities @ 31/12/01.

| Liabilities | value (£) |
|---|---|
| trade creditors[4] - one quarter's telephone bill | 114 |
| bank overdraft | 35,000 |
| medium term loan | 16,508 |
| total | 51,622 |

Apart from this money owed by the business there are also internal limitations (weaknesses) and external conditions (threats) which may hinder the manager in achieving his objectives. Douglas considers these constraints to be:

- limited windthrow risks
- disease and pests in nursery and forest
- vulnerability to a decline in the price of timber
- limited management time
- doubts about reliability of forest worker
- bridge strengthening may be required.

He now divides the estate into enterprises and cost centres as shown in Fig. 2.5.

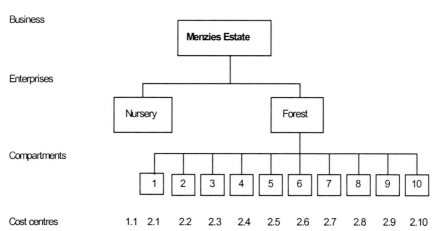

**Fig. 2.5** Enterprises and cost centres for the Menzies Estate.

---

[4] Money owed by the business to other individuals or organisations.

There are two enterprises, the nursery and the forest, the latter presently split into ten compartments. There are, therefore, eleven cost centres, comprising the nursery enterprise and the ten compartments of the forest enterprise.

At this stage a forest manager might be considering one course of action or several options. In this case, we assume that Douglas has already made some of the major decisions concerning options. Thus he has decided that thinning and clear cuts would be sold as standing sales. Therefore, we will not be considering alternative plans at this stage. Nevertheless, it would be wise for Douglas to periodically reassess his options. For options that affect the whole business, this might involve running through the first two, or even three, complete budgeting steps. For options which only affect part of the business and which might have short or long term effects, there are alternative ways of appraising their suitability - some of the techniques for such appraisal will be dealt with later in Chapter 12.

Douglas now proceeds to draw up a plan of operations for the next five years: this is shown in Table 2.5. More detail is given for the first year in terms of timings and resources required: this information is set out in Table 2.6.

Finally, Douglas wishes to make a production forecast for the next 20 years. Some of the information for the first five years is shown in Table 2.7.

Douglas has thus completed the first, planning, step and is now ready to proceed with the second step of the budget.

**Table 2.5** Plan of operations for Menzies Estate.

| ENTERPRISE /cost centre | 2002 operations: | 2003 | 2004 | 2005 | 2006 |
|---|---|---|---|---|---|
| NURSERY 1.1 | produce seedlings & transplants | ditto | ditto | ditto | ditto |
| FOREST | | | | | |
| cpt. 1  2.1 | | | | | |
| cpt. 2  2.2 | | | | | |
| cpt. 3  2.3 | restocking | weeding | weeding | | |
| cpt. 4  2.4 | | | | | measure, arrange sales, clear fell |
| cpt. 5  2.5 | | | | | |
| cpt. 6  2.6 | | | | marking, arrange sales, thinning | |
| cpt. 7  2.7 | | marking, arrange sales, thinning | | | |
| cpt. 8  2.8 | | | | marking, etc. | |
| cpt. 9  2.9 | | marking, etc. | | | |
| cpt. 10  2.10 | marking, arrange sales, thinning | | | | |
| OVERHEAD ACTIVITIES | roads, buildings, machinery & equipment maintenance staffing, budgeting and accounting activities; purchase 4WD vehicle. | ditto ditto | ditto purchase office equipment | ditto ditto | ditto ditto |

**Table 2.6** Detailed plan of operations and operation schedule for year 1 (2002).

| quarter | 1 | 2 | 3 | 4 | resources required |
|---|---|---|---|---|---|
| ENTERPRISE /cost centre | operations: | | | | |
| NURSERY | ground preparation plant sales (40%) transfer plants to forest | planting & transplanting fertilise & spray plant sales (10%) | plant sales (10%) spray | plant sales (40%) | forest worker, casual labour, tractor, trailer, tools & equipment, store, seeds, fertilisers, sprays, fuel, containers |
| FOREST cpt. 3 | fencing pre-plant weeding scarify plant seedlings | | | | forest worker, tractor, trailer, tools & equipment, sprays, fuel, transplants |
| cpt. 10 | | | Marking arrange sales | thinning | forest worker, vehicle, equipment, fuel |
| OVERHEAD ACTIVITIES | roads, buildings, machinery & equipment maintenance; purchase, sales, staffing, budgeting and accounting activities; purchase 4WD vehicle and sell old one | *ditto* | *ditto* | *ditto* | office, etc., secretary, misc. office and maintenance inputs |

**Table 2.7**  Thinning and clear fell volumes.

| time | cpt. | operation | age | area | average tree size | volume | total vol. |
|------|------|-----------|-----|------|-------------------|--------|------------|
| yrs | | | yrs | ha | $m^3$ | $m^3/ha$ | $m^3$ |
| 2002 | 10 | thinning | 32 | 40 | 0.275 | 56.0 | 2240 |
| 2003 | 7 | thinning | 37 | 30 | 0.446 | 56.0 | 1680 |
| | 9 | thinning | 27 | 30 | 0.141 | 56.0 | 1680 |
| 2004 | | - | | | | | |
| 2005 | 6 | thinning | 37 | 35 | 0.446 | 56.0 | 1960 |
| | 8 | thinning | 27 | 45 | 0.141 | 56.0 | 2520 |
| 2006 | 4 | clear cut | 47 | 20 | 0.839 | 345.5 | 2915 |
| . . . . | . . | . . . . | . . | . . | . . . . | . . | . . . . |

# Chapter 3

# Budgeting - Step 2 - Profit Budget Based on Cost Centres

The objective of the second step is to calculate an overall profit estimate for the business, and along the way to estimate the output, cost and profit for each cost centre and enterprise within the business. The reasons why we should wish to forecast this information are:

1.  to avoid errors by building up the profit estimate in a logical way from first principles. This is rather like considering each brick in the building that we are constructing
2.  to enable us to check output, operational cost and profit performance for each element of the business
3.  to estimate overall profit
4.  to help in taking the subsequent budgeting steps.

Some forest managers reading this may be saying to themselves, "budgeting for profit might be appropriate in other industries, but not in forestry. In fact, it is a waste of time." It is, therefore, worth taking a minute or two to consider the arguments which might be put forward to support this point of view and to weigh up their validity. To do this, let us continue the conversation between the forest manager (**F**) and the author (**A**):

**F** "Look, budgeting is about forecasting the performance of business in the future and controlling its direction. In forestry, cash flows can also be forecast and later compared to actual performance and cash flows can be manipulated by the manager in the short to medium term in order to control the business. Profit, however, is a different matter. You see, in forestry, one of the key elements contributing to profit is the change in the value of the growing stock of trees. Now, there does not seem much point in forecasting this change every year, since many forest managers will only be assessing the actual value every three, five or more years and so there will not be an annual 'actual' figure which can be compared with the forecast one. Furthermore, predicting the value is extremely difficult because of price changes and natural hazards which are so hard to predict. And as far as control is concerned, the growing stock is not really amenable to short-term manipulation and the hazards and price changes mentioned above are largely outside the manager's control.

"Therefore, my advice would be, forecast cash flow and use cash for short-term control of the business, but don't bother with profit, or capital either."

**A** "You are quite right, cash is the major aspect of the business which can be forecast and compared to actual outcomes and is subject to control in the short to medium term, so it is important to pay particular attention to it - we are coming to that in Chapter 6. Nevertheless, we do also need to plan for profit and capital as well as cash. Why is this? Even though there are difficulties in forecasting for profit, and especially for changes in the value of the growing stock, it is important that we have an idea of where the business is going in terms of profitability in the short to medium term - after all, it is unlikely that the owners of the business would be very impressed if we were to tell them that we didn't know what profit their investment could be expected to make over the next year or so. And when it comes to comparing the forecast against the actual outcome in a year's time, although we may not have a proper valuation at that time, the earlier forecast will provide a basis upon which to make a more accurate assessment in the light of experience during the year."

**F** "But how can we forecast when there are so many unknowns like price changes and natural hazards?"

**A** "Better an informed forecast than no forecast at all. Does the captain of an oil tanker, heading in a straight line across a wide stretch of ocean, not forecast where the tanker might be in 24 hours' time because it is impossible to know how the winds might change and whether there might be icebergs which will require avoiding action? At least, we then have a best estimate which can be amended in the light of future events."

**F** "Okay. But what about my criticism concerning short-term control?"

**A** "It is true that cash is the element most amenable to short-term adjustments, and it is therefore cash which will receive closest attention from the manager between one planning point and the next. However, periodically, when we are planning ahead for the next one year or so, it is important that we consider the implications for profit, cash and capital. For if we pay attention to manipulation of cash only, we may find that there are unforeseen implications for profit and capital. In fact, actions which have a positive impact on cash flows will often have a negative impact on other elements and actions which have a negative impact on cash flows will have a positive impact on other elements, although the effect might take some time to be felt. For instance, if we decide to harvest in the coming year, the cash flow is likely to be boosted considerably during the period, but, of course, the value of that stand will be reduced. Or if we decide to carry out certain operations, such as pruning or fertilising, on a number of compartments, or to upgrade the roading in the forest, then this will have a negative impact on cash flows, but will improve future volumes in the first case, and reduce the cost of future operations in the second. So, by all means control in the short term via the cash flow, but do plan for profit, cash and capital."

Having discussed the validity of budgeting for profit, we can now return to the practicalities of carrying out this second step, which we have termed the 'profit budget based on cost centres'. The procedure is, using the enterprises and cost centres identified in Step 1, to estimate the outputs and costs for each of these elements, then to calculate profits by cost centre, enterprise and business; Fig. 3.1 illustrates how the results might be tabulated. For calculation and comparison purposes figures should be presented, not only as totals for cost centres, enterprises and business, but also per unit. For instance, this may be per hectare, per cubic metre, per plant or per hour of labour input. Don't worry about the headings down the left-hand side; they will be explained as we come to them.

## Output

Output will include major products such as: thinnings and harvested timber according to the various categories in which it is sold, sawn timber, poles and posts and possibly subsidiary produce like firewood and firewood gleaning licences, bark, and other forest produce. Production grants should also be included as well as fees and rents from sporting rights, agricultural land, car parks and leisure facilities, allocated to the appropriate cost centre. The prices used in the calculations should be forecasts of those expected to pertain at the time of sales, which may be higher or lower than those at present.

Output does not only consist, however, of the value of what is expected to be sold and the value of grants to be received over the period under consideration, but also transfers, valuation changes and benefits in kind. Output can thus be classified as follows:

**Sales**: the value of all produce sold, both major and subsidiary items.

**Grants and subsidies**: government or quasi-government organisations may provide grants for planting, maintenance and harvesting and in agriculture, production subsidies may be claimed.

**Transfers**: sometimes there are transfers between cost centres - the nursery provides plants for compartments, compartments provide timber for the sawmill, and so on. Although enumeration of the values of these transfers will not affect the overall profit of the business, they will affect that of the cost centres. Therefore, if we wish to assess cost-centre profitability with reasonable accuracy, we must include the value of transfers as output from the producing cost centre and the same amounts as costs for the consuming cost centre.

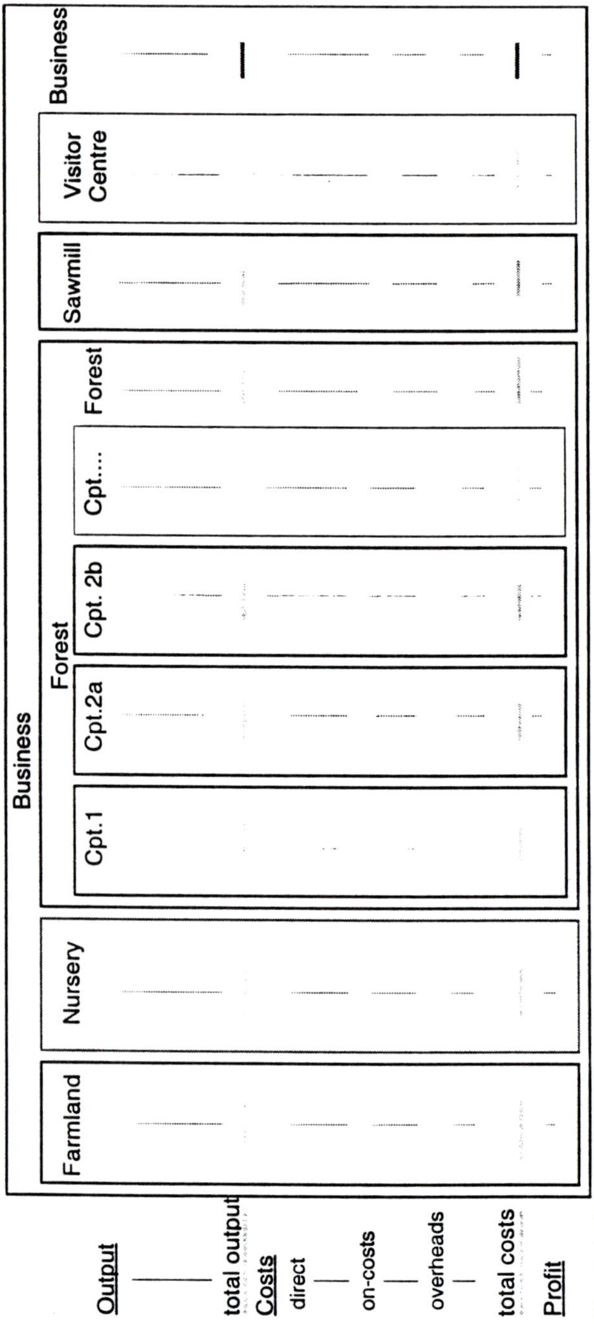

**Fig. 3.1** Profit budget based on cost centres.

Furthermore, for the same reason, it is most important that the price used is a realistic market price. If transfers were omitted or prices were too low, for instance, then the producing cost centre would appear to generate less output than it actually did and the consuming enterprise to incur lower costs, giving a false picture of cost-centre profitability.

**Valuation changes**: for production cycles overlapping several years, as is the case with forestry, the produce may not be sold in a particular year. Instead, at the end of the year, the produce is still growing or in store. Yet, if only what was sold were to be included in output, we would again get a false picture. What has happened in such an instance is that production may have taken place, but the value of the produce is embodied in the forest. In order to take account of this we need to estimate the increased value of the timber between the start and close of the period. So the compartment must be valued at those two points in time, or in the case of a budget, the value of the closing stock needs to be estimated. This 'valuation change' tends to be extremely important in forestry because of the extremely long production cycle. However, it is perhaps the most difficult and confusing aspect of budgeting and accounts and is therefore deserving of a chapter to itself - we will come back to valuation in Chapter 4. You will see from Fig. 3.2 that a separate table for forecasting valuation changes is required; the results are fed from here into the output sections of the compartment budgets.

**Benefits in kind**: in some businesses, especially those which are privately owned, the owner may take some of the produce for his or her private use, and also provide employees with an allocation. Such items are termed 'benefits in kind', 'perquisites' or 'perks', but they are still part of production and should therefore be valued as such. They are also, however, a form of payment, in lieu of wages or salaries and therefore are really also a cost, and should therefore be included as a cost as well. In that case, the output and cost effects will cancel out and not affect profit. So why bother, you might think. If the amounts are not significant they can be ignored, otherwise when assessing performance we may find that output and costs both appear to be low if these are excluded from our calculations.

Benefits in kind taken without permission by employees or outsiders have a different name: embezzlement or theft! This might appear to be hardly worth mentioning, but in some instances it can be a heavy drain on profitability[1].

---

[1] Shukla (1996), for instance, found illicit felling in India to be a major problem, although it can be deemed by some to be a useful means of transferring incomes to the poor if they are the beneficiaries!

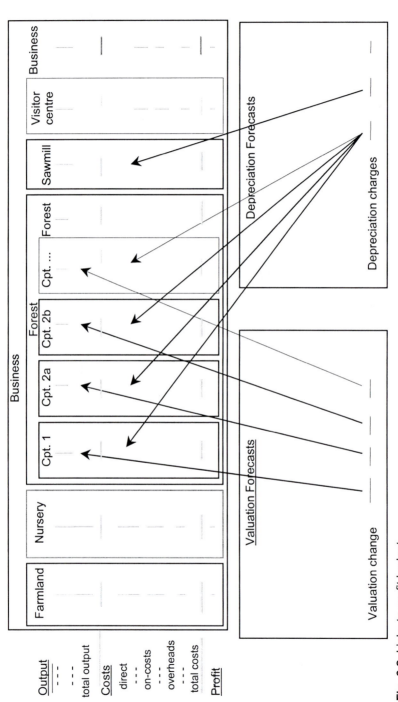

**Fig. 3.2** Links to profit budget

In summary, then, under the output heading of the cost-centre budget you should include the value of everything that is expected to be produced, along with production grants over the coming year or years. Although production may be sold immediately, kept in store, transferred within the business, or consumed as a benefit in kind, it should all be included under the heading 'output'. However, because changes in the growing stock and the land have to be calculated separately, you may wish to keep this value separate in the figures. Remember too, that 'actual' or 'current' prices should be used, that is, expressed in terms of the price level expected to prevail when the transaction occurs.

## Costs

You might expect that this section would be fairly straightforward; after all, to arrive at an estimate of profit all we need is a figure for total costs which we then subtract from output. If we were only concerned with an overall picture of the business, then that would be the case, but if we are concerned with a deeper understanding of the business, then we have to give more careful thought to costs. If we wish to be able to consider performance of enterprises and cost centres rather than only that of the organisation as a whole, then we must allocate costs to the appropriate sections of the business. Some costs, such as plants and chemicals, are readily divided between enterprises, but others, like supervision and office expenses, are not. So why go to the effort of allocating, which after all is likely to be somewhat arbitrary and will involve extra effort in recording and calculation? In farm management, for instance, the convention of only allocating certain costs was adopted many years ago. The response to this is that **full** or **absorption, costing** is necessary for:

- gauging the contribution of enterprises and cost centres to total costs and profit;
- some methods of compartment valuation; and
- fixing of prices or calculation of acceptable prices.

It is therefore recommended that all costs are allocated. However, the more detailed our budgeting and accounting, the more detailed must be our recording, and all of this costs time and money. Therefore, make sure your use of such figures justifies the effort involved.

Accuracy is also important. Although, the allocation of some costs might be criticised as there is no one agreed basis for sharing costs between cost centres, as Openshaw emphasises:

> "it is important that overheads be allocated correctly because with the large time period involved in forestry a misallocation could make a substantial difference to the profitability of a plantation."
>
> (Openshaw, 1980, p. 67)

Nevertheless, a high degree of accuracy can be expensive and we may therefore, in the interests of economy, have to accept a little less precision than we might like.

Costs in forestry can be categorised as **direct costs**, **on-costs** or **overhead costs**, although there are other terms used in accountancy, as Table 3.1 shows.

**Table 3.1** Forestry cost categories.

| Forestry terms | | Accountancy terms |
|---|---|---|
| **Direct costs** | Prime or directly traceable costs | Manufacturing costs |
| **On-costs** | | |
| **Overheads** | Production or manufacturing expenses | |
| | Operating and non-operating expenses | Non-manufacturing costs |

**Direct costs** come under the general accountancy heading of manufacturing costs. Direct costs are those which are readily identified with the product and include wages of production workers and raw materials. Although normally classified in other fields as production overheads, costs of machinery, such as skidders and graders, are commonly considered in forestry as direct costs.

As we will see later in Chapter 9, direct costs are allocated for accounting purposes by recording materials used or time expended on that cost centre. However, for budgeting, the process is different: material costs are allocated according to expected amounts required by the cost centre; this can be based on past experience or published standards and multiplied by expected prices. Similarly direct labour costs can be based on forecast hours per hectare, or per unit of production in the case of nursery and sawmill, and then multiplied by an hourly rate. The latter must take account of expected wage and associated on-costs (see next section).

Machine hours devoted to each cost centre are also estimated and then multiplied by the hourly costs of each category of machinery costs. Hourly costs of fuel are readily estimated, but those for repairs and the costs of the machines themselves (depreciation) involve rather more calculation. We will come back to depreciation in Chapter 5. As Fig. 3.2 indicates, **depreciation**[2] calculations are best carried out separately and the results fed into the profit budget.

**On-costs** are mostly associated with labour, and to some extent machinery. Slack or wet time, travel time, sickness and holiday pay, training, clothing, employers' insurance contributions and machinery tax and insurance are considered as on-costs. Although often considered in UK forestry as a category by themselves, the author would support the views of Openshaw (1980) and Price (1989) and the practice in other industries, that they should be subsumed under one of the other two categories, mainly by allocating to direct costs. However, for purposes of identification and control, it is worth entering them separately within the direct or overhead category.

Allocation of on-costs can be according to proportion of direct costs or the labour element of those. For any machinery on-costs they can be apportioned to cost centres by machine hours incurred.

**Overheads** are classified by industry accountants as either 'production/manufacturing expenses' (or non-direct production costs) or 'operating and non-operating expenses', (also termed non-manufacturing costs). Thus costs of production machinery and vehicles, supervision and other costs associated with the forest enterprise, would be considered to be 'manufacturing expenses', while costs which might apply to the whole estate or enterprise costs not related to production would be non-manufacturing expenses. The latter would include local and headquarters secretarial, office cleaning and administrative costs as well as interest on borrowed money.

These figures will tend to be estimated as totals for the business (e.g. estate office costs) or an enterprise (e.g. forest manager), again using past experience, standard figures and inflation forecasts. They must then be allocated to cost centres.

The ways in which overheads should be allocated vary, but should follow a general rule. Openshaw recommends,

> "that the major factors which influence overheads should be picked out and the costs allocated accordingly."                    (Openshaw, 1980, p.55)

In other words, what influences the level of overheads? Some costs do not, in fact, seem to vary with the size of the compartment or cost centre or with the volume of production: these are called **fixed** costs. However, most costs do vary with size or volume and so can be called **variable** costs. In fact, even fixed costs, such as those incurred in running the estate office, are likely to vary if the enterprise is increased sufficiently in size.

Are overhead costs, therefore, dependent upon the size of the cost centre, and should allocations therefore be made according to some measure of size, such as hectares, volume or value of production? Some costs, such as

---

[2] Depreciation - an estimated cost of the loss in value of a machine, building or similar item through wear, tear and obsolescence – see Chapter 5.

maintenance and protection costs related to the land, can be reasonably allocated by area. Others, such as haulage and marketing of produce, could be allocated, not perhaps by value of production, but by value of sales. But allocating most of the overheads by sales or production would mean that many forest enterprises would have little or no allocation during the major part of the rotation.

Thus, most overhead costs are best allocated in some other way. Hart (1991) and Price (1989) both suggest that the most common allocation base is according to the proportion of direct costs incurred by that cost centre or operation. So, for instance, if a compartment is budgeted to incur 10% of the direct costs, then it would also be allocated 10% of those overheads. Given that a lot of the costs of management, administration and so on are related to the production costs of the business - supervising and paying workers, and ordering contracting services, materials and spare parts - then it seems sensible to allocate overheads accordingly[3]. In fact, some overheads can be allocated directly themselves: that part of a manager's time involved in measuring, marking and supervising, if we are able to forecast the proportion of his or her time spent in each cost centre, can be allocated directly.

The supervision of labour, in particular, often takes up a large proportion of a manager's time and so, certain items can be more accurately allocated on the basis of direct labour rather than direct costs in general.

In summary, then, most of the overhead costs can be allocated in proportion to the various cost centres' direct costs or labour costs. Those costs which depend upon the how much we sell can be allocated according to estimated sales revenue, and those that are closely linked to area can be shared out on a per hectare basis.

But, in budgeting ahead, how do we decide what the overhead costs are going to be in the first place? After all, it is only *after* the event that we have overhead costs which need to be allocated. We can approach this in two ways. Some of the overhead costs are fairly fixed - we expect to continue needing a secretary, a manager, and the associated office equipment, for instance. We can then base our forecasts on last year's figures, with an allowance for inflation, and allocate the ensuing figures to enterprises and cost centres according to direct costs or whatever basis we have decided upon. On the other hand, if we are unsure as to what our managerial and secretarial requirements will be, we may take a published 'standard' cost[4] as a certain proportion of direct costs and so arrive at a total after deriving a figure for each cost centre. Many of the more variable overhead costs will be determined in the same way - starting with a per unit figure and then aggregating.

---

[3] You might say that overheads are closely related to the number of transactions, rather than the total value of those transactions, so allocation could be on that basis. But that would involve counting the numbers of both purchase and sales transactions and would omit the effect of other factors such as time needed for supervision.

[4] As a result of surveys of forestry business there may be published figures for average costs in forestry. These can be used as 'standard' costs to apply to our own business.

## Profits

As Fig. 3.2 shows, once output figures have been estimated and all costs allocated, profits can be calculated for cost centres, enterprises and the business as a whole. These can be presented in a 'per unit' and 'cost centre total' form. Inter-cost-centre comparisons of output, costs and profit figures can them be made, as well as comparisons with past performance and published industry standards. Later, these budgeted figures can be used for comparison with 'actual' performance, derived from the accounts.

## Menzies Example

Douglas now begins the second step of his budgeting exercise.

### Output

In line with the Plan of Operations in Table 2.5, output in the first year will come in the form of revenue from standing sales of thinnings for compartment 10 and sales and transfers of plants from the nursery. Changes in the value of the growing stock of trees and the land are also included as part of output. For the Menzies Estate for the coming year, valuation changes have been calculated, but the calculation will not be explained until the next chapter.

Table 3.2 shows Douglas' output figures for the different cost centres. Note that not all compartments are shown - to save space only a sample are shown here, along with the total for the forest enterprise and the whole estate, which comprises the nursery and the forest.

The figures for changes in the values of the growing stock and the land are derived from the valuation forecasts which Douglas will have to have made; these will be dealt with in Chapter 4. You will see on the right-hand side of the table that the estimated total closing value is greater than the opening value, resulting in a positive valuation change. For all compartments there is a positive valuation change except for compartment 10. If you look in the third column from the right of table you will see that the valuation is expected to decline by £53,786. This is because a thinning operation is expected to take place during the coming year. However, this decline is more than compensated for in the total output figure by the expected revenue of £88,258 from the thinning sales.

Revenue is expected over the year from the thinnings in compartment 10 as well as the plants from the nursery. The revenue of £21,000 for plants from the nursery includes not only sales to other businesses (£11,000), but also a transfer (£10,000) to compartment 3 where planting is due to take place.

**Table 3.2** The Menzies Estate - disaggregated output forecasts (£)

|  | nursery 3 ha | 1 35 ha | 2 40 ha | 3 40 ha | 4 20 ha | .. | 10 40 ha | forest 350 ha | estate 353 ha |
|---|---|---|---|---|---|---|---|---|---|
| **Opening valuation** | 49021 | 110816 | 77856 | 12214 | 351337 | .. | 508149 | 3111684 | 3160705 |
| **Closing valuation** | 49021 | 120951 | 86512 | 54242 | 374409 | .. | 454364 | 3282298 | 3331319 |
| valuation change | 0 | 10135 | 8655 | 42029 | 23072 | .. | -53786 | 170614 | 170614 |
| **Revenues** | | | | | | | | | |
| clear cut | 0 | 0 | 0 | 0 | 0 | .. | 0 | 0 | 0 |
| thinning | 0 | 0 | 0 | 0 | 0 | .. | 88258 | 88258 | 88258 |
| plants | 21000 | 0 | 0 | 0 | 0 | .. | 0 | 0 | 21000 |
| planting | | | | | | .. | | | |
| grants | 0 | 0 | 0 | 0 | 0 | | 0 | 0 | 0 |
| Total revenue | 21000 | 0 | 0 | 0 | 0 | .. | 88258 | 88258 | 109258 |
| Total output | 21000 | 10135 | 80655 | 42029 | 23072 | .. | 34473 | 258872 | 279872 |

Thus, for all cost centres except the nursery and forest compartment 10, output consists entirely of a valuation change. In fact, for the whole estate Table 3.2 shows that £170,614 out of the total output of £279,872 comes from the valuation change. This has implications for cash flows, as we will see later on.

**Costs**

*Direct costs*

The cost section of this second budgeting step is produced in a similar fashion. Douglas takes account first of direct costs. Table 3.3 shows the cost categories which Douglas considers to be direct costs - both for the compartments and sub-compartments of the forest and for the nursery enterprise. Note that, because the estate does not employ much of its own labour and machinery, and because he has classified the cost of the forest worker under overheads, Douglas has not classified any of the costs as on-costs.

In the coming year, although thinning is planned to take place in compartment 10, there are no direct costs associated with it because the timber is to be sold standing and the arrangements for the sale and the supervision of the work will be carried out by Douglas and the forest worker. There will be direct costs, however, for the restocking of compartment 3 and for the nursery.

**Table 3.3** Menzies Estate - direct costs allocated to cost centres.

|  | Nursery | compartment/sub-compartment | | | | | | | Forest | Estate |
|---|---|---|---|---|---|---|---|---|---|---|
|  | 3 ha | 1 35 ha | 2 40 ha | 3 40 ha | 4 20 ha | ... ha | ... ha | 10 40 ha | 350 ha | 353 ha |
| **Direct forest costs** | | | | | | | | | | |
| Clear felling | 0 | 0 | 0 | 0 | 0 | ⋮ | ⋮ | 0 | 0 | 0 |
| Thinning | 0 | 0 | 0 | 0 | 0 | ⋮ | ⋮ | 0 | 0 | 0 |
| Fencing | 0 | 0 | 0 | 10,000 | 0 | ⋮ | ⋮ | 0 | 10,000 | 10,000 |
| Pre-plant weed | 0 | 0 | 0 | 3,200 | 0 | ⋮ | ⋮ | 0 | 3,200 | 3,200 |
| Scarify | 0 | 0 | 0 | 4,000 | 0 | ⋮ | ⋮ | 0 | 4,000 | 4,000 |
| Purchase transplants | 0 | 0 | 0 | 10,000 | 0 | ⋮ | ⋮ | 0 | 10,000 | 10,000 |
| Planting | 0 | 0 | 0 | 8,000 | 0 | ⋮ | ⋮ | 0 | 8,000 | 8,000 |
| Weeding | 0 | 0 | 0 | 0 | 0 | ⋮ | ⋮ | 0 | 0 | 0 |
| **Direct nursery costs** | | | | | | | | | | |
| Planting material | 3,150 | 0 | 0 | 0 | 0 | ⋮ | ⋮ | 0 | 0 | 3,150 |
| Fertilisers and sprays | 750 | 0 | 0 | 0 | 0 | ⋮ | ⋮ | 0 | 0 | 750 |
| Other materials | 330 | 0 | 0 | 0 | 0 | ⋮ | ⋮ | 0 | 0 | 330 |
| Casual labour | 5,400 | 0 | 0 | 0 | 0 | ⋮ | ⋮ | 0 | 0 | 5,400 |
| Total direct costs | 9,630 | 0 | 0 | 35,200 | 0 | ⋮ | ⋮ | 0 | 35,200 | 44,830 |

*Overheads*

Douglas next estimates the amounts under the different overhead categories, but must then allocate them between the cost centres. Douglas decides to allocate most of the overhead costs to all cost centres on the basis of the relative size of the compartment or enterprise.

If we now look at some of the figures in Table 3.4 we should be able to see how they have been calculated. Take first the nursery enterprise column. Since the roading relates to the forest, no share of that cost has been apportioned to the nursery. The insurance cost of £13 is derived by multiplying the estimate for the total cost of insurance (see the far right column) of £1,500 by its proportion of the total area, 0.008 (i.e. 0.8% being 3 ÷ 353). This is the case for most of the other costs. However, in the case of the forest worker, Douglas estimates that he will spend one third of his time in looking after the nursery, so allocates that proportion of the total cost of £9,000 to the nursery enterprise, giving £3,000. And since the store is largely used for the nursery, he feels that 80% of the costs associated with it, namely depreciation and repairs, should be allocated to the nursery. Thus, 80% of the £960 depreciation charge for the store is £768.

Note that the depreciation charges which Douglas has entered into Table 3.4 have been first calculated in a depreciation table, which will be dealt with in Chapter 5.

Let us turn now to the forest enterprise and the compartment allocations of overhead costs. If we take compartment 1 as an example, the first figure we come across in the Table is £193 for road maintenance. This figure is arrived at by taking the proportion of the forest area within sub-compartment 1 (that is 35 hectares out of a total of 350, giving 0.1 or 10%) and multiplying it by the total road maintenance cost of £1,925, giving £192.50, which is rounded in the table to £193.

The next figure, £149 for insurance comes about slightly differently. The total insurance figure of £1,500 is allocated between all cost centres, including the nursery, so the proportion this time should be 35 divided by the total area of 353, which gives a slightly lower proportion than before, 0.099 or 9.9%. Most of the rest of the allocations are made in this way.

The exceptions are the costs of the store mentioned above and the forest worker cost. Given that one third of his wage is allocated to the nursery, the remaining two-thirds is allocated to the forest compartments on the basis of their share of the forest area. So for compartment 1, the figure is £600, which is 10% of £6,000 (£9,000 less the £3,000 allocated to the nursery).

Finally, there is one cost category missing from the list of overhead costs, namely overdraft interest. Douglas can only estimate this when he has set out his cash flow budget. So in this step of the budget, calculations are 'before overdraft interest'.

**Table 3.4** Menzies Estate - overhead costs allocated to cost centres

| | Nursery 3 ha | 1 35 ha | compartment 2 40 ha | 3 40 ha | 4 20 ha | 10 40 ha | Forest 350 ha | Estate 353 ha |
|---|---|---|---|---|---|---|---|---|
| Roads maint'nce | 0 | 193 | 220 | 220 | 110 | 220 | 1,925 | 1,925 |
| Insurance | 13 | 149 | 170 | 170 | 85 | 170 | 1,487 | 1,500 |
| *Salaries* | | | | | | | | |
| manager | 68 | 793 | 907 | 907 | 453 | 907 | 7,932 | 8,000 |
| secretarial | 34 | 397 | 453 | 453 | 227 | 453 | 3,966 | 4,000 |
| forest worker | 3,000 | 600 | 686 | 686 | 343 | 686 | 6,000 | 9,000 |
| *Vehicles* | | | | | | | | |
| depreciation | 35 | 410 | 469 | 469 | 235 | 469 | 4,105 | 4,140 |
| tax & insur. | 8 | 89 | 102 | 102 | 51 | 102 | 892 | 900 |
| fuel & oil | 7 | 79 | 91 | 91 | 45 | 91 | 793 | 800 |
| repairs | 3 | 40 | 45 | 45 | 23 | 45 | 397 | 400 |
| *Buildings* | | | | | | | | |
| store deprec. | 768 | 19 | 22 | 22 | 11 | 22 | 192 | 960 |
| repairs | 160 | 4 | 5 | 5 | 2 | 5 | 40 | 200 |
| office deprec. | 11 | 127 | 145 | 145 | 73 | 145 | 1,269 | 1,280 |
| equip deprec. | 4 | 50 | 57 | 57 | 28 | 57 | 496 | 500 |
| furniture deprec. | 1 | 8 | 9 | 9 | 5 | 9 | 79 | 80 |
| office repairs | 2 | 18 | 20 | 20 | 10 | 20 | 178 | 180 |
| Water | 3 | 40 | 45 | 45 | 23 | 45 | 397 | 400 |
| Electricity | 5 | 59 | 68 | 68 | 34 | 68 | 595 | 600 |
| Telephone | 4 | 50 | 57 | 57 | 28 | 57 | 496 | 500 |
| Misc. admin. | 17 | 198 | 227 | 227 | 113 | 227 | 1,983 | 2,000 |
| Loan interest | 14 | 164 | 187 | 187 | 94 | 187 | 1,637 | 1,651 |
| Total overhead costs | 4,157 | 3,486 | 3,984 | 3,984 | 1,992 | 3,984 | 34,859 | 39,016 |

**Profits**

Having calculated output and costs, Douglas can now bring these together to estimate profit. Table 3.5 summarises his results, which show the overall profit (before overdraft interest!) as well as the cost-centre profits. The total output is forecast at £279,872 and with costs at only £83,846, this leaves a profit of £196,026. Only £7,213 or under 4% of this profit is contributed by the nursery, although this is a much higher proportion than its relative area would suggest, while for the forest compartments, although all make a profit, the profit per hectare generally increases with the age of the stand.

**Table 3.5** Menzies Estate - output, costs and profit by cost centre.

| | | | | compartment/sub/compartment | | | | | |
|---|---|---|---|---|---|---|---|---|---|
| | Nursery 3 ha | 1 35 ha | 2 40 ha | 3 40 ha | 4 20 ha | ... | 10 40 ha | Forest 350 ha | Estate 353 ha |
| **Output** | | | | | | | | | |
| Total output | 21,000 | 10,135 | 8,655 | 42,029 | 23,072 | ... | 34,473 | 258,872 | 279,872 |
| **Costs** | | | | | | | | | |
| Direct costs | | | | | | | | | |
| Total direct costs | 9,630 | 0 | 0 | 35,200 | 0 | ... | 0 | 35,200 | 44,830 |
| Overhead costs | | | | | | | | | |
| Total overhead costs | 4,157 | 3,486 | 3,984 | 3,984 | 1,992 | ... | 3,984 | 34,859 | 39,016 |
| Total costs | 13,787 | 3,486 | 3,984 | 3,984 | 1,992 | ... | 3,984 | 70,059 | 83,846 |
| **Profit** | 7,213 | 6,649 | 4,671 | 2,845 | 21,080 | ... | 30,489 | 188,813 | 196,026 |

So far we have only looked at the disaggregated figures for the coming year. However, Douglas has carried out the exercise for a five-year time horizon and the figures that he has produced are shown in Table 3.6 below. As each of the forest compartments is growing older over the five-year period, their values are also growing and so, as a consequence, are the valuation changes. The effect of this, given that costs are not forecast to increase to match this, is to produce a growth in profits. Whether that is how it turns out remains to be seen.

**Table 3.6** Menzies Estate - five year aggregate output forecasts

|  | year | | | | |
|---|---|---|---|---|---|
|  | 2002 | 2003 | 2004 | 2005 | 2006 |
| **Output** | | | | | |
| Total output | 279,872 | 257,037 | 262,335 | 272,575 | 317,920 |
| **Costs** | | | | | |
| Direct costs | | | | | |
| Total direct costs | 44,830 | 13,630 | 13,630 | 9,630 | 13,230 |
| Overhead costs | | | | | |
| Total overhead costs | 39,016 | 37,808 | 36,985 | 35,897 | 34,949 |
| Total costs | 83,846 | 51,438 | 50,615 | 45,527 | 48,179 |
| **Profit** | 196,026 | 205,599 | 211,720 | 227,048 | 269,741 |

Douglas is now ready to move on to step 3 of the budget, but before we join him, we need to see how he arrived at his valuation and depreciation figures. These are the subjects of Chapters 4 and 5 respectively; we rejoin Douglas on step 3 in Chapter 6.

# Chapter 4

# Valuations

Before proceeding to the next, cash flow budgeting step, we need to pursue two of the points touched upon in the last chapter. This and the following chapter will deal with these topics.

When we discussed output, we mentioned that very often what is produced is not sold, but rather remains in the business at the end of the planning period. Thus, we may expect to have trees still in the ground, or in the form of felled or even processed timber, still somewhere on the estate. Later in the chapter we will see that we need to value not only trees, but everything that remains on the estate at the start and end of the planning period. This will include any materials that we have in store, plants, trees, timber and other forest products, tools, machinery, vehicles, buildings and even the land itself. The value of sporting and other amenities will also have to be valued. In brief, we need to estimate the value of these assets in order to assess the stock of wealth of the owner, and the change in the value of the assets as part of our profit calculations.

There are often a number of ways of valuing an item in the business and which method is most appropriate partly depends on what the item is to be used for. Valuation can be for tax, compensation, insurance, buying, selling or for financial management purposes; for some of these the lowest reasonable estimate is required, and for others the highest. Here, however, where we are concerned with financial management, we want the most realistic estimate[1]. But even here we find that there are a number of options available: we have to decide which method is best for our purposes and stick to it. Before we look more closely at some of the different valuation methods, it is worth pausing to consider the 'philosophy' behind the approach to valuation taken by the accountancy profession.

---

[1] As realistic as we can make it, that is, given limitations of time, cost and competence.

Accountants, as stewards of other people's assets, as reporters of financial performance and, increasingly, as members of management teams have established certain conventions. Of particular interest to us are:

- the 'going concern' convention - the assumption that the organisation is going to stay in business;
- the 'consistency' convention - using the same method each year, and making clear the effect if a different method is adopted; and
- the 'prudence' convention - an attitude to profits of 'don't count your chickens before they've hatched' and of erring towards the lower valuation estimate (Glautier and Underdown, 1986).

With these conventions in mind the accountant values assets according to the criterion of the 'value to the owner', which is defined as:

"the minimum loss that a firm would suffer if it were deprived of an asset."                                        (Edwards *et al.*, 1987,p.39)[2]:

To achieve this, it can be shown that the valuation should be based on one of the following:

- replacement cost (RC), which is the current cost if the asset were to be replaced;
- net realisable value (NRV), which is the amount the item could be sold for under normal trading conditions, net of selling expenses; and
- present value (PV), which is the value in today's money, of holding onto the asset, calculated by summing all of the costs and returns accruing to that asset over the future and converting those cash flows into their present value.

In forestry, however, there are various valuation methods in use, which do not seem, at first sight, to fit into these three categories. Nevertheless, as explained below, these methods can be categorised as giving RC, NRV or PV. Which measure we use in practice depends upon which we consider best reflects the 'value to the owner', and which we are able to measure. Once we have decided upon a method, we should be consistent in its application. We will now look at the different types of assets within the forest enterprise, the ways in which they are valued and the pros and cons of each method.

---

[2] Why minimum? Because that is what the asset is worth to the business.

# The Trees

For our cost-centre budget, we needed a value for each compartment (and sub-compartment if appropriate). Therefore, we are interested in valuing the growing stock in each compartment separately. For budgeting purposes we also want to estimate values for future years.

How do we value a stand? There are several approaches which we might take, and each can be put in the form of a question:

- What would we pay today to buy the whole forest enterprise? This is the **market price,** or **comparable sales** approach and ties in with the RC method above. Remember here, however, that this value would have to include the other costs of buying (transaction costs), such as agent's and solicitor's fees.
- What would we be able to sell the whole forest enterprise for? In the market, if a transaction takes place, the buying and selling price is the same. Yet because of transaction costs (which here would be subtracted from the total value) the sale value would be somewhat lower than that for purchase. This method ties in with the NRV approach;[3]
- For how much could we sell the trees as timber if they were to be felled today? The value arrived at here is known as the **devastation value**, or alternatively the **actual, liquidation,** or **stumpage value,** and is another way of deriving the NRV.
- How much would it have cost us to get the trees to that stage in their rotation? This might be termed the **accumulated net costs** approach and could be viewed as another approach to deriving the RC.
- What is the value to the business today of growing those trees on to maturity? Answering this question gives the **expectation** value, **holding** value, or **willingness to pay** and ties directly in with the PV.

Let us now look at each method in turn.

## The market price

Since we are here concerned with the value to the owner of the forest in this particular site, the net sale rather than the net purchase valuation will be used. This approach is straightforward: we simply take the *current* price of an identical or comparable estate or enterprise or the price that our estate or enterprise would be likely to be sold for *now*, net of transaction costs. As long as there is a market with a sufficient number of transactions to allow an estimate to be made with confidence, then such a valuation is acceptable. However, despite the recent

---

[3] Both of these 'market price' approaches also assume the 'going concern' convention. As Lorraine-Smith (1998) has pointed out, if purchasing or sale had to take place at a particular time, the seller or buyer might get a lower or higher market price respectively than in normal market circumstances.

move in many countries towards such a market valuation of land and standing timber, it would seem that very often the market is too small and variable to allow sufficiently accurate assessments to be made. Klemperer (1996) sums up the problem well:

> "...with forest properties, we often don't have a large enough sample of truly comparable sales to get a valid average price... for forests to be truly comparable, they need to be in the same time period and have the same site quality, acreage, timber species and age-class composition, timber quality, distance to market, slope, roading, and other features. That doesn't often happen."                              (Klemperer, 1996, p.348)

This is particularly the case when one considers what we are using the valuations for: we are not concerned simply with getting a 'ball-park' figure, but rather we wish for sufficient accuracy as to be able to monitor how the value is likely to change from one year to the next. Hart (1991) does suggest that once an initial valuation is made it can be updated each year by several percentage points to cater for growth increment, but this again seems rather an arbitrary way of determining profit and future capital stock. Alternatively, to obtain market valuations for the following year we would have to predict the market value of that combination of compartments and enterprises, *but one year later*, taking into account what happens (growth, thinning, felling) in the intervening period.

Apart from the difficulties of accurate estimation, this type of valuation also gives only an aggregate figure: for the land, trees, buildings and other assets attached to the land, and it is for the whole area, not for individual cost centres. This method does have its place, but for our purposes it would generally appear to give too broad brush a figure.

**Devastation value**

Turning now to the devastation value method (Petrini, 1953; Gane, 1966; SWOA, 1978). For a mature stand of trees, or one close to maturity, for which there would be saleable timber if it was harvested today, we first estimate the *current* volumes of the different categories of timber contained in it. Then we multiply these amounts by the timber prices, net of harvesting, transport and other costs, currently prevailing in that region.[4] As we are using these figures for budgeting we must also carry out the same calculations for the budgeted years - we follow the same procedure - estimating the volumes one, two, three years ahead and multiply by what we expect the prices to be *at that time*.

Figure 4.1 illustrates pictorially the devastation value approach for an example in which the trees are valued at year 30 of the 45-year rotation and a budgeted value for year 31 is also estimated.

Using prices at the time of valuation means that if we expect timber prices to go up (or down) by then, we must increase (or decrease) them accordingly.

---

[4] This 'net price' can be termed the 'standing' price.

Why is this important? Because our budgets for the next few years are meant to be predicting what will actually happen, and we will use them to monitor the business performance by comparing what does happen with what was expected to happen (actual versus budget). If we try to predict physical amounts, but leave the prices as they are today, it is therefore going to be rather unhelpful, particularly if the increase (or decline) of those prices is more than a few per cent. When we do include expected price changes we call it budgeting in **actual** or **nominal terms**.

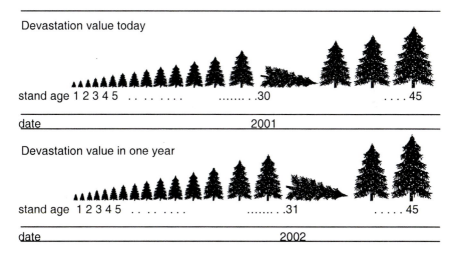

**Fig. 4.1** Devastation value illustration.

Some people criticise the devastation method as unrealistic, saying that we are never likely to fell the timber much before it is ready for harvesting. In fact, in some countries limitations would be imposed by the necessity of obtaining a felling licence, which might not be granted for environmental or other reasons. Supporters of the method would respond that at least it is fairly certain: we are not hoping for something far into the future, and this does fit in with the accountant's prudence convention.

For immature stands, we get to an age below which the trees have no 'devastation' value: the pole size is simply too small. In fact, we may even get a negative value as it would cost more to get the timber to market than it was worth: Fig. 4.2 illustrates a typical example of the 'devastation' value of a compartment over its rotation, as shown by the solid line[5].

In this instance, the method does not provide a reasonable solution. However, all is not lost as it is possible to move across to the next method. The

---

[5] Thinnings occur periodically, and although one might expect a short-term dip in yield (and devastation value) immediately after thinning, this does not appear in the results, probably because the program used interpolates between five-year estimates.

problem caused by the violation of the consistency convention in moving from one method to another will be dealt with later.

## Accumulated net costs value

The accumulated net costs approach (Petrini, 1953) has traditionally been followed by accountants when dealing with immature assets which could not readily be valued by other means. Using accumulated net costs as a measure of value seems to be following the implicit notion that, if the asset is to at least break even then it must be worth as much as it has cost to produce it.

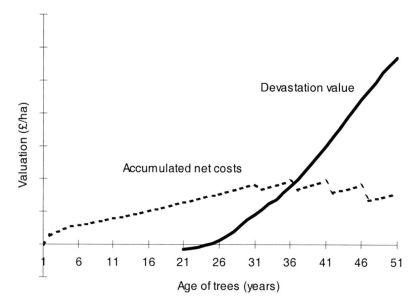

**Fig. 4.2** Devastation values of trees and net accumulated costs over rotation.

It was common in the past, and is still prevalent in some quarters, to simply add up all of the costs (net of any benefits such as grants)[6] so far incurred, with no further adjustment. This adherence to the 'historic cost basis', which means using the market prices prevailing when the item was originally acquired, rather than current prices, was made to look rather unsuitable by the inflation that hit many economies in the 1970s.

To understand why, imagine, for instance, that production costs for a compartment had reached £100,000 by 1995. If inflation averaged 15% over the

---

[6] Inclusion of benefits as well as costs (hence the term accumulated *net* costs) may seem strange but can be justified on a number of grounds. Firstly, the market value would, if it was that precise, tend to take account of whether a grant was about to be paid or had just been paid and, secondly, the present value (see later) would tend to dip (*ceteris paribus*) just after the grant had been paid.

intervening period, five years later, to produce the same stand would cost over £200,000. Yet the stand would still be deemed, if valued on the historic cost basis, to be worth only half of this. To take account of this, and at the same time to deal with the fact that laying out money for a number of years might incur interest charges, it has been suggested that costs should be updated by adding an interest charge to those costs at a compound rate (Openshaw, 1980; Price, 1989)[7]. The interest rate should be that rate at which the business might have borrowed money, or earned money if the money had not been tied up for the period, and given that this rate has inflation built into it, costs would be automatically brought up to date; that is, they would be converted to a 'current costs' basis. So, for instance, if we have a five-year-old stand whose costs have been £1,000 at the start, £150 for the next two years, partly counteracted by a grant of £100 coming in both those years, and £10 management costs for the following three years, and using an interest rate of 12%, the accumulated net costs would be calculated as follows:

At the end of the first year, the net accumulated costs would be the £1,000 incurred at the start, to which one year's interest (£120) would need to be added as well as the costs for the year of £150 less the grant of £100, thus:

£1,000 + £1,000 × 0.12 + £150 - £100 = £1,170

The accumulated costs at the end of the second year would be the £1,170 plus interest on that amount and again the cost of £150, for the second year, less the grant of £100 giving:

£1,170 + £1,170 × 0.12 + £150 - £100 = £1,360.40

The process would continue up to the present, as Table 4.1 illustrates. The calculations required for this method may seem to involve a lot of hassle, but if you have access to a spreadsheet such calculations are easy.

**Table 4.1** Tabular calculation of accumulated net costs.

| year | benefits | costs | net costs | interest charge @ 12% | net costs including interest | net accumulated costs @ year end |
|------|----------|-------|-----------|-----------------------|------------------------------|----------------------------------|
|      | £        | £     | £         | £                     | £                            | £                                |
| 1996 | 0        | 1,000 | 1,000     | 0.00                  | 1,000.00                     | 1,000.00                         |
| 1997 | 100      | 150   | 50        | 120.00                | 170.00                       | 1,170.00                         |
| 1998 | 100      | 150   | 50        | 140.40                | 190.40                       | 1,360.40                         |
| 1999 | 0        | 10    | 10        | 163.25                | 173.25                       | 1,533.65                         |
| 2000 | 0        | 10    | 10        | 184.04                | 194.04                       | 1,727.69                         |
| 2001 | 0        | 10    | 10        | 207.32                | 217.32                       | **1,945.01**                     |

This method would only tend to be advocated for dealing with very immature stands, otherwise you would get to the final year and there might be a big divergence between the valuation of the stand at the start of the year (based on the accumulated net costs approach) and the amount received for the timber, which would translate into a big jump in apparent profits. In order to smooth this

---

[7] This is considered further in Appendix 4.2.

out, you can change over from this approach to the devastation value approach at an earlier stage. Even then there could be a jump from the valuation at the start of the year according to one method and the valuation at the end of the year according to another (and it does not seem to follow the consistency convention very well, does it?). Refer to Fig. 4.2 again, where the dotted line shows accumulated net costs[8]. If the changeover of methods (from the dotted to the solid line) occurred at age 26, for instance, there would be a huge drop in the valuation. And if the changeover occurred at age 46, there would be a huge jump in the valuation.

Nevertheless, if the devastation value approach is followed for the later years of a rotation, there does not seem to be any alternative but to take the accumulated net costs approach for the earlier years of the rotation. And the jump, or drop, occurring at the changeover point does not have to be much of a problem if a point in the rotation was chosen at which both approaches gave a similar valuation: year 36 for instance in Fig. 4.2.[9]

**Expectation value**

This method would be preferred by economists, but is often avoided by others largely because it is seen as difficult to understand and calculate. And this is largely because it involves the dreaded **discounting**, the hub of forest economics. Although seen by many foresters as an almost incomprehensible concept, if it is explained and studied carefully it does not have to be so difficult to understand: Appendix 4.1 attempts to provide some clarification.

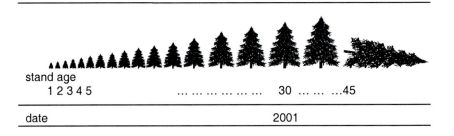

stand age
1 2 3 4 5                    … … … … … …    30 … … …45

date                                        2001

**Fig. 4.3** Expectation value illustration.

The expectation approach can be thought of as an answer to the question, "How do I value a stand on the assumption that I am not going to clear fell today,

---

[8] In case you are wondering why the curve shows a saw-tooth effect, it is because of the beneficial effects of thinnings revenue which periodically lower the accumulated net costs.

[9] This example will give some experienced forest managers a shock: "surely the man is not advocating using the accumulated net costs approach to such a late stage?" The answer, in this case is, "yes, as long as accumulated net costs are not soaring above the devastation value, then it is most appropriate to choose the changeover age as that at which the curves cross, in this case 36 years."

but rather will let the trees grow on to a later point (the end of the rotation)?" Figure 4.3 illustrates the valuation problem, again for someone wishing to value today at the end of year 30 of a rotation when the stand is expected to be clear cut at the end of 45 years (i.e. 15 years from now).

Based on that assumption, I want to know what the costs and benefits, which are expected to occur over the remaining years of the rotation, are worth to me *today*. Well, surely the answer would be, "list those costs and benefits and simply add up the costs and subtract them from the benefits", wouldn't it? For instance, imagine we are later in the rotation than in Fig. 4.3, so that we are only 3 years away from the end of the rotation, when the trees will be harvested. Then, if I have costs of £10 at the end of this and the remaining years, and in the final year I estimate harvesting receipts of £19,000 you might expect the expectation value to be £19,000 - £10 - £10 - £10 = £18,970.

*But it is not.*

Why?

All because of *time* and *interest*. And this is where *discounting* comes in. If you have never dealt with it before, or feel that you do not understand it properly, then it would be better to read Appendix 4.1 now before continuing with the rest of the chapter. Otherwise, we will continue assuming a basic understanding of discounting.

We should now be able to answer the question which was posed at the beginning of the section, namely; "How do I value a stand on the assumption that I am not going to clear fell today, but rather let the trees grow on to the end of the rotation?" We should list the expected costs and benefits relating to the particular compartment for the *remainder* of the rotation and then *discount* them back to the present. However, we do not go back to the start of the rotation, but instead we begin from the point in the rotation where we are *today*. In our example above, we might set out the discounted cash flow (DCF) procedure as shown in Table 4.2.

**Table 4.2** Discounted cash flow table - values at the start of the year.

| date | time | benefit | cost | net benefit | discount factor @ 6% | present value |
|------|------|---------|------|-------------|----------------------|---------------|
| end year | years | £ | £ | £ | £ | £ |
| 2001 | 0 | 0 | 0 | 0 | 1.0000 | 0.00 |
| 2002 | 1 | 0 | 10 | -10 | 0.9434 | -94.34 |
| 2003 | 2 | 0 | 10 | -10 | 0.8900 | -89.00 |
| 2004 | 3 | 19,000 | 10 | 18,990 | 0.8396 | 15,944.00 |
| | | | | | NPV @ 6% | 15,925.67 |

Notice that we take the starting point for discounting as zero and assume that the cash flows arise just before the end of the first, second and third years from now. The discount rate is 6%.

We would then be able to say that the expectation value of that stand today (i.e. at the end of time zero) is £15,925.67. In other words, it is the value to us in today's money of all the costs and benefits arising from that stand for the remainder of the current rotation[10].

But what about the expectation value of that stand in one year's time, which is the end of the first year of the budgeting period? It may help to appreciate what is required by referring back to Fig. 4.3 where we would now be looking at the expectation value in year 31, one year closer to the end of the rotation. To estimate the new value we have to imagine that a year has passed, so that 'today' is now no longer the end of 2001, but the end of 2002. We then simply go through the calculations again taking the end of year 2002 as time zero. Table 4.3 has the result.

**Table 4.3**  Discounted cash flow table - values at the end of the year .

| date | time | benefit | cost | net benefit | discount factor | present value |
|---|---|---|---|---|---|---|
| end year | years | £ | £ | £ | £ | £ |
| 2002 | 0 | 0 | 0 | 0 | 1.0000 | 0.00 |
| 2003 | 1 | 0 | 10 | -10 | 0.9434 | -94.34 |
| 2004 | 2 | 19,000 | 10 | 18,990 | 0.8900 | 16,901.10 |
| | | | | | NPV @ 6% | 16,806.76 |

Notice that, at the end of 2002 we will have just paid out £10, and as that is not included in the remaining cash flows we only have to consider the final two years' cash flows. Also note that we assumed that prices will not change between 2001 and 2002, otherwise we would have had to inflate all of the cash flows in line with what we expected prices to change by over that period: have a look at Appendix 4.3 if you want to know more.

The expectation value in 2001 is therefore £15,925.67 and the budgeted expectation value for one year from now (2002) is £16,806.76, so the valuation change is expected to be £16,806.76 - £15,925.67 = £881.09.

In Fig. 4.2 we saw an illustration of how the devastation value and accumulated net costs might change over a single rotation; Fig. 4.4 now has superimposed on that the expectation value as well.

Notice that the expectation value curve is generally above the devastation value curve, but they converge at the point of harvesting, i.e. the planned end of the rotation. The former will grow, after taking account of any intervening costs and revenues (thinnings in this case), by a percentage reflecting the discount rate.

This expectation value approach follows the third, 'value to the owner' option which we discussed at the beginning of the chapter, namely, the PV. It is seen as giving a more realistic answer than the previous two approaches since it values the most likely course of action, which is to let the trees grow on to the age of clear cut. It is also a method which allows us to set up a table of costs and benefits at the start of the rotation, which can then be used each year after amending it in the light of revised expectations of yields, costs and prices. Again,

---

[10] We need to estimate a realistic rotation length, remembering that it may not be the optimal period because of market, environment or other factors.

if we have access to a computer spreadsheet the effort involved is considerably reduced.

However, there are three main criticisms of this method: firstly, it assumes a certain future. What happens if there is windthrow, disease or price slump or what if the estimates are simply wrong? As Appendix 4.4 shows, amendments to the method to deal with risk complicate matters rather a lot. The other methods studied so far do not have this problem since they look at what is there now, not what might be there in the future. Secondly, this method makes profit rather too predictable from the outset. Except for changes due to unforeseen alterations to costs or adjustments for inflation, profit will be determined by the discount rate. Yet, except for the market price approach, the other methods can be criticised in a similar way: this is considered further in Appendix 4.5. Finally, the expectation value depends crucially on the discount rate used: using 3% instead of 6%, for instance, is likely to have a huge impact on the valuation.

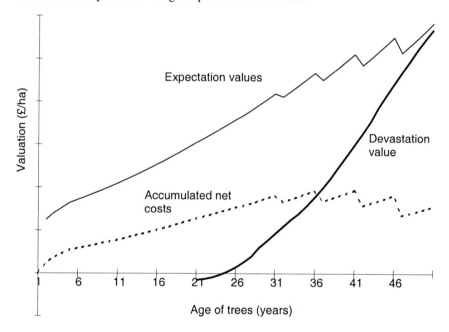

**Fig. 4.4** Expectation values, devastation values and accumulated net costs over one rotation.

*Discount rate*

Before we move on to the valuation of land, it is appropriate at this point to pause to consider how we decide upon a correct discount rate. The answer is straightforward, but how we actually decide upon a rate in a particular instance is not so simple.

The rate used for discounting should be the rate of interest which the business has to forgo by tying up money in this business, or the rate which the business can obtain elsewhere by delaying payment by the business. This rate is known as the **opportunity cost of capital** which is defined as:

> "the rate of return which the firm could have obtained on the funds…, if they had been used in the next most profitable opportunity open to the firm (whether internal or external)."  (Bannock *et al.*, 1978, p. 100)

Given that here we are dealing with investments of a long-term nature, we should be looking at the sort of return we could obtain over the long term on the next best use of funds. But what uses should we be looking at? If we have alternative projects which we otherwise could have carried out then we might use the estimated return on the next best alternative as our discount rate. It is more likely that we won't have much of a clue about what we would earn internally, so we have to look at what rates the markets are offering. The rates which you focus on depend upon the sort of investments you might consider and they can vary a lot (Price, 1993). An important indicator is the long-term yield on company shares or government securities. In Britain, for instance, the average real rates of return over the period 1963-1993 were between 6 and 7% in both cases[11]. A rate of 6% will be used here.

To summarise the methods considered above, the terms and their descriptions are tabulated in Table 4.4.

**Table 4.4** Forestry and accountancy valuation methods.

| term | alternative terms | accountants' term | method |
|---|---|---|---|
| **market price** | comparable sales | RC for purchases NRV for sales | value of business or enterprise according to market prices |
| **devastation value** | liquidation, actual, or stumpage value | NRV | value of what is there if it was sold today |
| **accumulated net costs** | | RC | sum of interest and inflation-adjusted costs incurred so far |
| **expectation value** | holding value, willingness to pay | PV | discounted present value of the stream of future costs and benefits accruing to that item |

---

[11] Based on the FT industrial share index and British government long dated securities: CSO, 1995.

# Land

The land on which the trees are grown and on which the various other enterprises take place is, along with the current stock of trees, one of the major assets to be valued. So as to separate the values of each of the different assets we need to think of the land without the present stock of trees as these are going to be valued separately, if possible[12]. We must, however, make sure that the valuation method we choose for land is consistent with the method we have used for the trees - it should become clear as to why this is important as we work through each of the valuation methods as applied to the land itself.

## Market value

If we have already decided to value the trees according to the market value method, it is likely that the valuation would have included the land as well - in which case we need go no further in trying to value the land separately. However, if we have used the devastation or accumulated net costs method for valuing the trees, then we do need a separate value for the land.

The replacement cost of the land in a bare state would be the price that we would have to pay for an identical plot of land; in other words, its **market price.** If prices were readily available for clear-felled or agricultural land then a suitable value could be chosen. If, however, the market for such land for forestry was small, and if there was a great variability in plots sold, it might not be possible to obtain an accurate market valuation.

Looking at the net realisable value (NRV) of the land, if it were to be clear felled, it might be suitable for agriculture or some other development, and if market prices are available for such land, a current market value (net of rehabilitation costs) could be assigned. On the other hand, it might only be suitable or likely to remain in forest use, so a forest land market price should be assigned.

This method may suffer from the same shortcomings described in the section on valuing the stock of trees, although it is more likely that we will be able to obtain a larger sample of market prices for the bare land than would be the case with land plus an assortment of stands. The valuation between the beginning and the end of the year would only change with market conditions, so we would need to be prepared to apply a predicted rate of inflation to the forecast value.

---

[12] Although sometimes in accounts you will come across a land valuation only - this means that the current and future stands have been valued altogether, i.e. trees have not been separated out from land.

**Devastation value**

If we have used the devastation value method for valuing the trees, we have done so on the assumption that we clear cut the trees today. Consequently, we would need to value the land in such a condition too: free of trees, but possibly needing destumping, particularly if sold for non-forestry uses. Here the NRV would be the market value and we would therefore need to value it in the way described above.

On the other hand, we might say to ourselves, "What would the clear felled land be worth to us?" In other words, what would we expect to get out of it if we were to put it back into forestry? This means that we are seeking the expectation value or PV of the land. Despite the fact that we have used the devastation value method for the trees, it is not a problem switching to a different method for valuing the land, *as long as our assumptions about the trees and the land are consistent*[13]. This takes us on to the expectation value approach.

**Expectation value**

We may come to this approach to valuing the land after valuing the trees by the RC, NRV or PV methods. If we have used either the RC or NPV we are now effectively in the position of valuing land assumed to be bare today. If, however, we have used the PV for the trees, we are assuming that they will be grown on to the end of the current rotation and this requires a slightly different approach. Let us examine the different approaches in turn.

Having used the *devastation value* or the *accumulated net costs method* for valuing the trees, we now need to imagine

a new rotation started today,

followed, when that was completed, by another full rotation

followed by another rotation,

followed by another rotation,

followed by another rotation,

and so on . . .

Figure 4.5 illustrates this situation.

---

[13] For instance, taking an expectation value approach for the trees would not allow us to use the current market value of the bare land since the former method assumes that the land will be retained until at least the end of the current rotation.

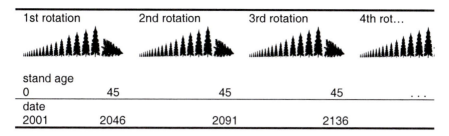

1st rotation      2nd rotation      3rd rotation      4th rot...

| stand age | | | | |
|---|---|---|---|---|
| 0 | 45 | 45 | 45 | . . . |
| date | | | | |
| 2001 | 2046 | 2091 | 2136 | |

**Fig. 4.5** Expectation value of land - an illustration.

So the value of the land can be viewed as the present value of an infinite series of rotations, or effectively, a series of rotations into the distant future. This is known as the **land expectation value (LEV)** or the soil expectation value (Nautiyal, 1988; Klemperer, 1996).

How do we calculate this value?

First we calculate the present value of the first full rotation. As before we list the costs and benefits in the years in which they are expected to occur, the only difference being that now we list the cash flows for a complete rotation, rather than just the remaining part of it.

For instance, in our example above for which we calculated the PV for the final three years of the current rotation, let us now tabulate the cash flows for each of the 45 years and then work out the PV: Table 4.5 shows some of the figures.

**Table 4.5** Discounted cash flow table - for a full rotation.

| date | time | benefit | cost | net benefit | discount factor | present value |
|---|---|---|---|---|---|---|
| end year | years | £ | £ | £ | @ 6% | £ |
| 2001 | 0 | 0 | 1,000 | -1,000 | 1.000 | -1,000.00 |
| 2002 | 1 | 100 | 150 | -50 | 0.943 | -47.15 |
| 2003 | 2 | 100 | 150 | -50 | 0.890 | -44.50 |
| 2004 | 3 | 0 | 10 | -10 | 0.840 | -8.40 |
| 2005 | 4 | 0 | 10 | -10 | 0.792 | -7.92 |
| 2006 | 5 | 0 | 10 | -10 | 0.747 | -7.47 |
| 2007 | 6 | 0 | 10 | -10 | 0.705 | -7.05 |
| 2008 | 7 | 0 | 10 | -10 | 0.665 | -6.65 |
| ... | ... | 0 | 10 | -10 | ... | ... |
| ... | ... | 0 | 10 | -10 | ... | ... |
| 2041 | 40 | 0 | 10 | -10 | 0.097 | -0.97 |
| 2042 | 41 | 0 | 10 | -10 | 0.092 | -0.92 |
| 2043 | 42 | 0 | 10 | -10 | 0.087 | -0.87 |
| 2044 | 43 | 0 | 10 | -10 | 0.082 | -0.82 |
| 2045 | 44 | 0 | 10 | -10 | 0.077 | -0.77 |
| 2046 | 45 | 19,000 | 10 | 18,990 | 0.073 | 1,386.27 |
| | | | | | NPV @ 6% | 159.11 |

First, the cash flows are listed, and the discount factors are calculated, using a rate of 6% and based on the number of years from the present (time zero). Next, present values are worked out (net benefit × discount factor) and these are summed to obtain the NPV.

The answer we get is £159.11, which is the present value of the stream of costs and benefits arising from a complete rotation, discounted at 6%.

We now have the net present value of one rotation, but we need to work out the present value of a whole series of rotations, one after the other. If we wanted we could produce a table showing these rotations, one after the other: in this case, for instance, we could list 10 rotations of 45 years over 450 years[14]. The present value then would be the LEV, or certainly very close to it.

To save us the trouble of listing a whole series of rotations we can simply take the PV of one rotation and then apply a LEV formula, thus:

$$ \text{LEV} = \text{PV} \times \frac{(1 + \text{discount rate})^{\text{years}}}{(1 + \text{discount rate})^{\text{years}} - 1} $$

where 'years' refers to the length of one rotation in years.

So, for instance, in the example we have an NPV of £159.11 and with a discount rate of 6% and rotation length of 45 years the formula would look like this:

$$ \text{LEV} = £159.11 \times \frac{(1 + .06)^{45}}{(1 + .06)^{45} - 1} $$

Now, as $1.06^{45}$ is 13.765, the formula becomes

$$ \text{LEV} = £159.11 \times \frac{13.765}{12.765} = £171.57 $$

What does this mean?

This is the *land expectation value*: the value of the land to the owner if it was retained into perpetuity. It means that, if the present value of one rotation, discounted at 6%, is £159.11, then the present value of an infinite series of rotations, one after the other, is £171.57. It doesn't seem to add very much to the PV for the single rotation, does it, especially when you think that there is an infinite series of rotations after the first? The reason for this is that the later rotations occur so far into the future that when discounted back to today they don't count for very much. Incidentally, if we had listed 10 rotations and worked

---

[14] We normally assume that all future rotations would be the same as the first. If they are not likely to be, we can still use the LEV formula, but base the NPV of a single full rotation on what crop we expect to follow the present one.

out their PV, as we suggested above, we would get the same answer as that using the LEV formula as above.

What if we now wanted to find the land value for next year for our budget? Think for a moment what you would expect it to be.

If we were to repeat the procedure in a year's time then we would still be assuming the land was cleared immediately and a new rotation begun. So, except for expressing things in terms of the price level in a year's time (i.e. taking account of how prices had risen over the year), nothing would have changed. Thus, apart from inflation, when we use this method, with the assumption of a fresh start from today, we will have a land value that doesn't change - and for our accounts that is quite convenient.

That is how we calculate an expectation value for the land if we have valued the trees by the devastation value or accumulated net costs method. If, instead, we have used the *expectation value of the trees*, the procedure is as follows.

The expectation valuation method used for the trees assumes that we are going to retain the trees to the end of the current rotation. You could say then that the expectation value of the whole lot, the land and the trees together, is the PV of all future costs and benefits - that would be for the current rotation and then all of the full rotations which follow after. But since we have taken out the value of the current rotation already as the value of the trees, then what is left we will call the value of the land. This value is the PV of all future rotations (an infinite series) after the current rotation has finished; Fig. 4.6 illustrates this.

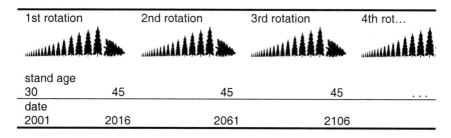

| 1st rotation | | 2nd rotation | | 3rd rotation | | 4th rot... |
|---|---|---|---|---|---|---|

| stand age | | | | | | |
|---|---|---|---|---|---|---|
| 30 | 45 | | 45 | | 45 | ... |

| date | | | | | | |
|---|---|---|---|---|---|---|
| 2001 | 2016 | | 2061 | | 2106 | |

**Fig. 4.6** Expectation value of current and future rotations - an illustration.

But isn't that the LEV? After all, that is the PV of an infinite series of rotations. Not quite. The LEV is for an infinite series of rotations *starting today*, whereas we are now talking about an infinite series of rotations *starting at the end of the current rotation*. So the difference is one of time - and when differences in time are involved it means that we must *discount*. So the LEV effectively occurs at the end of the current rotation and consequently we must discount that value back to today - by the number of years of the current rotation remaining.

$$\text{adjusted LEV} = \frac{\text{LEV}}{(1 + \text{discount rate})^{\text{years left}}}$$

by 'years left' we mean the number of years between now and the end of the current rotation, which could be defined as:

years left = rotation length - current rotation age

This adjusted LEV can be spelled out as: the present value of an infinite series of rotations which *commence at the end of the current rotation*. And *this adjustment is only necessary if we have used the expectation value for the trees*. Otherwise, the unadjusted LEV does reflect the value to the owner of retaining the land and therefore needs no adjustment.

In our example above, we assumed we were three years from the end of the current rotation. Now if the LEV at the start of the series of full rotations is £171.57 then we need to adjust it like this:

$$\text{adjusted LEV} = \frac{£171.57}{(1+.06)^3} = \frac{£171.57}{1.191} = £144.06$$

Notice that we used the same discount rate as in the full LEV calculation, namely 6%, assuming that the discount rate would be the same every year, and that 'years left' is 3. The adjusted LEV is therefore about 16% lower (£144 compared to £172) than the LEV because we want the present value of a figure based on a point three years from now.

To estimate the adjusted LEV in one year's time, we must ask ourselves, "What is different?" The answer is, apart from any change in the price level, the only difference is that in one year we will be one year closer to the end of the current rotation. In other words, in our formula the 'years left' term is one less. You might now like to ask yourself, "How will the adjusted LEV this year differ from the adjusted LEV next year (apart from the change in the price level over the period)?" To find out let us look at the following example.

Calculation of the adjusted LEV at a point one year from now, involves using 'years left' as 2 instead of 3 in the formula, thus:

$$\text{adjusted LEV} = \frac{£171.57}{(1+.06)^2} = \frac{£171.57}{1.124} = £152.64$$

Being 1 year closer to the end of the rotation, the adjusted LEV for next year is bigger. But by how much? The difference is £152.64 - £144.06 = £8.58, which happens to be 6% of this year's figure. And of course, that is what we might have expected it to be, since discounting at 6% means reducing the value by 6% each year. Figure 4.7 illustrates how the LEV used as the land value when adopting the devastation value method for the trees compares with the adjusted LEV used when the expectation method is adopted for the trees. Note that the former is constant, whereas the latter rises as the end of the rotation approaches.

This illustrates one problem of using the expectation method for both trees and land - other things being equal, the valuations of both grow by the discount rate percentage each year until the end of the rotation. This means that, unless we also adjust our expectations values in the light changing circumstances and expectations each year, profits are largely pre-determined from the outset.

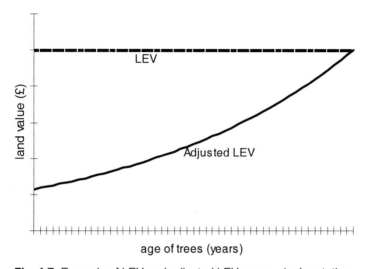

**Fig. 4.7** Example of LEV and adjusted LEV over a single rotation.

At this point it is worth listing some of the advantages and disadvantages of the different valuation methods described above; Table 4.6 overleaf lists them.

One final comment on the methods for valuing trees and land: how do they tend to compare? We have seen a comparison of an example of devastation and expectation values for trees in Fig. 4.4: the expectation value tends to be above the devastation value until the end of the rotation. For land, as Fig. 4.7 illustrates, the LEV would be constant (apart from inflation) when the devastation value is used for trees, but only reaches that level at the end of the rotation when the expectation method is used for the trees.

However, it is hard to say how the market value (which values trees and land together) compares with the two methods. The market price that an estate or part of an estate achieves depends upon the forces of supply and demand. Those supplying, the sellers, will wish to obtain at least as much as they deem it to be worth - which would be the expectation value if they were to retain the trees until the end of their optimum rotations.

Table 4.6 Advantages and disadvantages of valuation methods.

| attribute | valuation method | | |
| --- | --- | --- | --- |
| | Market Value | Devastation Value (and Accumulated Net Costs) | Expectation Value |
| Accuracy | Sufficient data on similar sites may not be available | Dependent on sampling technique, yield estimation method and current price information | Dependent on sampling technique, final yield estimation method and future price estimates. Also highly dependent on discount rate chosen |
| Simplicity | Straightforward, but requires detailed market information and expertise | Requires annual yield and price estimation for each compartment | Requires annual reconsideration of estimates in the light of experience. Discounting complexities can be avoided by use of computer spreadsheet |
| Realism | Realistic market picture | Trees unlikely to be felled before maturity, especially if environmental regulations restrict this | Realistic view regarding when trees are likely to be felled |
| Certainty | Based on current values | Based on what is there now and on current prices | Based on uncertain future |
| Consistency | One method | Different methods required for immature and mature stands | One method |
| Use in profit calculations | Unlikely to be sufficiently detailed for valuation changes and could therefore give wide variability in annual profits | Recalculation for each year allows valuation change calculation, but may produce wide variability in annual profits | Recalculation for each year allows valuation change calculation. Annual profit stream is relatively smooth |
| Degree of detail | Overall figure doesn't allow cost-centre detail nor separation of trees and land | Trees and land and compartments separately valued | Trees and land and compartments separately valued |

On the other hand, those demanding, the buyers, will not want to pay any more than, and preferably less than, the present value of the money it is likely to generate for them if they buy and retain it - again the expectation value. This would suggest that, in a free market, a price is likely to be agreed upon at or close to the expectation value. In practice, however, the price may differ considerably from the expectation value. Reasons for this may be that the two parties may work with different estimates and discount rates, other factors may influence their assessment (such as the effects of tax, shooting rights, alternative land uses, and difficult to quantify costs and benefits of land ownership), different attitudes to risk and uncertainty, and the relative bargaining strengths (linked to how desperate each party is to buy or sell that particular piece of land).

Thus, a forest may fetch a price well above its expectation value if, for instance, such land is in short supply, there are many buyers, it has hunting or other rights attached, and there are tax advantages involved. Conversely, its price may fall well below the expectation value (and even below the devastation value) if it is in an unattractive area, many estate owners are trying to sell at the same time, and windthrow, fire or other hazards are seen to pose a serious risk[15].

## Infrastructure

Roading, bridges, drains, fences and similar infrastructure are assets, which have involved the outlay of funds in the past and enable production to take place in the future, so they too must be valued. However, in arriving at a value for the land and the trees we should have done so in the light of the infrastructure that was in place at the time. Consequently, the value of that infrastructure should already have been accounted for and, therefore, need not be valued separately.

For instance, imagine a compartment about to be felled early in the coming year. If adequate roading exists at the start of the year then the £50,000 that we estimate as the likely income for the standing timber is the value of that compartment.[16] However, if that roading had not existed at the start of the year we would have had to put down roading before felling, at a cost of £20,000[17]. The valuation for that compartment would then have been only £30,000. This means that the presence of the roading effectively raises the value of the trees by £20,000.

Similarly, the existence of fences, drains and so on either reduces future cost outlay or raises the productivity of the land - both effects enhance the value of the trees.

---

[15] However, the expectation value calculations can take account of many of these variables and so give a value closer to the market price: see Appendix 4.4.

[16] Effectively both the devastation and expectation value.

[17] Or the timber purchaser would have had to pay for roading and therefore would have offered a lower price for the timber to take account of this; the effect is the same.

**Fig. 4.8** Roading does not need to be valued separately. Forest road network, Vancouver Island, Canada (photo: Tom Jenkins).

If account is properly taken of the effects of infrastructure in this way, then infrastructure should not be valued separately: to do so would mean double-counting.

## Buildings and Machinery

Buildings, machinery, tools and equipment (including computers and office furniture) could be valued in a similar way to other assets. However, for reasons which will be explained later, they are usually valued rather differently, as detailed in Chapter 5.

## Materials

A range of different materials are used in a forestry business: not only are there seedlings, fertilisers and sprays, but there are also fuel and oil for vehicles, fencing materials, spare parts for machinery and equipment, and even stationery and software for the office. At any particular point in time, such as the beginning or end of the year, there are likely to be stocks of some of these inputs as well as stocks of ready-for-sale or semi-finished produce, such as logs and poles. These must be valued, but how do we do it?

Stocks of materials are conventionally valued in a certain way according to whether they are inputs, semi-finished goods or finished products.

Stocks of inputs are generally valued in terms of their replacement cost, which should be what one would currently pay for them, but since they are likely to have been acquired within the last year this is often approximated for by using their original cost. Fertiliser and fuel, for instance, would fall into this category.

Stocks of semi-finished goods or 'partially processed materials' may be at varying stages. Those early in the production process might be valued on the basis of the sum of the costs so far incurred, which could be termed the RC; those at the end of one process, awaiting further processing, such as nursery seedlings awaiting planting out or planks awaiting planing, might actually have a market value, so could be valued at the cost of replacement (RC) or the price they could be sold for less marketing costs (NRV); and those goods or materials close to completion might also be valued at NRV, this being the final expected price less remaining costs to be incurred. The PV is not generally used, discounting not being worthwhile for the relatively short periods involved. Note also that we are not here dealing with trees, even if they are only in recently planted compartments - they will have already been valued using one of the methods considered in the earlier section.

Finished products are valued in terms of their NRV in the same way as products close to completion.

## Valuing for Other Purposes

So far we have been concerned with valuing the assets of the business for management purposes. There are, of course, other reasons why we might want to carry out a valuation - for insurance, tax or compensation purposes, for instance.

Which method we use, and whether we diverge from the ones set out so far, depends upon the objective of the valuation. Once we have determined the latter, we can then ask ourselves the question, "which is the most appropriate method?"

One valuation problem deserves particular attention - that is, valuation for sale or purchase decisions. The market for forestry property involves interaction between buyers and sellers. Whether the sale is made by auction, private treaty, tender or by some other method there is likely to be competition and often negotiation. In these conditions, we need to have in mind how much we want to obtain or how much we want to get rid of the property, what our competitors are likely to bid or agree to, and the value that we place upon it. As we saw earlier in the chapter, we will also want to cover transaction costs. We will then enter the market with a desire to go no higher than a certain figure in buying (buyer's maximum) or to go no lower than a certain figure in selling (seller's minimum). If our figure does not overlap that of the person with whom we are negotiating, then no sale is likely (a in Fig. 4.9), whereas if there is overlap there is likely to be a sale at a price somewhere between the two positions (b in Fig. 4.9).

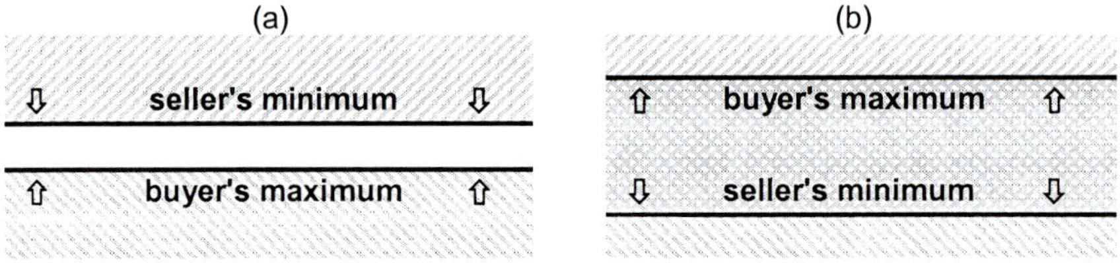

|   | (a) |   |
|---|-----|---|
| ⇩ | **seller's minimum** | ⇩ |
| ⇧ | **buyer's maximum** | ⇧ |

|   | (b) |   |
|---|-----|---|
| ⇧ | **buyer's maximum** | ⇧ |
| ⇩ | **seller's minimum** | ⇩ |

**Fig. 4.9** Negotiating positions in forest property sale.

Thus, before we enter the market for a property we should attempt to value it, both from the point of view of what price it is likely to fetch and what we feel it is worth. The first viewpoint can be initially addressed by using a market valuation, although if sufficient comparable sales data are not available it is likely that resort will have to be had to other methods. Perhaps the best way of valuing the property for ourselves is the expectation method - after all, this tells us what the stream of costs and benefits is worth in today's money. This would involve calculating the expectation value of all of the assets being sold and summing them in line with what we or any future buyers are likely to do with them. So all compartments and other pieces of land and what is contained upon them need to be valued, as well as any other assets such as materials, machinery and animals.

As a buyer I may be prepared to go up to, but no further than, my valuation in my bid. If I were to obtain the property for exactly this amount this would mean that, if my expectations about the future are correct, the return from my investment would be exactly equal to the discount rate used in my calculations. On the other hand, I would probably wish to pay well below this for a number of reasons, including:

1. Any reduction in the purchase price would raise the rate of return on my investment which means increasing the profits obtained from the property.

2. If my calculations did not take account of risk, then the valuation figure obtained is likely to overestimate its value. Appendix 4.3 shows how to take account in the valuation of the estimated probabilities of different hazards (such as windthrow) occurring in the future.

Sometimes a buyer will, in fact, pay above their valuation, especially if he wants the property in order to gain tax advantages or is extremely keen on purchase for non-financial reasons.

As a seller, I may not wish to go below my valuation, but may have to be prepared to do so if there is not much competition amongst buyers, or a lot of properties on the market, especially if I am desperate to sell. Anyway, if risks are not insubstantial a lower valuation is probably more reasonable.

# Conclusion

Apart from the valuation of trees and land there is little controversy concerning which valuation method to use. However, when valuing trees and land we are faced with three alternatives - market value, devastation value (along with accumulated net cost) and expectation value. Which should we choose? On the first page of this chapter it was suggested that we should seek the most realistic method, within our time, cost and competence limitations, so the following comments are made in the light of this.

Market valuation is currently being promoted and adopted by some major organisations and in estimating a value when buying or selling it can be useful, but its accuracy is suspect because of inadequacy of data and it cannot really cope with year to year changes. As an economist, I would tend towards the expectation value, but because of the uncertainty involved (remembering the 'prudence' convention) I am drawn towards a method giving a valuation of what is there now. Nevertheless, because environmental restraints have become much more stringent than in the past, it is now highly unlikely that permission would be granted for early felling, which the devastation approach assumes. Therefore, I would come down in favour of the expectation value: despite its drawbacks, it is *marginally* preferable to the devastation method.

Whichever method you choose you should stick to it and employ it to as high a degree of precision as is warranted by the time and effort involved relative to the benefits of the level of accuracy achieved.

# Menzies Example

In the previous chapter we saw how Douglas carried out step 2 of his budget. There he calculated profit (overall and for each cost centre), but in doing so he had to have figures for the opening and closing valuations of the trees and land in each compartment. We can now follow the technique which he used to arrive at these figures. Let us use compartment 1 as an example.

Since Douglas has decided to use the expectation method he first sets out the costs and benefits for a full rotation of Knots pine, YC16. The expected costs and benefits per hectare are shown in Table 4.7. Note that, all costs and benefits are assigned to a particular point in time, measured in years from the start of the rotation. Thus, because the initial costs are expected to occur in the first half of the first year they are assigned to time zero (i.e. the start of the first year). The revenues, sales costs and overheads are expected to occur in the second half of the year.

The overhead charges have been calculated on a per hectare basis by taking the total overheads for the forestry enterprise in Table 3.4 in the last chapter (£34,859) and dividing this by the total forest hectares (350) to give £99.60 per hectare. Although overheads are expected to change somewhat over the next few years, basing the figure on that expected over the next year seems reasonable.

**Table 4.7**   Knots pine rotation - costs and benefits per hectare.

| time (years) | operation | cost £ | benefit £ |
|---|---|---|---|
| 0 | fencing | 250.00 | |
| | pre-plant weeding | 80.00 | |
| | scarification | 100.00 | |
| | plants | 250.00 | |
| | planting | 200.00 | |
| 1 | weeding | 100.00 | |
| 2 | weeding | 100.00 | |
| | planting grant | | 375.00 |
| 22 | thinning | | 185.76 |
| 27 | thinning | | 1,369.73 |
| 32 | thinning | | 2,206.46 |
| 37 | thinning | | 3,055.04 |
| 47 | sales costs | 180.00 | |
| | clear cut | | 23,944.51 |
| all | overheads | 99.60 | |

Now, at the start of the budget year (2002 in this case), compartment 1, planted in 1992, will be 10 years old. So, to calculate the expectation value of the stand at that point, Douglas follows a number of steps, as follows:

1. He sets out the expected costs and benefits over the remaining years of the rotation - the first six columns of Table 4.8 illustrate this (these are taken, of course, from Table 4.7). So, for instance, in year 22 we have the annual cost of £99.60 and thinnings revenue of £185.76.

2. The values must then be discounted from the future back to today. Douglas has decided to use a discount rate of 6% and has worked out the discount factor for each of the remaining years of the rotation using the formula:

$$\text{discount factor} = \frac{1}{(1+\text{discount rate})^{\text{years left}}}$$

Thus, in the penultimate column, the discount factor for the thinnings and overheads occurring at the end of year 22, 12 years from the current date is:

$$\text{discount factor} = \frac{1}{(1+0.06)^{12}} = \frac{1}{2.012} = 0.497$$

The net benefit for each year is then multiplied by the discount factor to give the present value. Thus for year 22 the overhead cost of £99.60 is subtracted from the revenue of £185.76, giving a net benefit of £86.16, which is then multiplied by the discount factor, 0.497, to give a present value of £42.82.

**Table 4.8** Calculating the expectation value of compartment 1.

| time* | direct costs | overhead costs | total costs | revenue | net benefit | discount factor | present value |
|---|---|---|---|---|---|---|---|
| years | £ | £ | £ | £ | £ | @ 6% | £ |
| 10 | 0 | 0.00 | 0.00 | 0 | 0.00 | 1.000 | 0.00 |
| 11 | 0 | 99.60 | 99.60 | 0 | -99.60 | 0.943 | -93.92 |
| 12 | 0 | 99.60 | 99.60 | 0 | -99.60 | 0.890 | -88.64 |
| 13 | 0 | 99.60 | 99.60 | 0 | -99.60 | 0.840 | -83.66 |
| 14 | 0 | 99.60 | 99.60 | 0 | -99.60 | 0.792 | -78.88 |
| 15 | 0 | 99.60 | 99.60 | 0 | -99.60 | 0.747 | -74.40 |
| 16 | 0 | 99.60 | 99.60 | 0 | -99.60 | 0.705 | -70.22 |
| 17 | 0 | 99.60 | 99.60 | 0 | -99.60 | 0.665 | -66.23 |
| 18 | 0 | 99.60 | 99.60 | 0 | -99.60 | 0.627 | -62.45 |
| 19 | 0 | 99.60 | 99.60 | 0 | -99.60 | 0.592 | -58.96 |
| 20 | 0 | 99.60 | 99.60 | 0 | -99.60 | 0.558 | -55.58 |
| 21 | 0 | 99.60 | 99.60 | 0 | -99.60 | 0.527 | -52.49 |
| 22 | 0 | 99.60 | 99.60 | 185.76 | 86.16 | 0.497 | 42.82 |
| 23 | 0 | 99.60 | 99.60 | 0 | -99.60 | 0.469 | -46.71 |
| 24 | 0 | 99.60 | 99.60 | 0 | -99.60 | 0.442 | -44.02 |
| 25 | 0 | 99.60 | 99.60 | 0 | -99.60 | 0.417 | -41.53 |
| 26 | 0 | 99.60 | 99.60 | 0 | -99.60 | 0.394 | -39.24 |
| 27 | 0 | 99.60 | 99.60 | 1,369.73 | 1,270.13 | 0.371 | 471.22 |
| 28 | 0 | 99.60 | 99.60 | 0 | -99.60 | 0.350 | -34.86 |
| 29 | 0 | 99.60 | 99.60 | 0 | -99.60 | 0.331 | -32.97 |
| 30 | 0 | 99.60 | 99.60 | 0 | -99.60 | 0.312 | -31.08 |
| 31 | 0 | 99.60 | 99.60 | 0 | -99.60 | 0.294 | -29.28 |
| 32 | 0 | 99.60 | 99.60 | 2,206.46 | 2,106.86 | 0.278 | 585.71 |
| 33 | 0 | 99.60 | 99.60 | 0 | -99.60 | 0.262 | -26.10 |
| 34 | 0 | 99.60 | 99.60 | 0 | -99.60 | 0.247 | -24.60 |
| 35 | 0 | 99.60 | 99.60 | 0 | -99.60 | 0.233 | -23.21 |
| 36 | 0 | 99.60 | 99.60 | 0 | -99.60 | 0.220 | -21.91 |
| 37 | 0 | 99.60 | 99.60 | 3,055.04 | 2,955.45 | 0.207 | 611.78 |
| 38 | 0 | 99.60 | 99.60 | 0 | -99.60 | 0.196 | -19.52 |
| 39 | 0 | 99.60 | 99.60 | 0 | -99.60 | 0.185 | -18.43 |
| 40 | 0 | 99.60 | 99.60 | 0 | -99.60 | 0.174 | -17.33 |
| 41 | 0 | 99.60 | 99.60 | 0 | -99.60 | 0.164 | -16.33 |
| 42 | 0 | 99.60 | 99.60 | 0 | -99.60 | 0.155 | -15.44 |
| 43 | 0 | 99.60 | 99.60 | 0 | -99.60 | 0.146 | -14.54 |
| 44 | 0 | 99.60 | 99.60 | 0 | -99.60 | 0.138 | -13.74 |
| 45 | 0 | 99.60 | 99.60 | 0 | -99.60 | 0.130 | -12.95 |
| 46 | 0 | 99.60 | 99.60 | 0 | -99.60 | 0.123 | -12.25 |
| 47 | 180 | 99.60 | 279.60 | 23,944.51 | 23,664.91 | 0.116 | 2,745.13 |
| | | | | | | NPV @ 6% | 3,135.16 |

* from the start of the rotation.

However, one year's figure is omitted from the calculation. Although there is an overhead cost of £99.60 occurring at the end of year 10, if we are at the threshold between year 10 and 11 that cost will already have occurred so it should not be included in the calculation, since we should be only including costs and benefits still to occur. Thus, in the table a figure of zero has been inserted for year 10.

The present values are summed (i.e. all the values in the present value column) to give the NPV of the current rotation of £3,135.16/ha.

3. Next, Douglas wishes to find the value of the land on which the trees stand. Remember that, to do this, you need to calculate the NPV for a complete rotation, convert this to a perpetual series of rotations and then discount this value from the end of the rotation back to today. Therefore, he first lists in the first six columns of Table 4.9 the costs and benefits for a complete rotation.

**Fig. 4.10** Measurement has to take place as the basis for valuation

4. Douglas then calculates the discount factors; this time they are not for the period from the end of year 10 until the point in time when the cost or benefit occurs, but from the start of the rotation. So, for instance, the discount factor for the year 22 net benefit of £86.16 is

$$\text{discount factor} = \frac{1}{(1+0.06)^{22}} = \frac{1}{3.604} = 0.278$$

which gives a present value of £23.95. The present values are calculated in the same way as before and summed to give the NPV for the whole rotation which, in this case is £293.84.

**Table 4.9** Calculating the LEV for compartment 1.

| time | direct costs | overhead costs | total costs | revenue | net benefit | discount factor | present value |
|---|---|---|---|---|---|---|---|
| years | £ | £ | £ | £ | £ | @ 6% | £ |
| 0 | 880 | 0.00 | 880.00 | 0.00 | -880.00 | 1.000 | -880.00 |
| 1 | 100 | 99.60 | 199.60 | 0.00 | -199.60 | 0.943 | -188.22 |
| 2 | 100 | 99.60 | 199.60 | 375.00 | 175.40 | 0.890 | 156.11 |
| 3 | 0 | 99.60 | 99.60 | 0.00 | -99.60 | 0.840 | -83.66 |
| 4 | 0 | 99.60 | 99.60 | 0.00 | -99.60 | 0.792 | -78.88 |
| 5 | 0 | 99.60 | 99.60 | 0.00 | -99.60 | 0.747 | -74.40 |
| 6 | 0 | 99.60 | 99.60 | 0.00 | -99.60 | 0.705 | -70.22 |
| 7 | 0 | 99.60 | 99.60 | 0.00 | -99.60 | 0.665 | -66.23 |
| 8 | 0 | 99.60 | 99.60 | 0.00 | -99.60 | 0.627 | -62.45 |
| 9 | 0 | 99.60 | 99.60 | 0.00 | -99.60 | 0.592 | -58.96 |
| 10 | 0 | 99.60 | 99.60 | 0.00 | -99.60 | 0.558 | -55.58 |
| 11 | 0 | 99.60 | 99.60 | 0.00 | -99.60 | 0.527 | -52.49 |
| 12 | 0 | 99.60 | 99.60 | 0.00 | -99.60 | 0.497 | -49.50 |
| 13 | 0 | 99.60 | 99.60 | 0.00 | -99.60 | 0.469 | -46.71 |
| 14 | 0 | 99.60 | 99.60 | 0.00 | -99.60 | 0.442 | -44.02 |
| 15 | 0 | 99.60 | 99.60 | 0.00 | -99.60 | 0.417 | -41.53 |
| 16 | 0 | 99.60 | 99.60 | 0.00 | -99.60 | 0.394 | -39.24 |
| 17 | 0 | 99.60 | 99.60 | 0.00 | -99.60 | 0.371 | -36.95 |
| 18 | 0 | 99.60 | 99.60 | 0.00 | -99.60 | 0.350 | -34.86 |
| 19 | 0 | 99.60 | 99.60 | 0.00 | -99.60 | 0.331 | -32.97 |
| 20 | 0 | 99.60 | 99.60 | 0.00 | -99.60 | 0.312 | -31.08 |
| 21 | 0 | 99.60 | 99.60 | 0.00 | -99.60 | 0.294 | -29.28 |
| 22 | 0 | 99.60 | 99.60 | 185.76 | 86.16 | 0.278 | 23.95 |
| 23 | 0 | 99.60 | 99.60 | 0.00 | -99.60 | 0.262 | -26.10 |
| 24 | 0 | 99.60 | 99.60 | 0.00 | -99.60 | 0.247 | -24.60 |
| 25 | 0 | 99.60 | 99.60 | 0.00 | -99.60 | 0.233 | -23.21 |
| 26 | 0 | 99.60 | 99.60 | 0.00 | -99.60 | 0.220 | -21.91 |
| 27 | 0 | 99.60 | 99.60 | 1,369.73 | 1,270.13 | 0.207 | 262.92 |
| 28 | 0 | 99.60 | 99.60 | 0.00 | -99.60 | 0.196 | -19.52 |
| 29 | 0 | 99.60 | 99.60 | 0.00 | -99.60 | 0.185 | -18.43 |
| 30 | 0 | 99.60 | 99.60 | 0.00 | -99.60 | 0.174 | -17.33 |
| 31 | 0 | 99.60 | 99.60 | 0.00 | -99.60 | 0.164 | -16.33 |
| 32 | 0 | 99.60 | 99.60 | 2,206.46 | 2,106.86 | 0.155 | 326.56 |
| 33 | 0 | 99.60 | 99.60 | 0.00 | -99.60 | 0.146 | -14.54 |
| 34 | 0 | 99.60 | 99.60 | 0.00 | -99.60 | 0.138 | -13.74 |
| 35 | 0 | 99.60 | 99.60 | 0.00 | -99.60 | 0.130 | -12.95 |
| 36 | 0 | 99.60 | 99.60 | 0.00 | -99.60 | 0.123 | -12.25 |
| 37 | 0 | 99.60 | 99.60 | 3,055.04 | 2,955.45 | 0.116 | 342.83 |
| 38 | 0 | 99.60 | 99.60 | 0.00 | -99.60 | 0.109 | -10.86 |
| 39 | 0 | 99.60 | 99.60 | 0.00 | -99.60 | 0.103 | -10.26 |
| 40 | 0 | 99.60 | 99.60 | 0.00 | -99.60 | 0.097 | -9.66 |
| 41 | 0 | 99.60 | 99.60 | 0.00 | -99.60 | 0.092 | -9.16 |
| 42 | 0 | 99.60 | 99.60 | 0.00 | -99.60 | 0.087 | -8.67 |
| 43 | 0 | 99.60 | 99.60 | 0.00 | -99.60 | 0.082 | -8.17 |
| 44 | 0 | 99.60 | 99.60 | 0.00 | -99.60 | 0.077 | -7.67 |
| 45 | 0 | 99.60 | 99.60 | 0.00 | -99.60 | 0.073 | -7.27 |
| 46 | 0 | 99.60 | 99.60 | 0.00 | -99.60 | 0.069 | -6.87 |
| 47 | 180 | 99.60 | 279.60 | 23,944.51 | 23,664.91 | 0.065 | 1,538.22 |
| | | | | | | NPV @ 6% | 293.84 |

5.   The LEV is calculated using the formula

$$LEV = PV \times \frac{(1 + \text{discount rate})^{years}}{(1 + \text{discount rate})^{years} - 1}$$

which is here

$$LEV = £293.84 \times \frac{(1 + 0.06)^{47}}{(1 + 0.06)^{47} - 1} = £293.84 \times 1.069 = £314.11$$

6.   Since the LEV represents the value of a perpetual stream of rotations based at the start of a full rotation, whereas compartment 1 will not be in a position to commence a new rotation for 37 years (as we are currently at the end of year 10 of the rotation), then the LEV has to be adjusted to take account of this. That is, Douglas has to discount the LEV back 37 years. The calculation for this is therefore:

$$\text{adjusted LEV} = \frac{£314.11}{(1 + 0.06)^{37}} = £36.37$$

7.   Finally, to arrive at the complete opening valuation for compartment 1 Douglas must take the NPV of the current rotation and the adjusted LEV, which are expressed per hectare, and multiply by the area, which is 35 hectares:

Opening valuation of trees and land =
$$(£3,135.16 + £36.37) \times 35 = £3,171.53 \times 35 = £111,004$$

   If we had not rounded the overhead costs and the discount factors we would have obtained a slightly different figure of £110,816. If you go back to Table 3.2 in the last chapter you will see that this is the figure used for the opening valuation of compartment 1. The figures for the opening and closing valuations for all compartments are calculated in the same way.
   That is how Douglas deals with the valuation of the trees and the land, but what about all of the other things in the estate - the buildings, the machinery, the office furniture, the plants in the nursery and the stocks of chemicals and other bits and pieces? Well, for the plants he employs the same method as for the trees, except that the time before they are sold or transferred is shorter. For the chemicals and other stores he simply estimates the market value. And for the buildings, machinery, equipment and furniture he uses a procedure known as depreciation - this is the subject of the next chapter.

## Appendix 4.1 Taking Account of Time and Interest: Discounting

To repeat the question posed in the text: in calculating the value of a series of future costs and benefits, why should we not simply add them? The short answer was: because of time and interest. A more detailed answer is as follows.

Those cash flows are not received and paid out today - they occur in the future, and because of that they mean less to me. Take £100 in a year's time, for instance. That £100 payable one year from now means less to me than £100 payable today. Why? If I had to pay £100 today and borrow the money to do so, at say 6% per annum, then by the end of the year I would have owed £100 + £6 = £106. Or, looked at another way, if I used my own money to pay the £100 today, then I would forgo, or miss out on, the opportunity of investing the money somewhere and earning interest on it. Again, if I could get a rate of 6%, the £100 would become £106 in a year's time. This can be expressed in different ways:

Paying out £100 today is the same to me as paying out £106 in one year's time.

I would be indifferent between £100 paid today and £106 paid after one year.

At 6% interest, £100 paid today is equivalent to £106 paid in one year's time.

This can be expressed mathematically in words as:

future value = present value + (present value × decimal interest rate)

which is the same as saying:

future value = present value × (1 + decimal interest rate)

Okay. So now think how I would owe £100 in a year's time if I paid a bill today and borrowed the money at 6% to do so. In other words, I have to solve this mathematical formula for 'something':

'something' × (1 + 0.06) = £100

therefore, dividing both sides by (1 + 0.06) we get

'something' = £100 ÷ (1 + 0.06)

which gives an answer of £94.34.

Hence, if I borrow money at 6% or could earn 6% on my own money, £100 payable (or receivable) in one year's time is to me equivalent to £94.34 payable today. I should not mind paying either way, as they ultimately have exactly the same effect on my bank account.

So just as we had an equation for the future value, we can move the terms around and derive one for the present value, thus:

present value = future value ÷ ( 1 + decimal interest rate)

Let us now take our example a stage further. What about the £100 payable after two years - how do I work out what that is equivalent to today? The procedure is the same as before, only for two years rather than one year:

If I had to pay the £100 today and borrowed the money at 6%, by the end of two years I would owe £100 + £6 = £106 after one year, all of which would have interest charged against it for the second year, thus:

(£100 + £6) + (£100 + £6) × 0.06 = £106 + £6.36 = £112.36

Therefore, we are saying again that, if the interest rate is 6%, then £100 paid today is equivalent to £112.36 payable in two years' time.

This can be expressed more generally as:

future value = present value × (1 + decimal interest rate) × (1 + decimal interest rate)

or

future value = present value × (1 + decimal interest rate)$^2$

We can turn this upside down again and ask, "What is today's equivalent of £100 payable in two years, if the interest rate is 6%?"

The formula is £100 ÷ $1.06^2$ , which gives an answer of £89.

Again the general formula becomes:

present value = future value ÷ ( 1 + decimal interest rate)$^2$

These future value and present value formulae can be expressed even more generally, like this:

future value = present value × ( 1 + decimal interest rate)$^{years}$

and

present value = future value ÷ ( 1 + decimal interest rate)$^{years}$

one simply being the 'upside down' or reciprocal of the other. The first calculation is known as **compounding** and the second as **discounting**[18]. And the interest rate we use for the discounting is called the **discount rate**. Discounting

---

[18] Incidentally, discounting appears to have been 'invented' in the mid-1800s by a German forester by the name of Martin Faustmann.

is thus a way of converting cash flows at different points in time to one common measure - today's money. You see, because of the effect of interest over time, amounts of money expressed at different points in time are not comparable - it is rather like having a number of sums of money in different currencies - dollars, sterling, rupees and shillings. People would think we were stupid if we simply added them up - we would first need to convert them into a common currency: in Caledonia this would be most easily understood if the amounts were all converted into Caledonian £. Similarly, it helps if we convert amounts of money accruing at different points in time into the currency which we most readily understand - that of the present. Hence, we express amounts in terms of their present values.

You should now be a little clearer as to why we could not simply add up those amounts in our example in the main text: they occur at different points in time and therefore need to be converted into a common currency before they can be summed. Let us go through the calculations:

The present value of the £10 payable in one year, at 6%, is:

$$£100 \div (1 + 0.06) = £9.43$$

The present value of the £100 payable after two years was calculated as

$$£100 \div (1 + 0.06)^2 = £8.90$$

At the end of the third year we have two cash flows: £10 going out and £9,000 coming in, so the calculation is:

$$(£19,000 - £10) \div (1 + 0.06)^3 = £18,990 \div 1.191 = £15,944.58$$

We can now take the sum of the present values (remembering that some are negative) to obtain the net present value (NPV):

$$NPV = £15,944.58 - £8.90 - £9.43 = £15,926.25$$

Compare this with the figure of £18,970 we obtained earlier by simply summing the cash flows regardless of timing: quite a difference, isn't there?

Before we return to look at what this all means for the expectation value approach, there are three further points to mention:

1. Notice that we used a figure of 1.191 to discount the third-year cash flow. This was derived from the formula $1.06^3$. Similarly, the figure for two years is 1.124 (from $1.06^2$) and for one year is 1.06. This can be readily worked out by using the $y^x$ button on your calculator[19] or in a spreadsheet (using the expression

---

[19] For instance, for the three-year figure we type 1.06 followed by pressing the $y^x$ button, then 3, then the = button.

'=1.06^ 3'). Although the procedure is fairly straightforward if you have a modern calculator, if you do not have access to one you may need to refer to a 'ready reckoner' table, which is included in many economics and accounting textbooks including this one. You may find them confusing however, but only because they give the answers in a different form to that shown above. For instance, the figure for three years at 6% would be 0.840.

The explanation is quite simple: conventionally, **discount factors**, as they are called, are expressed as:

$$\frac{1}{(1 + \text{discount rate})^{\text{years}}}$$

instead of:

$$(1 + \text{discount rate})^{\text{years}}$$

This makes no difference to the answer we get, it is simply that our figure has to be *divided* into the amount whereas with the discount factor we have to *multiply* it by the amount instead. Thus, for our third-year cash flow our calculation was:

£18,990 ÷ 1.191 = £15,944.58

whereas, using the discount factor from the tables, the calculation would be:

£18,990 × 0.840 = £15,951.60

The answers are slightly different because the discount factors were rounded.

2. Notice that *the further into the future our cash flows occur, the smaller the present value becomes*: Table 4.10 illustrates this. Thus, the present value of the £10 paid after two years was less than the present value for that paid after one year. This is because we are effectively taking off a bigger interest charge for the cash flow in the second year compared to that in the first year.

Also, *present values become smaller as we raise the discount rate*. Remember our third-year cash flow discounted at 6% was £15,944.58. If we discount using 9% instead the calculation becomes:

(£19,000 - £10) ÷ (1 + **0.09**)$^3$ = £18,990 ÷ **1.295** = £14,664.09

and, if we discount at 3%, the answer is:

(£19,000 - £10) ÷ (1 + **0.03**)$^3$ = £18.990 ÷ **1.405** = £13,516.01

Again, raising the discount rate effectively means that we are taking off a higher interest charge in converting a future value to its value today.

Table 4.10 and Fig. 4.11 illustrate the effects that raising the discount rate and extending the time have on the present value of a future amount. The column on the left-hand side of Table 4.3 shows when in the future the cash flow is to occur, and the numbers within the table show the present value of £100 occurring at that time and discounted back to today at the given discount rate. So, for example, the present value of £100 occurring in 30 years at a rate of 10% is only £5.73, whereas a rate of 0% means that the present value is exactly the same £100 as the amount occurring in the future.

**Table 4.10** The effect of discount rate and time on present value.

| time | discount rate | | | |
|------|------|------|------|------|
| (years) | 0% | 3% | 5% | 10% |
| 0 | £100.00 | £100.00 | £100.00 | £100.00 |
| 10 | £100.00 | £74.41 | £61.39 | £38.55 |
| 20 | £100.00 | £55.37 | £37.69 | £14.86 |
| 30 | £100.00 | £41.20 | £23.14 | £5.73 |
| 40 | £100.00 | £30.66 | £14.20 | £2.21 |
| 50 | £100.00 | £22.81 | £8.72 | £0.85 |
| 60 | £100.00 | £16.97 | £5.35 | £0.33 |
| 70 | £100.00 | £12.63 | £3.29 | £0.13 |
| 80 | £100.00 | £9.40 | £2.02 | £0.05 |
| 90 | £100.00 | £6.99 | £1.24 | £0.02 |
| 100 | £100.00 | £5.20 | £0.76 | £0.01 |

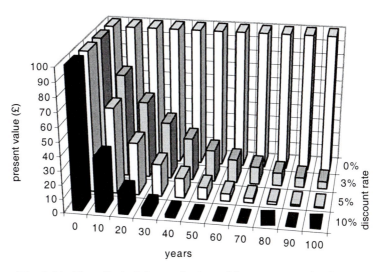

**Fig. 4.11** The effect of discount rate and time on present value.

Notice that when cash flows occurring more than 50 years in the future have even a relatively low discount rate applied, the present value is less than one quarter of their original value. This relationship is only accentuated as the discount rate rises. A discount rate of 10% makes the present value of any cash flow occurring 30 or more years in the future very small.

3. All of the future cash flows have been expressed in **real terms**, that is, without inflation. Put another way, we have expressed the future cash flows in terms of today's spending power of money, even though we know that prices in the future may well change. For instance, I might currently face labour costs of £6 per hour. Although these might go up by, say, 5% next year to £6.30 and a further 5% the following year to £6.62, if the general level of prices is expected to go up by the same percentages, then the spending power of that hourly wage rate has not changed - it stays the same *in real terms*. It is easier to work in real terms, rather than trying to predict inflation rates into the distant future. As Appendix 4.3 shows, as long as we use the real discount rate (the interest rate without inflation) rather than the actual (nominal rate), then we get the same valuation as we would if we had used nominal values and the nominal discount rate.

## Appendix 4.2   Accumulated Net Costs: With or Without Interest?

We discussed earlier the use of accumulated net costs as a means of valuing an immature stand before a meaningful positive devastation value was available. The method advocated involved not simply adding up the net costs so far, but also adding a cumulative interest charge. The reason for this was twofold - to ensure that the costs were inflated to bring them up to the current price level[20] and also to add an interest charge for the period between the original outlay and the present. The latter is justified in the same way as the discounting to today of future values - just as money tomorrow is worth less in today's terms, so money yesterday is worth more in today's terms. In other words, in the time interval between when the money was paid out and the present, I have either foregone the interest that I might have earned on that money by investing it elsewhere, or alternatively, I have had to pay interest on that amount borrowed from the bank over the period.

Table 4.11 and Fig. 4.12, following on from Table 4.1, illustrate the effects of the inclusion of interest in accumulated net costs. As before, interest is calculated based upon the accumulated net costs at the start of the year and using a rate of 12%. Accumulated net costs are then calculated for each year, excluding interest in the penultimate column and including it in the final column.

---

[20] Costs are inflated by simply including inflation in the interest rate; i.e. the nominal rather than real rate is used: See Appendix 4.3 for further explanation.

**Table 4.11** Accumulated net costs - exclusion and inclusion of interest.

| year | benefits | costs | net costs | interest charge @12% | net costs including interest | accumulated net costs excluding interest | accumulated net costs including interest |
|------|----------|-------|-----------|----------------------|------------------------------|------------------------------------------|------------------------------------------|
| | £ | £ | £ | £ | £ | £ | £ |
| 1996 | 0 | 1,000 | 1,000 | 0.00 | 1,000.00 | 1,000.00 | 1,000.00 |
| 1997 | 100 | 150 | 50 | 120.00 | 170.00 | 1,050.00 | 1,170.00 |
| 1998 | 100 | 150 | 50 | 140.40 | 190.40 | 1,100.00 | 1,360.40 |
| 1999 | 0 | 10 | 10 | 163.25 | 173.25 | 1,110.00 | 1,533.65 |
| 2000 | 0 | 10 | 10 | 184.04 | 194.04 | 1,120.00 | 1,727.69 |
| 2001 | 0 | 10 | 10 | 207.32 | 217.32 | 1,130.00 | 1,945.01 |

Both the table and the figure illustrate the way in which the inclusion of interest causes the accumulated net costs to diverge at an increasing rate, such that by the end of year 2001 the inclusion of interest gives rise to a figure more than 70% greater than its non-interest counterpart. In fact, if the figures were projected to year 20 of the rotation the former figure would be more than eight times the latter. It is therefore suggested, that if you do use accumulated net costs along with the devastation method, then interest should be included.

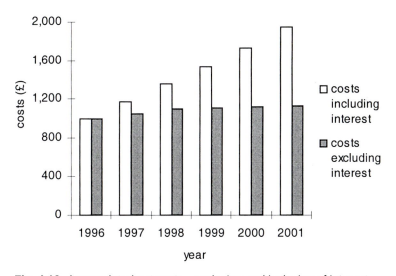

**Fig. 4.12** Accumulated net costs - exclusion and inclusion of interest.

## Appendix 4.3 Real or Nominal Terms Discounting

It was suggested earlier in the chapter that discounting should be carried out in real terms, which means that we set out the estimated real values of the stream of costs and benefits in the future and discount them back to the present using the real discount rate, i.e. the rule is: if we are using *real* terms (with inflation taken out) then everything must be in *real* terms, including the discount rate.

However, if we did want to set out the costs and benefits in nominal terms, i.e. in terms of the prices which we expect to prevail at each time period in which the costs and benefits occur, then we can do so. But then we have to employ the same rule as above, but replace 'real' with 'nominal', i.e. if we are using nominal terms (with inflation included) then everything must be in nominal terms, including the discount rate. So, in this case, we should be using the nominal discount rate. The important point which we will illustrate in a moment, is that, in whichever terms we carry out the calculations, as long as we do not mix nominal and real, then we arrive at the same answer: the same NPV.

As an example, imagine a forest compartment in which the cost and revenue structure is quite straightforward: establishment costs occur over the first two years, followed by a long gap until year 50, when the trees are ready for harvesting. At that point there will be felling costs and harvest revenue.

The two tables below show the costs and benefits and the effects of discounting in real terms (Table 4.12) and nominal terms (Table 4.13). The nominal discount rate used is 9.18%, and with an expected inflation rate of 3% this gives a real discount rate of:

$$\text{real discount rate} = \left( \frac{1 + 0.0918}{1 + 0.03} \right) - 1 = 1.06 - 1 = 0.06 \text{ or } 6\%$$

Thus, in the real-terms example, a discount rate of 6% is used and none of the cash flows are inflated, whereas in the nominal-terms example the discount rate is 9.18% and the cash flows are inflated by 3% per year.

**Table 4.12** Discounting in real terms.

| time | costs | benefits | net benefits | discount factor | present value |
| years | £ | £ | £ | @ 6% | £ |
|---|---|---|---|---|---|
| 0 | 500 | | -500 | 1.00 | -500.00 |
| 1 | 200 | | -200 | 0.943 | -188.68 |
| 2 | 200 | | -200 | 0.890 | -178.00 |
| .. | .. | | .. | .. | .. |
| 50 | 800 | 18,000 | 17,200 | 0.054 | 933.76 |
| | | | | NPV @ 6% | 67.08 |

In Table 4.12, when the present values for each year are added to give the Net Present Value, the figure of £67.08 is obtained. You may be surprised to find that when the same calculation is carried out for Table 4.13 we get the same NPV of £67.08. Actually, this is not really surprising when you think about it, because in the real-terms example we are inflating into the future by 0% and discounting back to the present by 6%, whereas in the nominal terms case we are inflating by 3% and discounting back by 9.18% - the net effect of which is the same. Therefore, it does not matter in which terms we carry out our discounting as long as we express everything in those terms. Nevertheless, many practitioners prefer to stick to the real-terms approach as it involves less adjustment and only having to forecast an average real rate of interest over the period, rather than both a nominal discount rate and an inflation rate.[21]

**Table 4.13** Discounting in nominal terms.

| time | costs | benefits | inflated costs | inflated benefits | inflated net benefits | discount factor | present value |
|---|---|---|---|---|---|---|---|
| years | £ | £ | £ | £ | £ | @9.18% | £ |
| 0 | 500 | | 500.00 | | -500.00 | 1.000 | -500.00 |
| 1 | 200 | | 206.00 | | -206.00 | 0.916 | -188.68 |
| 2 | 200 | | 212.18 | | -212.18 | 0.839 | -178.00 |
| . . | . . | | . . | | . . | . . | . . |
| 50 | 800 | 18,000 | 3,507.13 | 78,910.31 | 75,403.18 | 0.012 | 933.76 |
| | | | | | | NPV @ 9.183% | 67.08 |

One final point. If you expect prices to rise faster or slower than the general rate of inflation, then the values should be adjusted accordingly. If the analysis is in nominal terms you simply inflate the expected future costs and benefits by whatever rate you expect them to rise (or fall), but still continue to use the nominal discount rate. If the analysis is in real terms, then you inflate (or deflate) by the percentage by which you expect the values to diverge above (or below) the general rate of inflation, but you still use the real discount rate[22].

For instance, in Table 4.12 the prices on which the revenue calculation was based were expected to rise in line with the general rate of inflation of 3%, and so remain constant in real terms. But what if, in fact, we now decide that timber prices are likely to fall in real terms by 1% per annum? In other words, if general prices in the economy rise by 3% a year, timber prices will rise by approximately 2%. This means that timber prices will fall in real terms by year 50 to about 60.5% (i.e. $[1 - 0.01]^{50}$) of their current level[23]. The figure of £18,000 should therefore be adjusted down to this level, giving £10,890 in real terms.

To put this into words: working in real terms, if prices used in cash flows are expected to diverge from the general rate of inflation, the rate of divergence

---

[21] Remember though that you should normally carry out the discounting in terms of the prices at the start of the period, i.e. time zero. If you are using the calculation for valuing a stand of trees at a particular point in time then the analysis should be carried out in terms of the prices at that time. If you then wish to value for a year (or more) later, you should use the price levels that you expect in a year's (or more) time.

[22] An alternative, suggested by Price (1989), is not to inflate or deflate the cash flows but to discount them by different real discount rates, adjusted for the expected inflation rate affecting that item. If you do things this way you will arrive at exactly the same answer as using the method suggested here.

[23] If you want to be really exact then the calculation is:

$$\text{real decline} = \frac{(1 + \text{timber price inflation})^{years}}{(1 + \text{general inflation})^{years}} - 1 = \frac{1.02^{50}}{1.03^{50}} - 1 = 0.614$$

should be applied for the number of years in the future when they are expected to occur.

## Appendix 4.4  Risk and Uncertainty and Expectation Value

Valuation of trees and land involves a certain amount of uncertainty: if we use the market or the devastation approach we are not sure that the figures we arrive at would definitely be those which we would obtain if we were to sell the land or the standing timber today. And if we use the expectation approach we can only estimate what yields, prices and costs we will face into the future.

If we are faced with *uncertainty* as defined by economists, that is a series of possible outcomes with no idea of the probability of them occurring, then the calculations that we have made so far, based on our best estimates, although possibly subject to a good deal of uncertainty, are the best we can hope for. But if we do have some idea about the probability of different outcomes, a situation that according to the economist's definition involves *risk* rather than uncertainty, then it is possible to derive a more accurate valuation by taking those probabilities into account.

Now, although most of us do not have accurate figures on the probabilities of different outcomes in a forestry context, with some thought and research we could probably make rough estimates. Despite this, it is rare to see a valuation which attempts to take account of risk, for two main reasons - because people do not understand how to deal with risk and because of the complex calculations involved.

Here the objective is to show how valuations taking account of risk can be calculated and the difference in results compared to not doing so.

For market and devastation valuation approaches we can make a reasonably accurate estimate of the physical values - how much land is there, what are the areas, stocking rates, ages and volumes of trees, etc. The source of risk is more in terms of the prices which we would be likely to be receive. Now the price we have used so far is likely to be the one we deem to be the most likely, and if we estimated the probabilities of lower and higher prices to be equally balanced either side of that price, then the price we have used is the appropriate one.

Thus, if we calculated the risk-adjusted price as the weighted average of all possible prices, weighted by their respective probabilities, then we would find that it gave the same value as the best estimate which we had made in the first place. Imagine for instance a range of prices and probabilities as shown in Table 4.14 and Fig. 4.13.

In this case, the probability-weighted average price, which is termed the *expected price*[24] (Klemperer, 1996), turns out to be £10, the same as if the most likely price had been chosen.

---

[24]Or more generally, the expected value - not to be confused with the expectation value!

**Table 4.14** Probability-weighted average price calculations.

| price | probability | weighted value |
|---|---|---|
| 1 | 0.00 | 0.00 |
| 2 | 0.00 | 0.00 |
| 3 | 0.00 | 0.00 |
| 4 | 0.01 | 0.04 |
| 5 | 0.02 | 0.10 |
| 6 | 0.04 | 0.24 |
| 7 | 0.08 | 0.56 |
| 8 | 0.10 | 0.80 |
| 9 | 0.15 | 1.35 |
| 10 | 0.20 | 2.00 |
| 11 | 0.15 | 1.65 |
| 12 | 0.10 | 1.20 |
| 13 | 0.08 | 1.04 |
| 14 | 0.04 | 0.56 |
| 15 | 0.02 | 0.30 |
| 16 | 0.01 | 0.16 |
| total | 1.00 | 10.00 |

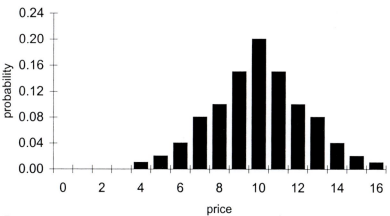

**Fig. 4.13** Price probabilities

If, however, to take an extreme example, the distribution of probabilities was skewed, then the result would be rather different, as Table 4.15 and Fig. 4.14 show. Here, although the best estimate might be a price of £10, the probability weighted average price would be £8.29. However, it is likely that when we make

**Table 4.15**  Probability-weighted average price calculation - skewed distribution.

| price | probability | weighted value |
|-------|-------------|----------------|
| 0 | 0.00 | 0.00 |
| 1 | 0.00 | 0.00 |
| 2 | 0.01 | 0.00 |
| 3 | 0.02 | 0.06 |
| 4 | 0.04 | 0.16 |
| 5 | 0.07 | 0.35 |
| 6 | 0.09 | 0.54 |
| 7 | 0.11 | 0.77 |
| 8 | 0.13 | 1.04 |
| 9 | 0.16 | 1.44 |
| 10 | 0.20 | 2.00 |
| 11 | 0.12 | 1.32 |
| 12 | 0.04 | 0.48 |
| 13 | 0.01 | 0.13 |
| 14 | 0.00 | 0.00 |
| 15 | 0.00 | 0.00 |
| 16 | 0.00 | 0.00 |
| total | 1.00 | 8.29 |

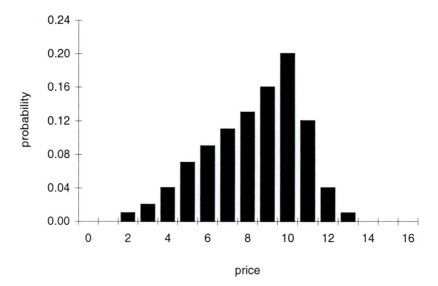

**Fig. 4.14**  Price probabilities - skewed distribution.

an estimate of the expected price in the first place, we would probably subconsciously take account of the probabilities. If not, then it would be worth using the methodology employed here.

Turning to the expectation valuation method, if the risk is seen in terms of the variability of the prices that might be received or the costs expended at a particular date, the problem is not really any more complex than the one just dealt with - we simply work out a probability-weighted average price and use this in the analysis.

A more complicated problem arises with the expectation valuation method when there is a risk of various hazards occurring which may cause a shortening of the rotation and a reduction in the revenue; windthrow and disease are examples. How would we work out the expected value then?

Some practitioners get round some hazard problems by insuring against them. Although this raises costs, it does mean that if the hazard should occur then some or all of the lost income will be reimbursed. Others (see Reed, 1984 for instance) would suggest simply raising the discount rate by the annual risk rate - if the discount rate is 6% and the annual risk of hazard is 2% then the discount rate should be 8%. But this is only acceptable if the risk rate is constant throughout the rotation. So, in many situations we are still left with the question posed at the end of the previous paragraph - how to account for risk in the expected value calculations.

If only the current rotation were to be considered, the expected net present value ($NPV_E$) would be the probability-weighted sum of the present values of the different outcomes, thus:

$$NPV_E = NPV_1 p_1 + NPV_2 p_2 (1-p_1) + NPV_3 p_3 (1-p_1)(1-p_2) +...+ (1-p_1)...(1-p_{n-1})$$

where the subscripts 1, 2, etc. refer to the different outcomes at different stages in the rotation, probabilities of those outcomes are denoted by p, and the subscript n refers to the final outcome, if the planned rotation is successful.

In other words, we work out the present values of each of the different outcomes, weight them by their probabilities, and add them together. For instance, imagine a 50-year rotation, with two risky events, the first being crop failure due to disease in year 5 with probability 0.1, the second being windthrow in year 40, with probability 0.2. This means that the probability of failure in year 5 is 0.1, in year 40 it is 0.18 (i.e. 0.2 × the probability of reaching year 40, which is 1 - 0.1 or 0.9), and the probability of reaching harvesting age at year 50 is 0.72 (i.e. 1 - 0.1 - 0.18). Table 4.16 shows the cash flows associated with the different events and their present values, discounting at 5%.

The expected net present value is worked out by multiplying the NPVs by their probabilities and summing them, thus:

$$NPV_E = 0.1 \times -100.0 + 0.18 \times 27.8 + 0.72 \times 74.4 = £48.58$$

a very different result from the £74.4 obtained under the assumption of no risk.

**Table 4.16** Discounting for risk (@5%).

| outcome: | disease | | windthrow | | full rotation | |
|---|---|---|---|---|---|---|
| time | cash flow | present value | cash flow | present value | cash flow | present value |
| (years) | £ | £ | £ | £ | £ | £ |
| 0 | -100 | -100.0 | -100 | -100.0 | -100 | -100.0 |
| 5 | 0 | 0.0 | - | - | - | - |
| 40 | - | - | 900 | 127.8 | - | - |
| 50 | - | - | - | - | 2000 | 174.4 |
| | NPV | -100.0 | NPV | 27.8 | NPV | 74.4 |

This, however, is not all. If events which shorten the rotation might occur, then cash flows from successor crops will occur earlier, and successor crops themselves may also be subject to risk. In order to visualise the implications of this, consider an example. Imagine that the optimum rotation is 50 years, and the probability of the trees reaching that age is 0.8, whereas the probability of windthrow occurring at age 40 is 0.2. If these probabilities are taken to apply to future as well as current rotations, then the possible outcomes for the first three rotations which need to be considered can be shown diagrammatically as in Fig. 4.15.

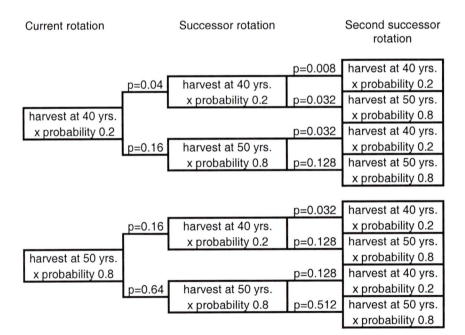

**Fig. 4.15** Outcomes and probabilities - windthrow example.

Here we have only looked at two successor generations - if we were to bring in more, then the picture would expand further and the calculations become even more complex. Fortunately, a general rule can be derived which enables us to calculate the *risk-adjusted LEV, expected LEV*, or what Price (1989) terms the *Mean Expected Value (MEV)*. The general formula can be written:

$$LEV_E = NPV_{E_c} + NPV_{E_s} \frac{A}{(1-A)}$$

where the first NPV term refers to the current rotation (calculated according to the formula on the previous page) and the second refers to the successor rotation (these may not be the same, if a different species is likely to be planted as successor, or if re-establishment costs are likely to be different from the initial establishment costs) and

$$A = \frac{p_1}{(1+r)^{t_1}} + \frac{p_2(1-p_1)}{(1+r)^{t_2}} + \frac{p_3(1-p_1)(1-p_2)}{(1+r)^{t_3}} + ... + \frac{p_n(1-p_1)...(1-p_{n-1})}{(1+r)^{t_n}}$$

that is, the sum of the discounted probabilities of all outcomes over the rotation.

This calculation can be made easier if broken into a series of steps:

Step 1   Calculate the expected NPV of the current rotation;
Step 2   Calculate the expected NPV of the successor rotation;
Step 3   Calculate A; and
Step 4   Combine the NPV's and A in the expected LEV equation.

Taking the example above, and assuming that re-establishment costs are 40 instead of 100, the results from each step are:

Step 1   The expected NPV for the current rotation, calculated earlier, was £48.58

Step 2   The expected NPV for the successor rotation is simply £60 greater because of the difference between initial establishment and re-establishment costs, giving £108.58

Step 3   There are three possible outcomes - failure in year 5 because of disease, premature harvest of a damaged crop in year 40 due to windthrow, and successful harvest in year 50. The calculation of A is therefore:

$$A = \frac{0.1}{(1.05)^5} + \frac{0.2(1-0.1)}{(1.05)^{40}} + \frac{(1-0.1)(1-0.2)}{(1.05)^{50}} = 0.078 + 0.026 + 0.063 = 0.167$$

Step 4   The expected LEV is now derived as:

$$LEV_E = 48.58 + 108.58 \frac{0.167}{(1 - 0.167)} = £70.31$$

Now compare this to the LEV which would have been obtained by assuming no risk. The unadjusted NPV for the current rotation, as we saw earlier, was £74.40, whereas for the successor crop the figure would be £60 greater, £134.40. If all rotations gave this latter NPV we would simply multiply £134.40 by 1.0955, which is the LEV formula given in the main part of this chapter. This would give £147.25, but since the current rotation has an establishment cost £60 greater than that for all successor rotations, this must be subtracted from the £147.25 to give a LEV of £87.25. In this example then, although the expected NPV of £48.58 was about two thirds of the unadjusted NPV of £74.40, the expected LEV is about four fifths of the unadjusted LEV, i.e. the gap is narrower because the negative effect of disease and windthrow is partly reduced by the earlier receipt of returns from successor rotations.

For some further developments along these lines refer to Bright and Price (2000).

## Appendix 4.5  Effects on Profits of Valuation Approaches

The valuation method used affects profit, since the valuation change is used in the profit. The following example will help to illustrate the effects of the valuation method.

Using the same data as was used to derive Fig. 4.4, but with a discount rate of 3%, profits for each year of the rotation have been calculated using three different valuation methods: expectation method, devastation method and adjusted devastation method. As suggested in the chapter, the devastation method here is combined with the net accumulated costs (including interest) until year 35.

The expectation method produces a profit which grows fairly smoothly over the rotation - in fact it grows directly in line with the change in valuation. Unless predictions of costs and revenues in the year ahead, for the remaining years of the rotation and also for successor rotations (although the effects of the latter will be limited because they are so far into the future) change, then profits calculated each year will not diverge from the predictions made at the start of the rotation.

The profit stream derived under the devastation valuation method, is much less smooth, however. Although, profits will grow fairly smoothly during the early years when net accumulated costs are used, at the point of changeover from the latter to the devastation method there may be a large jump or decline in profits. There will also be wide variation in later years because of the thinning revenues. The latter occur partly because published yield models are often produced for five-year intervals and are then interpolated between without taking account of the drop in value immediately after thinnings have taken place. To allow for this here, the valuations were adjusted in an attempt to take account of thinnings, but as Fig. 4.16 shows, although the variation is reduced it is not completely removed.

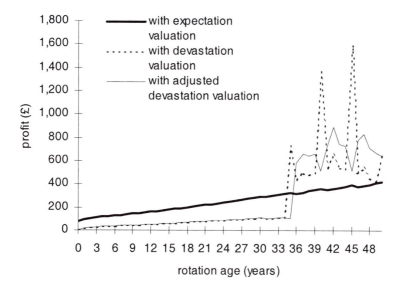

**Fig. 4.16** Profits calculated using different valuation methods.

Again, apart from the causes of change mentioned above, the profit would be completely predictable from the outset. However, this is not really a problem, but rather a truism. What we are really saying is this: if things go according to plan then they are predictable! It does, though, mean that if we want each year's profit to be meaningful, we do need to change the predictions in the light of revised expectations. Thus, if we had predicted at the outset that clear fell revenue would be £10,000, but now we believe that prices will be lower, then we should revise our figures, accordingly.

As far as profit calculations when derived under a market valuation approach are concerned, it is likely that the valuation figures will not be sufficiently precise to give figures for each age of a rotation; rather values may be quoted for age ranges. If so, the figures are likely to give rise to wide variations in profit figures, rather than the smoother pattern derived under the expectation approach. Figure 4.17 shows what would happen under the market valuation approach if valuation figures were only available for five-year periods. If such is the case, then although market valuations might be acceptable for other uses, unless they were interpolated in an informed way, then they would not be acceptable for annual profit calculations.

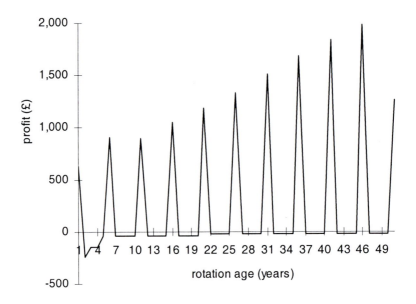

**Fig. 4.17** Profits calculated using a market valuation method.

So, if we were to judge valuation methods on this issue only, the expectation valuation would come out on top.

# Chapter 5

# Depreciation

Some assets, trees for instance, go up in value from one year to the next, some may have a constant value (land, materials in store), while others lose value because they are used up or worn out. This loss of value through wear and tear is known as **depreciation**. And assets, such as buildings and machinery, that depreciate are known as **wasting assets**.

Whether assets are appreciating, maintaining value or depreciating should not make any difference to the valuation process used - they can be valued at the beginning and end of the period and the change in value over this time can be calculated - the only difference being that some will exhibit a positive valuation change, some no change, and others will show a decline in value. The former will be a benefit which will boost profits whereas the latter will effectively be a cost which will serve to reduce profits.

However, for buildings and machinery, the valuation may not be as straightforward as for other items - we may not know the replacement value of a machine that is several years old and second-hand buildings will be unlikely to be sold apart from the land which they occupy. If instead we were to try to work out the present value of these items, it would be difficult to quantify the stream of costs and, particularly, benefits attributable solely to them. One way round this would be to value all assets as part of an overall expectation value of the whole business, just as we do with roads and fences. However, accountants and managers prefer to be able to separate out the values of such items so that they can see what the total valuation is made up of.

In attempting to solve this problem of valuing buildings, machinery and similar medium- and long-term wasting assets, accountants use a method, which instead of directly calculating the asset's value at a point in time, estimates the change in value between one period and the next: this is known as a depreciation charge. Once this figure is known the valuation at the end of the period can then be readily calculated.

Although there are a number of methods available for carrying out the depreciation calculation[1], accountants tend to use two main depreciation techniques: the **straight line method** for buildings and the **diminishing balance method** for machinery. Let us see how and why.

## Buildings - the Straight Line Method

This method is based on the assumption that a building has a useful life in the business, after which it will have a value of zero, since it is highly unlikely to be sold as a separate entity. The accountant also assumes, for simplicity, that the building will fall in value by equal amounts each year of its useful life. The depreciation charge for a particular building is therefore the initial value or cost of the building on erection divided by the number of years of its expected life, and the valuation at the end of the period, known as the *book value* or **written down value**, is the value at the start of the period less the depreciation charge.

More formally we can show these calculations as formulae:

$$\text{Depreciation charge} = \frac{\text{initial value}}{\text{expected life}}$$

or we can first calculate a depreciation rate as the reciprocal of the expected life (1 ÷ expected life) and multiply this decimal by the initial value, thus:

Depreciation charge = initial value × depreciation rate

and the value at the end of the period is

Closing value = opening value - depreciation charge

So, for example, if we erect a building at a cost of £20,000 and estimate that it will have a useful life of 20 years, then each year's depreciation charge will be:

$$\text{Depreciation charge} = \frac{£20,000}{25} = £800$$

---

[1] Some alternatives are considered in Appendix 5.1

or, we arrive at the same answer if we use the depreciation rate of $(1 \div 25) = 0.04$ or 4%, then:

Depreciation charge = £20,000 × 0.04 = £800

and the value after one year would be:

Closing value = £20,000 - £800 = £19,200

Since the depreciation charge is the same every year the valuation will fall by the same amount each year, as Table 5.1 and Fig. 5.1 illustrate.

**Table 5.1**  Depreciation schedule - straight line method.

| age of building years | depreciation charge £ | closing value £ |
|---|---|---|
| 0 | 0 | 20,000 |
| 1 | 800 | 19,200 |
| 2 | 800 | 18,400 |
| 3 | 800 | 17,600 |
| 4 | 800 | 16,800 |
| 5 | 800 | 16,000 |
| .. | 800 | .. |
| .. | 800 | .. |
| 23 | 800 | 1,600 |
| 24 | 800 | 800 |
| 25 | 800 | 0 |

The straight line method thus reduces the value of the building until it reaches zero at the end of its accounted life. However, what if, at the end of the accounted life, the building is not only still standing, but also still in use? Well, given that we will have accounted for the full cost of this asset over the previous years we should leave it at that: the book value is now zero. However, it might suggest that we should have used a longer accounting life in the first place, which leads us on to the question of just that: what should the accounting life or depreciation rate be?

Conventionally, many of the more traditional accountants use an assumed lifetime for buildings of 10 years. However, even though some buildings might be only expected to last for 10 years or less, it does seem to be rather too conservative for most buildings, and a figure or 20 or 25 years might be more realistic. In fact, we may, with sufficient regular repair and maintenance, be able to keep a building in use indefinitely. By extending the life of the building we can reduce annual depreciation charges, but this will be, more or less, counteracted

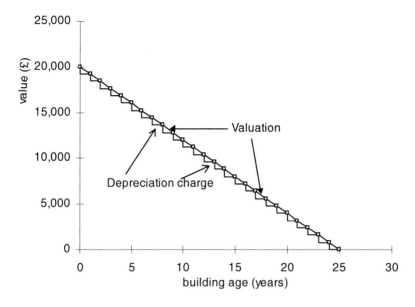

**Fig. 5.1** Building depreciation charges and closing values - straight line method.

by higher annual repair and maintenance costs. Therefore, when we put up a building, we need to estimate its useful life, in the light of the sort of maintenance programme we are likely to operate.

For depreciation of buildings it is probably best to maintain a depreciation record for each building, such as that summarised in Table 5.2. Any buildings that are erected during a particular year will need to be added to this list. Although they will not have been present in our opening valuation they should be there in the closing valuations. But should we charge depreciation for that year? If we have had use of the building for a substantial part of the year, then we should calculate a depreciation charge, if not we can assume that the closing value is the same as the cost of erection. Alternatively, if we wish to be more exact, we might carry out **fractional depreciation**. This impressive term simply means calculating depreciation for the fraction of the year for which the complete building was present in the business. The depreciation charge is therefore adjusted like this:

$$\text{Fractional depreciation charge} = \text{initial value} \times \text{depreciation rate} \times \frac{\text{months present}}{12}$$

So, if we finished erection of a £80,000 building after three months of our financial year, and so used it for nine months before the year end, the calculation would be:

Fractional depreciation charge = £80,000 × 0.04 × $\frac{9}{12}$ = £3,200 × $\frac{9}{12}$ = £2,400

However, although this is a perfectly feasible method to use, you may well deem that is unnecessarily complicated and so decide to depreciate for only a full year or none.

There is another point that arises when we erect buildings during the year - our closing valuation is no longer just opening valuation less depreciation, we must now also include any purchases.

Closing value = opening value + erections - depreciation charge

In this case (using fractional depreciation) the closing value would be:

Closing value = £0 + £80,000 - £2,400 = £77,600

Conversely, if we were to sell the building during the year or if it were destroyed by fire or other hazard, the book value[2] of this would have to be subtracted to arrive at the closing valuation. So an all-encompassing closing valuation formula is:

Closing value = opening value + erections - sales - losses - depreciation charge

**Table 5.2** Building depreciation table.

| item description | date erected | expected life | initial cost £ | 31/12/01 valuation £ | deprec. £ | 31/12/02 valuation £ |
|---|---|---|---|---|---|---|
| Machinery shed | 1987 | 25 | 20,000 | 8,800 | 800 | 8,000 |
| Chemical store | 1992 | 10 | 7,000 | 700 | 700 | 0 |
| Toilet block | 1995 | 15 | 12,000 | 7,200 | 800 | 6,400 |
| Sawmill | 2002 | 25 | 80,000 | - | 2,400 | 77,600 |
| Total buildings | | | | 16,700 | 4,700 | 92,000 |

Finally, what do we do about inflation? After all, in times of inflation the building which we put up 10 years ago, would cost much more to put up today, and so our valuations on this *historic basis* would not give an accurate picture of values in terms of today's money. Furthermore, the calculated valuation change or depreciation charge would be falsely low since it was based on old, rather than new, higher prices and consequently this would make profits look better than they really were. Except in times of relatively low inflation (up to about 4%) we

---

[2]If the amount received was more or less than the book value in the accounts, then the difference would result in the closing assets being that amount more or less than the budgeting or accounting calculations would estimate. An adjustment, known as holding gain or loss would have to be made in what is known as the *capital account*. We will deal with this procedure in Chapter 8.

cannot ignore inflation in the vain hope that its effects will cancel themselves out - they won't! However, so as not to distract you from the main thrust of this chapter, adjustments for inflation in depreciation calculations are dealt with in Appendix 5.2.

## Machinery - the Diminishing Balance Method

Unlike buildings, machinery and equipment may be sold second hand and so a market value can be placed upon them. However, although it is known that machinery prices drop very quickly in the early years of their lives but level out later and are unlikely to reach zero within the expected life in the business, the typical market values of specific items at particular ages are only known to experts. Therefore, what is needed is a depreciation method which mirrors market values fairly well without requiring an inordinate understanding of second-hand machinery markets. The **diminishing** or **reducing balance** depreciation method does this reasonably well[3], and although some accountants continue to use the straight line method for machinery as well as buildings, the former is now widely used. The diminishing balance method requires an estimate of the rate of depreciation which is then applied to the value of the asset at the start of the period. Because the depreciation is a constant proportion of the opening, rather than the initial value, as is the case with straight line depreciation, the depreciation charge goes down each year at a diminishing rate, much like the machinery market values.

The diminishing balance depreciation calculation can be expressed mathematically as:

Depreciation charge = opening value × depreciation rate

and the valuation at the end of the period as:

Closing valuation = opening valuation - depreciation charge

For example, if a machine is purchased for £13,500 and the depreciation rate is estimated to be 25% then the calculations are:

Depreciation charge = £13,500 × 0.25 = £3,375
and
Closing valuation = £13,500 - £3,375 = £10,125

However, look what happens to the depreciation charge for the following year:

---

[3] Appendix 5.3 gives an example of market values compared to valuations arrived at using the diminishing balance method.

Depreciation charge = £10,125 × 0.25 = £2,532.25

This is lower than the previous year because the opening value on which it is based is lower. The closing value at the end of this following period is therefore:

Closing valuation = £10,125 - £2,531.25 = £7,593.75

**Fig 5.2** Harvester in Black Forest, Germany (photo Jeremy Williams).

Table 5.3 and Fig. 5.2 illustrate the pattern over a number of years. Note that the annual depreciation charge, and consequently the valuation, declines at a declining rate, and that the valuation *never reaches zero* although it does get very small. So beware of drawing the conclusion, as some do, that a 25% depreciation rate, for instance, implies a machine life of four years - it does not!

**Table 5.3** Depreciation charges and valuations - diminishing balance method.

| age of machine | annual depreciation charge | closing valuation |
|---|---|---|
| years | £ | £ |
| 0 | | 13,500.00 |
| 1 | 3,375.00 | 10,125.00 |
| 2 | 2,531.25 | 7,593.75 |
| 3 | 1,898.44 | 5,695.31 |
| 4 | 1,423.83 | 4271.48 |
| 5 | 1,067.87 | 3,203.61 |
| 6 | 800.90 | 2,402.71 |
| 7 | 600.68 | 1,802.03 |
| 8 | 450.51 | 1,351.52 |
| 9 | 337.88 | 1,013.64 |
| 10 | 253.42 | 760.23 |

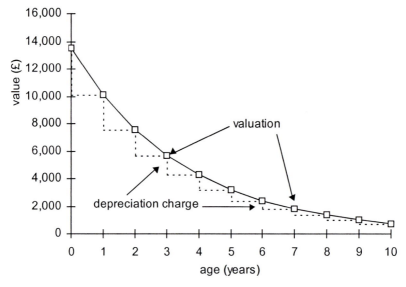

**Fig. 5.3** Depreciation charges and valuations - diminishing balance method.

What depreciation rate should be used for machinery? Although percentage[4] rates range from 10% to 30% or more, perhaps the most common rate would be 25% and some accountants would use this rate for all types of machines. Studies for farm machines in the UK and USA (Cunningham and Turner, 1995; Yule, 1995), however, would suggest that resale values depreciate at closer to 10% after a very heavy first-year drop in value. For forwarders and harvesters in UK forestry, Appendix 5.3 points to a figure of 14% after an initial decline of 21-35%.

The rate at which machinery values decline depends not only upon how much and how intensively they are used, but also how vulnerable they are to wear and tear (complex machines with many moving parts do seem to lose value more quickly than others) and also how carefully used and maintained they are. Consequently, in a business with a range of machines it can be helpful to employ different rates for different groups. So, for instance, we might choose to use a rate of 15-20% for simple machines, with light use, 20-25% for those used fairly frequently only on roads, while complex machines, used intensively and in difficult conditions would have a rate of 25-30% applied to them.[5] To show what

---

[4] The equations have expressed the depreciation rate as a decimal. These can also be expressed as a percentage by multiplying by 100. Thus, for instance, a rate of 0.25 is equivalent to 25%.

[5] As Openshaw (1980) suggests, if we are able to make a reasonably accurate estimate of when and for how much the machine is likely to be sold we can estimate the depreciation rate directly from the equation:

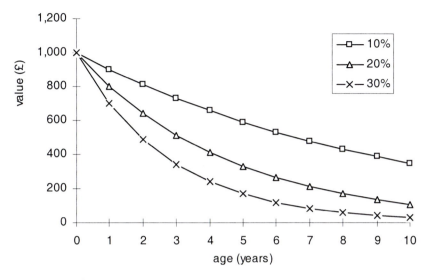

**Fig. 5.4** Effect of varying depreciation rates.

effect varying the depreciation rate has on the depreciation charge and the valuation of a machine, Fig. 5.4 graphs the annual figures for a £1,000 machine for rates of 10%, 20% and 30%.

Now what about items purchased, or sold, during the year - is fractional depreciation relevant for machinery too? The answer is yes: for items bought or sold during the year, we may either assume that they have been in the business for a whole year or none, or calculate depreciation based upon the proportion of the year for which they were in the possession of the business.

The formula for fractional depreciation for a new machine[6] is exactly the same as the one we used for buildings:

$$\text{Fractional depreciation charge} = \text{initial value} \times \text{depreciation rate} \times \frac{\text{months present}}{12}$$

---

$$\text{Depreciation rate} = 1 - \left(\frac{\text{sale price}}{\text{purchase price}}\right)^{\frac{1}{\text{age at sale}}}$$

e.g. £8,000 machine sold at 5 years of age for £2,000 gives a depreciation rate (DR) of

$$DR = 1 - \left(\frac{£2,000}{£8,000}\right)^{\frac{1}{5}} = 1 - 0.25^{0.2} = 1 - 0.76 = 0.24$$

[6] Strictly speaking, the depreciation rate for, say, half of the year is not quite the annual rate divided by two - it is rather more complicated than that. Thus the half yearly rate for an annual depreciation rate of 20% would not be 10%, but 10.5571%! However, for all practical purposes the method we have adopted in the text is sufficiently accurate.

However, we may also sell a machine as well, in which case we need to work out the amount of depreciation while it is still in the possession of the business. In this case we simply exchange the term 'valuation at the start of the year' for 'initial value' in the formula above. This is what we would do for budgeting purposes and this would then give us an estimate of what the machine would sell for. But if we are calculating figures for our accounts, we will already know what the item sold for, so, instead of using the formula we could simply calculate the depreciation charge as the valuation at the start of the year minus the sale price[7].

The formula for calculating the closing value of any machine, whether bought or sold, is similar to that for buildings, thus:

Closing value = opening value + purchases - sales - losses - depreciation charge

So, for example, if we expect to purchase a machine for £30,000 in the fourth month of the coming year, using a depreciation rate of 20%, the fractional depreciation charge is:

Fractional depreciation charge = $£30,000 \times 0.2 \times \frac{8}{12} = £4,000$

and the valuation at the end of the year is:

Closing value = £0 + £30,000 - £0 - £0 - £4,000 = £26,000

Similarly, if we have a machine valued at the start of the year at £9,000, depreciating at 30% per annum, and expect to sell it half way through the year, then the calculations are:

Fractional depreciation charge = $£9,000 \times 0.3 \times \frac{6}{12} = £1,350$

and

Closing value = £9,000 + £0 - £7,650 - £0 - £1,350 = £0

In other words, by the end of the budgeted year, having sold the machine for the amount for which it was valued in the accounts, the valuation would be zero.

Although the diminishing balance method would allow us to group together, or **pool,** machines with the same depreciation rate for calculation purposes, it is probably best to maintain a depreciation record for each machine as we have done with depreciation of buildings. An example is given in Table 5.4. Any

---

[7] If, in our accounts, we were to use the depreciated value for the value of the machine at sale, yet did in fact sell it for more or less than this amount, then we would need later to adjust for this difference by showing 'profit (or loss) on sale' in the accounts.

**Table 5.4** Machinery depreciation table.

| item description | date purchased | depreciation rate % | initial cost £ | 31/12/01 valuation £ | depreciation £ | sale £ | 31/12/02 valuation £ |
|---|---|---|---|---|---|---|---|
| Circular saw | 1990 | 14 | 5000 | 952 | 133 | 0 | 819 |
| ATV | 1993 | 25 | 13500 | 1352 | 338 | 1014 | 0 |
| Trailer | 1995 | 15 | 4500 | 1697 | 255 | 0 | 1442 |
| Land Rover | 2002 | 20 | 30000 | 0 | 4000* | 0 | 26000 |
| Total machinery | | | | 4001 | 4726 | 1014 | 28261 |

\* fractional depreciation applied.

machines that are purchased during a particular year will need to be added to this list.

## Summary remarks

Depreciation, then, is normally applied to machinery, equipment, fixtures, fittings and buildings. The straight line method, basing depreciation charges on the original value, is applied to the latter three and the diminishing balance method, basing depreciation on the value at the start of the year, to the first two.

Fractional depreciation can be applied if a more accurate picture of depreciation and valuation is required. Inflation adjustments should also be made, particularly when inflation is likely to be running at more than about 4% (see Appendix 5.2 for more on this).

Note that, because we have calculated a charge for the year for these items, a charge which will be inserted as a cost in the profit budget, then we *do not* also need to put in the item's full cost when we buy it (or include the revenue in the profit calculations if we plan to sell), otherwise we would be double counting. Imagine, for instance, buying a computer at the start of the year for £3,000 and applying a straight line depreciation rate of 33.333% per year. The depreciation charge for this year would be £1,000, as it would be for the following two years, by which time its value would be calculated as zero. This annual charge of £1,000 would be inserted as a cost in the profit budget - and the whole cost would be covered in the accounts over its three-year life. However, imagine if we also put down as a cost in the coming year's profit budget the £3,000 which we actually plan to spend on the computer. That would mean that we had applied costs of £4,000 this year, £1,000 next year and £1,000 in the third year - a total of £6,000, double the actual cost of the computer. The conclusion is therefore, if you apply depreciation, don't apply the purchase and sales costs and revenues as well. Incidentally, neither should you include a valuation change figure for machinery, etc. as well as depreciation, because that would again be double counting since depreciation is effectively the valuation change, albeit a negative one.

Finally, depreciation tells us something about the maintenance of productive capacity. Sometimes we might have too much machinery or surplus building capacity. However, if we are 'running a tight ship', that is, trying to run the business as efficiently as possible, then if we run these down it is likely that our ability to maintain profits at the current level will also decline. Consequently, on average we should be spending enough to match depreciation, so as to keep the value of machinery, buildings, etc. at more or less the same level.

For instance, if we have twenty chain saws, costing £500 each, and expect to discard them after 2 years, then we should charge £250 depreciation on each one every year: £5,000 for all 20. To maintain capacity how many should we buy each year? Ten, of course. Costing how much? Yes, £5,000, the same as the depreciation charge. Conclusion: if we are running at close to full capacity then we should be aiming to match depreciation with spending on replacements.

## Menzies example

We have already seen that Douglas inserted depreciation charges into his profit budget for the coming year. Here we will see how he arrived at those figures. In Table 5.5. Douglas has listed in each row the existing machinery, equipment and buildings as well as those items planned for purchase over the next five years. The opening valuations of those assets in the possession of the business at the start of the year are listed in the fifth column.

For the machinery and equipment the diminishing balance method is used with rates of 20% and 30% respectively. Thus the depreciation on the tractor is:

**Fig. 5.5** Some items depreciate more slowly than others.

£3,000 × 0.20 = £600
with the closing value
£3,000 - £600 = £2,400.

Similarly depreciation on the equipment is :

£800 × 30% = £240
giving a closing value of
£800 - £240 = £560.

Douglas plans to sell the four-wheel-drive vehicle early in the year and replace this with a new one. He has listed these in separate rows, as 4WD-1 and 4WD-2. Since the first is sold early on, there is no depreciation and the closing value is:

£6,000 (opening value) - £0 (depreciation) - £6,000 (sales) = £0

For the new vehicle, as it will be brought into the business early in the year, rather than using fractional depreciation, Douglas applies a full year's depreciation at 20%, giving £3,200, which then leaves a closing value of £12,800.

Summing the depreciation for all of the vehicles and equipment, Douglas obtains a figure of £4,140, which he uses in the profit budget (see Table 3.4).

Table 5.5 Depreciation on Menzies Estate machinery, equipment and buildings.

| item description | dr | date acquired | deprec. method | original value | ov | purchases | sales | deprec. | cv |
|---|---|---|---|---|---|---|---|---|---|
| | % | £ | | £ | £ | £ | £ | £ | £ |
| vehicles & equipment | | | | | | | | | |
| tractor | 20 | - | db | - | 3000 | - | - | 600 | 2400 |
| 4WD -1 | 20 | - | db | - | 6000 | | 6000 | 0 | 0 |
| 4WD -2 | 20 | - | db | - | - | 16000 | - | 3200 | 12800 |
| trailer | 20 | - | db | - | 500 | - | - | 100 | 400 |
| equipment | 30 | - | db | - | 800 | - | - | 240 | 560 |
| office | | | | | | | | | |
| office equipment | 25 | 2000 | sl | 2000 | 1500 | - | - | 500 | 1000 |
| new office equipment | 25 | 2004 | sl | 1800 | 0 | - | - | 0 | 0 |
| furniture | 10 | 2008 | sl | 800 | 560 | - | - | 80 | 480 |
| buildings | | | | | | | | | |
| store | 4 | 1984 | sl | 24000 | 7680 | - | - | 960 | 6720 |
| office | 4 | 1996 | sl | 32000 | 25600 | - | - | 1280 | 24320 |

dr = depreciation rate; ov = opening valuation; cv = closing valuation

For the office equipment, furniture and buildings the straight line method is used with rates of 25%, 10% and 4%, implying an expected useful life of 4, 10 and 25 years respectively. Remember that with this method we have to base the depreciation on the original value, not the value at the start of the year, and that is why those values have been shown in the fifth column of the table, with the year of purchase[8] in the third column.

Thus, the current office equipment has an opening value of £1,500, depreciation is

£2,000 × 0.25 = £500,

and the closing value is

£1,500 - £500 = £1,000.

Similarly, for the store, the opening value is £7,680, depreciation is

£24,000 × 0.04 = £960

and the closing value is

£7,680 - £960 = £6,720.

If you now refer back to Table 3.4 in Chapter 3 you will be able to pick out the various depreciation figures shown above. The depreciation figures for the subsequent four years have been calculated in the same way, based each time upon the closing figures for the previous year and the planned purchases and sales as noted in Table 5.5.

## Appendix 5.1 Alternative Depreciation Methods

Apart from the conventional straight line and diminishing balance depreciation methods there are several others which could be used. They are not advocated here, but you may find it useful to know what they are in case you come across their use or decide to use them for yourself. The methods to be considered here are:

a)   sum of the digits
b)   adjusted straight line and
c)   annuity.

### Sum of the digits

This method, which would typically be used for machinery depreciation calculations, involves several steps:

First we must decide upon the expected life of the machine within the business, say six years.

Next add up the numbers over that period, e.g. 1 + 2 + 3 + 4 + 5 + 6 = 21.

---

[8] Assuming previous purchases occurred towards the end of the year.

Finally, we reverse the stream of numbers (6, 5, 4, 3, 2, 1) and each years depreciation is the proportion of the starting value determined by the relevant number divided by the sum of the numbers.

So the proportions would be 6/21, 5/21, 4/21, 3/21, 2/21, 1/21 giving 0.29, 0.24, ... Thus, if the machine originally cost £3,000, then depreciation in year 1 would be

£3,000 × 0.29 = £870,

in year 2 it would be £720 and so on.

Because the depreciation charge diminishes each year, a curve showing the valuation over time would look like that for the diminishing balance method, except that the sum of the digits value would reach zero in year 6 - Fig. 5.6 illustrates this. Because of this latter weakness, it is possible to adjust the method so that the valuation diminishes to some given final value at the end of the period, instead of zero. To make this adjustment, the depreciation in a particular year would be calculated as the proportion, not of the original value, but of the original value less the final value. Figure 5.6 also illustrates how the sum of the digits valuation adjusted to produce a value at the end of year 6 of £2,600 compares closely to the valuation series derived using a diminishing balance rate of 20%.

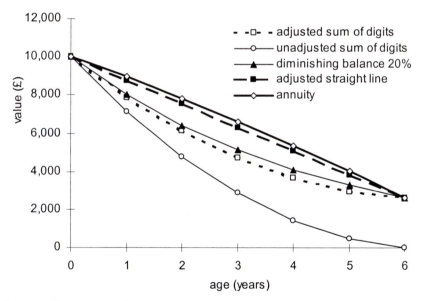

**Fig. 5.6** Alternative and conventional depreciation methods compared.

Despite the fact that at some, but not all, rates of depreciation, the adjusted sum of digits method gives similar depreciation and valuation figures to those derived using the diminishing balance method, it is still a puzzle as to why anyone would want to use it!

**Adjusted straight line**

We have seen that because market values are unlikely to decline to zero, the straight line method is inappropriate for use in a machinery context. However, it is possible to adjust the method, just like we did with the sum of the digits, so that the valuation reaches a desired value at a certain age. This is simply engineered by making the annual depreciation charge a constant proportion, not of the original value, but of the original value less the desired final value. Thus, if the machine cost £10,000 and is expected to have a value of £2,600 in year 6, then the annual depreciation figure is (£10,000 - £2,600) ÷ 6 = £1,233.33.

   Again, the resulting valuations are shown in Fig. 5.6, but in this case the diminishing balance and adjusted straight line series differ widely. Therefore, although this latter method might give a reasonable valuation of the machine when it was sold, the depreciation charges in the intervening period would appear to be rather inaccurate. Despite this, the method is currently employed within the Forestry Commission in the UK.

**Annuity**

It might be suggested (see Price, 1989) for instance, that the annual charge in the accounts for a machine should be the amount that would be needed to ensure that it was paid for over its lifetime. This amount would therefore need to cover not only the net capital cost of the machine (initial cost less value for which it might be sold at the end of its life in the business), but also interest. The amount could be calculated as an annuity (Audsley and Wheeler, 1978; Price, 1989; Bright, 1992) which is, like loan repayments, the equal annual amount required to pay off a lump sum (Bannock *et al.*, 1978). The formula for such an annuity is:

$$A = \left( K - \frac{S}{(1+r)^n} \right) \times \frac{(1+r)^n \times r}{(1+r)^n - 1}$$

where
A = the annuity or equal annual charge
K = the initial value
S = the salvage or final value after the specified number of years
r = the real[9] interest rate; and
n = the lifetime of the machine within the business in years

Thus, in the example here, using a real interest rate of 6%, the annuity would be:

$$A = \left( 10,000 - \frac{2,600}{(1+0.06)^6} \right) \times \frac{(1+0.06)^6 \times 0.06}{(1+0.06)^6 - 1} = (10,000 - 1,832.90) \times 0.2034 = 1,660.88$$

---

[9] i.e. with inflation taken out.

The amount outstanding at the end of each year[10] is shown in Fig. 5.6 as if this were the valuation; notice this method gives a slightly convex, rather than concave, curve.

Although such an annuity would certainly exactly pay off the capital and interest over the lifetime of the machine[11], it is not the appropriate measure to use here for depreciation purposes. Remember, what we are trying to do is estimate the amount by which the value of the machine falls each year, not how we are going to pay for it - that is a separate issue. "But", you might argue, "what about the interest we will incur in buying the machine?" If we borrow money to buy the machine, then the interest paid each year will be taken account of in our budgets and accounts, along with interest paid on any other borrowed money. Interest is one of the costs that come under the overhead costs heading. If, however, we have not borrowed money to acquire the machine, then no charge is made in the accounting process. So, if we were to cover the interest element within the annuity charge, we would either be double counting (because it was also charged for elsewhere) or would be costing something that was not, in fact, paid.

If this method is not correct for depreciation purposes, then neither can it be correct for valuations. The figures which we have inserted in Fig. 5.6 do not, in fact, show a valuation of the machinery at all. Rather, they show the position of a debt - which as we will see later is a *liability* rather than the value of the machine, which is an *asset*.

## Appendix 5.2 Inflation and Depreciation

The easiest way to deal with inflation in accounting is to ignore it. However, although we may omit it from our estimates, it will still affect machinery, buildings and similar items in the higher prices we will pay or receive when buying or selling them and in terms of the realistic value of those items which we have in the business at any particular time. In times of low inflation ignoring inflation does not do too much harm, but otherwise if we do not deal with it properly, then it can render our accounts at best inaccurate and at worst misleading or even meaningless.

To ignore inflation is to adopt the 'historical basis' for valuation and depreciation. In other words, we base our calculations on the prices we paid when the assets were originally acquired. The main alternative to this is to follow 'current cost accounting (CCA)', which, as the term suggests, involves expressing values in terms of current prices and values. So whether we are budgeting forward or constructing accounts in retrospect we need to adjust the figures each year.

---

[10] calculated by taking the opening amount borrowed as the initial value of the machine, then each year adding interest on the amount outstanding at the start of the year, less the annuity.

[11] hence it could be useful in helping to determine a charge for hiring out the machine, for instance.

So today's values are expressed in today's money, depreciation over the coming year is inflated to reflect expected price changes, and values at the end of the year are expressed in terms of the price level reached at that time. This will, of course, cause profits and other indicators derived using these figures to require careful interpretation - we will come to this in later chapters.

For buildings, machinery or other depreciated assets, the treatment is the same, so in the following section we will just talk about machinery.

**Depreciation**. For machines present within the business at the start of the year, the depreciation figure is increased by the expected amount of inflation, thus:

inflated depreciation = depreciation × (1 + inflation rate)

where the rate of inflation is the expected increase in the prices of that particular type of machine. For example, if the opening value of a machine is £10,000 and depreciation is 15%, then the depreciation charge would be £1,500. If inflation is expected to be about 8%, then:

inflated depreciation = £1,500 × (1 + 0.08) = £1,620.

For machines to be acquired during the coming year and for which fractional depreciation has been calculated, then the depreciation figure is only inflated by the proportion of the year for which the machine is to be present in the business.

**Closing value**. In the same way, the closing value is inflated by a full year:

inflated closing value = closing value × (1 + inflation rate)

In the above example, where the closing value calculated without inflation would be £8,500, the inflated figure would be:

inflated closing value = £8,500 × (1 + 0.08) = £9,180

Again, for machines to be acquired during the year, the amount of inflation should reflect this.

The only other calculation which will need to be made is that of the **holding gain**. Later on we will see that, during inflationary times, the assets of the business will grow in value by more than the profits would suggest, simply through the inflationary gain made by those in possession of assets. This growth is known as the 'holding gain' and is calculated as:

holding gain = closing value + inflated depreciation + sales - purchases - opening value

Which, in the example, is:

holding gain = £9,180 + £1,620 + £0 - £0 - £10,000 = £800

We do not need this figure at the moment, but it is used later when we are trying to tie in the profit and loss statement with the balance sheet.


## Appendix 5.3 Market Values and Depreciation

There have been a number of studies in agriculture of the market for second-hand machines, which enable one to compare how the depreciation charges compare with actual market prices. However, little appears to have been done in forestry. To remedy this to a limited extent, data collected by Farley (1993) for forwarders and harvesters sold in the UK have been used here to derive equations of value against age. Using regression analysis, the following equations were derived for the two types of machine:

forwarders: value $= 0.79 \times (0.855)^{years}$

harvesters: value $= 0.65 \times (0.858)^{years}$

The $R^2$ values, which give a measure of the percentage of the variation explained, were 0.70 and 0.55 respectively, suggesting that age is a major determinant, but that there may also be other important factors influencing the market value. However, when average hours of use were introduced into the equation they did little to improve the explanatory power of the equations and their coefficients were statistically insignificant.

These equations have been superimposed on the scatter of data points in Figs 5.7 and 5.8.

What does this tell us about depreciation rates? If we subtract the term in the brackets in the above equations from 1, then that gives us an estimate of the typical rate by which these machines depreciate. A quick calculation will show you that in both cases the depreciation rate is about 14%. However, the equations also show, in the constant terms, that there is an immediate drop in value (to 79% and 65%) when the machines are purchased new. As Yule (1995) suggests, it is probable that a large amount of this apparent decline is because studies usually compare second-hand prices with manufacturers' list prices. However, buyers typically can obtain a sizeable discount on the list price, which can be as much as 25%. Nevertheless, it is also common for there to be a very high rate of depreciation in the first year and so these equations reflect both of these facts.

To take account of this difference between the effective depreciation in the first year and the lower rate of about 14% in subsequent years one can either employ a high first-year rate and a lower rate for the following years or just apply a slightly higher rate overall, say 16 or 17%. It is important to remember also, that these figures can only give a rough guide to actual depreciation rates and users should decide on an appropriate rate in the light of their own circumstances.

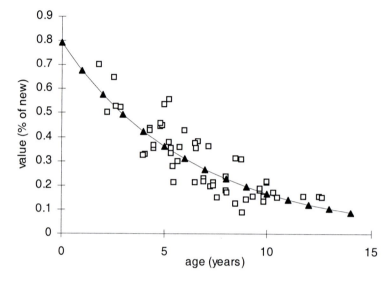

**Fig. 5.7** Forwarders - market values.

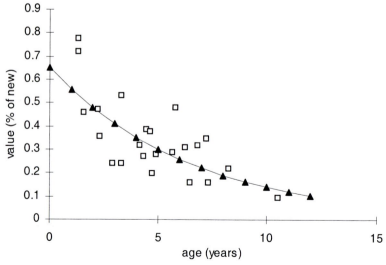

**Fig. 5.8** Harvesters - market values.

# Chapter 6

# Budgeting - Step 3 - Cash Flow Budget

After the diversions in Chapters 4 and 5 to look at related issues, we now move back to building up the budget in a series of steps. You will recall that Chapter 2 dealt with step 1 of the budgeting process, which was the outline plan. Chapter 3 then went on to show how we can produce a forecast of cost centre and overall profits in the cost-centre budget, which is the second step. We now want to forecast how the cash position of the business is likely to change over the coming year or years - this we do by constructing a cash flow budget, the third step.

The objective of this next step is to provide a forecast of the amounts of cash flowing into and out of the business over the next one to five years and from this information to show how the bank balance of the business is likely to fluctuate over that period. This forecast is an extremely important management tool as it enables us to do the following:

1.     Take steps to *optimise liquidity*. We saw earlier that cash is important to oil the wheels of the business. However, we do not require cash only to meet the bills for inputs of labour, sprays, fuel and so on, but also to make investments in longer term items such as machinery, buildings, roads and even land itself, as well as providing a surplus to enable the business to pay shareholders a reasonable dividend on their investment.

If the forecast liquidity during the period seems to be insufficient we might amend the plan so that products will be sold earlier or inputs purchased later, assets might be sold off (liquidated), a loan taken out or overdraft facility arranged with the bank. Such forward planning is likely to put much less of a strain on the business (and the manager's blood pressure) than later having to carry out 'fire brigade' actions when we suddenly find the business facing cash flow problems.

Conversely, too much cash is not a good thing either, as it suggests that we are losing out on the opportunity of earning a return on it by putting it to profitable use. If substantial amounts of surplus cash are forecast to be available, then plans can be made to invest some of this surplus either within the business or elsewhere.

2.     *Monitor and control financial performance* - once the plan is put into effect we can compare the budgeted with the actual performance on a regular basis, and if things do not appear to be going according to plan we can then trace where the problem lies and take steps to put things right. This enables a tighter control of the business than would occur if we put the plan into effect and didn't check on performance until the end of the period.

3.     *Monitor, by proxy, technical and biological performance* - this is really covered by the previous point, but is worth mentioning separately. Since our budget is built using forecasts of the technical and biological aspects as well as financial aspects, then a comparison of budgeted versus actual financial performance indicates whether the non-financial aspects are also reaching the planned levels. And if the cash flow turns out to be less than forecast, the weakness, whether financial, technical or biological can be pinpointed and corrective action or damage limitation steps taken. Thus, for instance, if spray costs turn out to be much lower than expected we may check further and discover that the area sprayed had been smaller than planned. Steps could then be taken to discover the reason for this and to do something about it[1].

This forecast of the liquidity of the business is called the Cash Flow Budget, and is defined as:

"A statement showing a forecast of the movement of funds into and out of the business over a specified period."

Table 6.1 shows how the budget lists the cash flows under the different categories of payments and receipts for the periods in which they occur. Overdraft interest charges are calculated and each period's cash flows are summed to give the net cash flows and from these figures estimates of the closing bank balance for each period are arrived at; all this will be dealt with later. Note that the specific cash flow headings are merely examples which may or may not appear in the user's actual situation.

The time horizon for the Cash Flow Budget should fit in with the earlier budgeting steps. A useful approach is to budget for a three to five year period, but to make the cash flow forecasts for years 2-5 on an yearly basis, whereas the

---

[1] However, it is also wise to monitor the technical and biological position as well, since, particularly in situations in which there is little activity for long periods, cash flow monitoring may not pick up problems quickly enough.

first year will be broken into quarters or months. In this way the manager is able to sketch out the medium-term liquidity picture, whilst focusing more closely on the immediate future. The cash flow budget can then become a 'rolling' budget, such that each year a further year is added to the end of last year's forecast and more detail filled in to the budget for the year ahead.

**Table 6.1** Cash flow budget format.

|  | q1 | q2 | Year 1 q3 | q4 | Total | Year 2 Total | Year 3 Total | Year 4 Total | Year 5 Total |
|---|---|---|---|---|---|---|---|---|---|
| **Receipts** | | | | | | | | | |
| Trading Receipts | | | | | | | | | |
| *sawlogs* | | | | | | | | | |
| *fence posts* | | | | | | | | | |
| *planting grant* | | | | | | | | | |
| *..* | | | | | | | | | |
| *..* | | | | | | | | | |
| Capital Receipts | | | | | | | | | |
| *loan* | | | | | | | | | |
| *machinery sale* | | | | | | | | | |
| *..* | | | | | | | | | |
| Total Receipts | | | | | | | | | |
| **Payments** | | | | | | | | | |
| Trading Payments | | | | | | | | | |
| *sprays* | | | | | | | | | |
| *seeds* | | | | | | | | | |
| *wages* | | | | | | | | | |
| *fuel* | | | | | | | | | |
| *electricity* | | | | | | | | | |
| *loan interest* | | | | | | | | | |
| *overdraft interest* | | | | | | | | | |
| *..* | | | | | | | | | |
| *..* | | | | | | | | | |
| Capital Payments | | | | | | | | | |
| *loan principal* | | | | | | | | | |
| *machinery* | | | | | | | | | |
| *purchase* | | | | | | | | | |
| *..* | | | | | | | | | |
| Total Payments | | | | | | | | | |
| Net Cash Flow | | | | | | | | | |
| Opening Bank Balance | | | | | | | | | |
| Closing Bank Balance | | | | | | | | | |

Building up the quarterly or monthly figures for the year ahead is obviously the most intricate task; once that has been done the annual figures for the following years can be filled in using a similar, but less detailed, approach.

Now we come to the construction of the Cash Flow Budget. The steps we need to follow are:

1. Annotate
2. Insert

Then for each period

3. Calculate overdraft interest
4. Sum receipts and payments
5. Calculate net cash flow
6. Calculate closing bank balance for the period.

Each of these steps will now be considered in more detail.

## 1. Annotate

In order to ensure that our Cash Flow Budget covers all cash flow items, no more and no less, we should go through the information set out under steps 1 and 2 and ask ourselves the question, "what is likely to happen to this item over the coming year?" This applies to all of the elements in the Cost Centre Profit Budget as well as the opening assets and liabilities and any other spending plans in the Plan in Step 1 which are not covered in the Profit Budget. This annotation then helps us to insert the correct figures into the Cash Flow Budget without missing or double counting anything. It also helps us to keep track of items which, although not coming into the cash flow budget, are needed for later steps of the budget.

You can invent your own annotation terms or use the ones suggested here. In answer to the question above, "what is likely to happen to this item over the coming year?", the responses and suggested annotations are shown in Table 6.2 below:

**Table 6.2** Annotations for cash flow budgeting.

| event | annotation |
|---|---|
| money received or paid during the year, in quarters or months 1, 2, 3,... | *q1, q2, q3,.... or m1, m2, m3, ....* |
| item still present in the business at the end of the year, i.e. appearing as a stock valuation | *v* |
| item owed by the business (creditor) or to the business (debtor) at the end of the year | *c or d* |
| item transferred to or from another cost centre and used up | *t* |
| item given during the year to the owner of business or staff for their own consumption as a 'benefit in kind' | *b* |

Table 6.2 is largely self-explanatory, but deserves a little explanation. Note first that one item might have several annotations - for instance chemicals might be purchased during the year, the invoice is paid in quarter 4, and therefore the annotation '*q4*' applied. However, most or all of that item might be expected to remain in the chemical store at the year end, and consequently the annotation '*v*' would also be applied.

Secondly, unless all of the value of the item were to be covered by the one annotation we would need to put an amount next to it. For instance, if thinnings revenue of £100,000 was to be received over quarters 1 and 2, with the bulk occurring in the first quarter, we might annotate as '*q1 £80,000, q2 £20,000.*' On the other hand, if an item, such as manager's salary, was to be paid in equal monthly amounts, we might simply annotate it as '*m=*'.

The third point to note relates to the terms 'creditor' and 'debtor'. Because goods sold by or received by the business are not usually paid for immediately, at any particular point in time there are likely to be amounts owed by or to the business. *Amounts owed by the business to other organisations or individuals* are known as **trade creditors** (or accounts payable), while *Amounts owed **to** the business by other organisations or individuals* are known as **trade debtors** (or accounts receivable). Incidentally, you might also come across the terms **accruals** and **prepayments**. These are really special kinds of creditors and debtors respectively, the former referring to amounts owed by the business, but for which no invoice has yet been issued, the latter referring to payments which have been made in advance of receipt of the good or service. So, for instance, if the telephone bill is paid in arrears, the business will have built up a debt before the bill is received - this is termed an accrual, and if the business pays rent 6 months in advance then two months after paying the rent the business will effectively be 'owed' four months worth of rent - this is a prepayment.

Transfers may occur over the year between cost centres. Therefore, although in the profit budget you would need to put down the amount produced as output for one cost centre and the same amount as a cost for the receiving cost centre, when it comes to the cash flow, there will obviously be none associated with the transfer since it has not gone out of the business. You will need to annotate the items for both the producing cost centre, to show how much of the production should not be included in the cash flow, and the receiving cost centre, to show that that amount will not have to be purchased from outside.

Finally, **benefits in kind**, also known as 'perquisites' or 'perks', are items given to staff or sometimes taken for home use by the owners of small businesses. They are usually small amounts and because they often cancel out because they can be considered as both an output (firewood, for instance) and a cost (an extra payment for labour) at the same time, they can be ignored. However, if they are substantial they must be taken account of.

So much for the possible annotations; now for the annotation process. Table 6.3 shows possible annotations for the profit budget and outline plan. It might help you to initially cover the right-hand column to see if you would arrive at the same annotations.

Note that there might be several annotations to one item if the whole amount is not treated in the same way. For instance, we might plan to buy 40 tonnes of fertiliser during the year, but in several instalments. We might buy four batches of 10 tonnes and pay for three of these in quarters 2, 3 and 4, with the final batch being delivered in quarter 4, but not being paid for or used until the following quarter.

**Table 6.3** Annotations of profit budget and outline plan items.

### For items in the Cost Centre Profit Budget:

IF <u>during the coming year</u> the item is:                                    **THEN:**

| | | | |
|---|---|---|---|
| produced | and sold | and the money is received | q1,q2,. . |
| | | but the money is not received | d |
| | and still there | | v |
| | and transferred out | | t |
| | and given as benefit in kind | | b |
| inputs purchased | and paid for | and the money is paid | q1 q2,. |
| | | but the money is not paid | c |
| | and still there | | v |
| | and given as benefit in kind | | b |
| transferred in | | | t |

### For Items in the Outline Plan/Plan of Operations:

IF <u>during the coming year</u> the item is:                                    **THEN:**

| | | | |
|---|---|---|---|
| opening creditor | and bill is paid | | q1,q2,. . |
| opening debtor | and bill is paid | | q1, 2, . . |
| opening valuation | and stock is sold | and the money is received | q1, 2, . . |
| | | but the money is not received | d |
| | and still there | | v |
| | and given as benefit in kind | | b |
| machinery/building purchase | and paid for | and money paid | q1, 2, . . |
| | | but money not paid | c |
| machinery sale | and sold | and the money is received | q1,q2,. . |
| | | but the money is not received | d |
| loan taken out | and money received | | q1,q2,. . |
| loan owing at start | and annual repayments (loan and interest) | | q1,q2,. . |
| other money transferred into or out of the business | | | q1,q2,. . |

If the price was £120/tonne the annotations (shown on the right hand side) might be:

40 tonnes @ £120/tonne = £4,800 |*q2 £1,200; q3 £1,200; q4 £1,200; c £1,200; v £1,200*

## 2.  Insert

The next step is simply to go through all of the annotated items and where a '*q*' or '*m*' is found then the amount is entered in the Cash Flow Budget in the appropriate column for the period concerned and in a row labelled according to what the cash flow item is. You may have noticed in Table 6.1 however, that there are two types of payments and receipts mentioned there, namely trading and capital. **Trading cash flows** are not very helpfully defined as '*those cash flows of a trading nature*'; what this means is those cash flows which relate to the production and selling activities of the business (as well as the costs of servicing the finance borrowed to run the business), which encompasses most of the items. Thus, receipts from sales of timber and timber products, farm produce, rents and fees received from contracting work which might have been done for somebody else, as well as production grants from government would be classed as trading receipts, while payments for fertilisers, chemicals, seeds, wages and salaries, fuel, insurance, interest payments and so on would be regarded as trading payments. **Capital cash flows**, on the other hand, are cash flows which relate to purchases and sales of machinery, buildings and any other items which are normally depreciated, as well as receipts of loans and repayments of loan principal (the money borrowed, as opposed to the interest on the money borrowed).

Sometimes, there may also be another category of cash flows: if the business is owned by individuals rather than shareholders, a form of business which might be called a sole trader or partnership, then the owners will probably take money out of the business for their own personal use or for paying tax on their personal income (income tax as opposed to company or corporation tax) - such items come under the heading of **personal cash flows**. In companies owned by shareholders, the latter type of cash flows will not pertain; if anyone, even the managing director, were taking funds out of the business for their own personal use, this would have another name - theft! Nevertheless, if you were to use these cash flow headings for a company, then this one could be used for the payment of dividends and receipt of funds from the issue of shares.

For larger companies the simple division of cash flows between the trading and capital headings is replaced by an allocation under four headings. We will continue to use the former, but if you want to know more about the latter, Appendix 6.1 has more details.

So far, we have only dealt with the annotations *q* and *m* which relate to cash flows expected to occur over the coming year. What about the other letters used - *v*, *c*, *d* and *b*? Items annotated according to these categories do not come into the projected cash flow, but they will need to be brought into some of the later steps.

In order to keep a logical record of these we may wish to add extra columns onto the right-hand side of the cash flow budget to cover 'non-cash items' - Table 6.4 illustrates how this might be done - the shaded columns show the additions. This format has the advantage that it enables us to see where items are coming from (if there at the start of the year) and where they go to.

**Table 6.4**  Cash flow budget format - with non-cash items.

| | opening valuations | opening debtors & creditors | q1 | q2 | q3 | q4 | total | closing valuations (v) | closing debtors & creditors (d&c) | benefits in kind (b) |
|---|---|---|---|---|---|---|---|---|---|---|
| **Receipts** trading receipts *sawlogs fence posts* .. .. | | | | | | | | | | |
| total receipts | | | | | | | | | | |
| **Payments** trading payments *sprays seeds* ... | | | | | | | | | | |

### 3.   Calculate overdraft interest

The only item that could not be brought into the cash flow budget from information given in steps 1 and 2 is overdraft interest, since we can only estimate this with any degree of accuracy once we know what the cash flow pattern is likely to be. Thus overdraft interest is determined *within* the cash flow budget. Now, although overdraft interest is calculated by banks on a daily basis, this is too complex a way of doing things for us. A much more straightforward, but still reasonably accurate, way of calculating this charge is to work out the quarterly or monthly interest based on the amount owing at the start of each period.

Thus the formula is:

$$\text{overdraft interest} = \text{negative bank balance @ start of period} \times \frac{\text{interest rate}}{\text{periods per year}}$$

For example, if the bank balance was £1,000 overdrawn at the start of the first quarter, interest was 12% and the calculations were to be carried out on a quarterly basis, then the interest charge for the first quarter would be:

$$\text{overdraft interest} = £1,000 \times \tfrac{0.12}{4} = £1,000 \times 0.03 = £30$$

Note that there would obviously not be any interest charge if the account was not overdrawn[2]!

For the first period of the year we already know the opening bank balance because that is the bank balance now, at the start of the year. Once we have calculated the interest for the first quarter or month, we go through the remaining steps, coming back to the calculation of the interest for the second period once we have worked out the bank balance at the end of the first. Interest charges for the rest of the periods in the year are calculated in the same way as the first, based, of course, on the projected bank balance at the start of that particular period.

If you are carrying out a less detailed annual budget for later years, overdraft interest is simpler as there is then only one period in the year.

## 4.   Sum receipts and payments

Once the overdraft interest has been calculated, the cash flow figures for that quarter or month are then summed – individual categories first (trading payments, capital payments, trading receipts, etc.) then total payments and total receipts.

## 5.   Calculate net cash flow

Net cash flow is simply total receipts minus total payments. This is calculated for each period and then for the whole year.

## 6.   Calculate closing bank balance for the period

Finally, the closing bank balance for each period is calculated as opening bank balance plus net cash flow, and then becomes the opening bank balance for the following period.

Steps 3 to 6 are followed for each month or quarter in turn, since overdraft interest, if any, has to be calculated each time. The closing bank balance for the final period of the year is the figure for the end of the year.

---

[2]Some banks pay interest on a positive balance, but usually at a very low rate and then only if the balance stays above a certain minimum amount. Nevertheless, if you wanted to carry out these calculations you would use the same formula as above, but with the relevant interest rate, and this 'interest received' would go in the cash flow budget under receipts, rather than payments.

This might seem rather a long-winded procedure, but it can be considerably speeded up if a spreadsheet is used - setting up the cash flow budget is reasonably quick, and thereafter the calculations are automatic.

What do the figures in the cash flow budget tell us? There are three particular sets of information below which can be gathered from the cash flow budget. The first two tie in with the points made at the beginning of the chapter, the third relates to a use made of the information which will be considered in Chapter 8:

1. the bank balance figures for each quarter or month and for the year show whether enough funds are likely to be available to pay debts as they fall due, to make investments, and to pay a reasonable dividend to shareholders;

2. the figures for each cost and revenue category show what the cash flow items are expected to be and when we expect them to occur. As the year progresses these can then be compared with the actual figures that arise, and, if necessary, steps taken to put the business 'back on track'; and

3. the closing bank balance for the end of the year gives some balance sheet information about what we own (a positive bank balance) or owe (overdraft) which will be used later in the budgeted balance sheet.

## Menzies Example

### Annotate

To construct the cash flow budget for the coming year, Douglas follows the steps suggested above. So, firstly, he annotates the items of the cost centre budget using the letters $q$, $d$, $c$, $t$ and $v$. Table 6.5 below shows the annotations against the headings from the profit budget in Tables 3.2, 3.3 and 3.4. To save you having to go back to the tables in Chapter 3, the values are printed in the right hand column of Table 6.5. The valuation change and depreciation headings, however, have not been included since they are calculated separately and therefore do not need annotation.

Most of the annotations are self-explanatory, the thinnings revenue of £88,258, for instance, being predicted to occur in quarter 4 and the £400 for vehicle repairs is expected to be paid in equal amounts of £100 each quarter. A few of the figures are a little more complex.

Plant production is expected to be worth £21,000. Of this there will be peaks of sales (£4,400) in quarters 1 and 4 with smaller amounts (£1,100) in quarters 2 and 3. But this only totals £11,000. The remaining £10,000 worth of plants will, this coming year, be used in compartment 3 where planting is due to take place. Hence the annotation letter $t$ denoting transfer. To balance this

**Table 6.5** Annotation of profit budget headings.

| Heading | Annotation | Cost-centre figure £ |
|---|---|---|
| **Revenues** | | |
| clear cutting | - | 0 |
| thinning | *q4 £88,258* | 88,258 |
| plants | *q1 £4,400; q2 £1,100; q3 £1,100; q4 £4,400; t £10,000* | 21,000 |
| planting grants | - | 0 |
| **Costs** | | |
| *direct forest costs* | | |
| Clear felling | - | 0 |
| thinning | - | 0 |
| fencing | *q1 £10,000* | 10,000 |
| pre-plant weed | *q1 £3,200* | 3,200 |
| scarify | *q1 £4,000* | 4,000 |
| plants | *t £10,000* | 10,000 |
| planting | *q1 £8,000* | 8,000 |
| weeding | - | 0 |
| *direct nursery costs* | | |
| planting material | *q1 £3,150* | 3,150 |
| fertilisers and sprays | *q2 £670, v -£80* | 750 |
| other materials | *q2 £330* | 330 |
| casual labour | *q1 £1,080; q2 £3,240; q3 £1,080* | 5,400 |
| *overheads* | | |
| roads maintenance | *q4 £1925* | 1,925 |
| insurance | *q3 £1,500* | 1,500 |
| salaries forest manager | *q= £8,000* | 8,000 |
| secretarial | *q= £4,000* | 4,000 |
| forest worker | *q= £9,000* | 9,000 |
| vehicles | | |
| tax & insurance | *q2 £900* | 900 |
| fuel & oil | *q= £800* | 800 |
| repairs | *q= £400* | 400 |
| buildings | | |
| repairs | *q= £200* | 200 |
| office | | |
| office repairs | *q= £180* | 180 |
| water | *q= £400* | 400 |
| electricity | *q= £600* | 600 |
| telephone | *q2, q3, q4 £125, c £125* | 500 |
| misc. admin. costs. | *q= £2,000* | 2,000 |
| loan interest | *q= £1,651* | 1,651 |

transfer you will see that for the sixth cost heading, 'plants', the material will not be purchased, but will instead be transferred in.

For the 'fertilisers and sprays' cost heading, although it is expected that £750 worth will be used, the annotations show that only £670 will have to be spent (in quarter 2), since the remainder will be material currently in the store.

The annotation *v -£80* denotes that £80 worth will be used from the store and so the closing valuation will have to reflect a decline by this amount.

The only other item to need explanation is the telephone expenditure. Although the amount incurred over the coming year is expected to be £500, because the bills are paid quarterly in arrears, three equal amounts will be paid in quarters 2, 3 and 4 and the fourth will be outstanding at the end of the year - payable in the following quarter.

Besides cash flows arising from the items in the profit budget, there are also a few others which arise from the Plan of Operations - these are listed in Table 6.6.

**Table 6.6**  Annotations of items from the plan of operations.

| item | annotation |
| --- | --- |
| Opening debtors (clear cut) | q1 £95,058 |
| Opening creditors (telephone) | q1 £114 |
| Machinery purchase | q1 £16,000 |
| Machinery sale | q1 £6,000 |
| Outstanding loan principal | q= £3,557 |

Although there is no clear cut planned for the coming year, it did take place in compartment 3 during 2001. Consequently the company which purchased the standing timber still owes £95,058 which should be paid in the first quarter of 2002.

As mentioned above, the telephone bill is paid quarterly in arrears, so the amount now owing at the start of the year and payable in quarter 1 is £114.

A new four-wheel-drive vehicle is planned for purchase at the beginning of the year. The old one will be sold at the same time.

The final item is the loan which currently stands at £16,508 (Table 2.2). The annual payment to the bank on the loan is £5,208. The interest part of that for the coming year depends upon the interest rate on that particular loan, which is 10%, and the amount outstanding at the start. 10% of £16,508 is £1,651 which is the amount shown in Table 6.5 against loan interest. That is a trading payment, whereas the principal element, which will be £5,208 - £1,651 = £3,557, is a capital payment. This, like the interest, will be paid in equal quarterly amounts.

**Insert**

The next step is for Douglas to use the annotations to construct the cash flow budget for the year ahead - Table 6.7 shows the completed budget.

**Calculate overdraft interest**

Although the cash flow budget is shown in Table 6.7, we have not yet gone through all of the steps for its completion. Douglas must next calculate overdraft interest.

**Table 6.7** Completed cash flow budget.

| opening | | | quarter | | | | | closing | |
|---|---|---|---|---|---|---|---|---|---|
| val | d/c | RECEIPTS | 1 | 2 | 3 | 4 | total | d/c | val |
| | | *trading receipts* | | | | | | | |
| | 95058 | clear felling | 95058 | 0 | 0 | 0 | 95058 | 0 | |
| | | thinning | 0 | 0 | 0 | 88258 | 88258 | | |
| | | plants | 4400 | 1100 | 1100 | 4400 | 11000 | | |
| | | planting grants | 0 | 0 | 0 | 0 | 0 | | |
| | | *capital receipts* | | | | | | | |
| | | vehicle sales | 6000 | 0 | 0 | 0 | 6000 | | |
| | | total receipts | 105458 | 1100 | 1100 | 92658 | 200316 | | |
| | | PAYMENTS | | | | | | | |
| | | *trading payments* | | | | | | | |
| | | clear Felling | 0 | 0 | 0 | 0 | 0 | | |
| | | thinning | 0 | 0 | 0 | 0 | 0 | | |
| | | fencing | 10000 | 0 | 0 | 0 | 10000 | | |
| | | pre-plant weed | 3200 | 0 | 0 | 0 | 3200 | | |
| | | scarify | 4000 | 0 | 0 | 0 | 4000 | | |
| | | planting | 8000 | 0 | 0 | 0 | 8000 | | |
| | | weeding | 0 | 0 | 0 | 0 | 0 | | |
| | | planting material | 3150 | 0 | 0 | 0 | 3150 | | |
| 80 | | fertilise and sprays | 0 | 0 | 670 | 0 | 670 | | 0 |
| 100 | | other materials | 0 | 330 | 0 | 0 | 330 | | 100 |
| | | casual labour | 1080 | 3240 | 1080 | 0 | 5400 | | |
| | | roads maintenance | 0 | 0 | 0 | 1925 | 1925 | | |
| | | crop insurance | 0 | 0 | 1500 | 0 | 1500 | | |
| | | salaries: | | | | | | | |
| | |    forest manager | 2000 | 2000 | 2000 | 2000 | 8000 | | |
| | |    secretarial | 1000 | 1000 | 1000 | 1000 | 4000 | | |
| | | forest worker | 2250 | 2250 | 2250 | 2250 | 9000 | | |
| | | tax & insurance | 0 | 900 | 0 | 0 | 900 | | |
| | | fuel & oil | 200 | 200 | 200 | 200 | 800 | | |
| | | vehicle repairs | 100 | 100 | 100 | 100 | 400 | | |
| | | building repairs | 50 | 50 | 50 | 50 | 200 | | |
| | | office repairs | 45 | 45 | 45 | 45 | 180 | | |
| | | water | 100 | 100 | 100 | 100 | 400 | | |
| | | electricity | 150 | 150 | 150 | 150 | 600 | | |
| | 114 | telephone | 114 | 125 | 125 | 125 | 489 | 125 | |
| | | misc. admin. costs | 500 | 500 | 500 | 500 | 2000 | | |
| | | loan interest | 413 | 413 | 413 | 413 | 1651 | | |
| | | overdraft interest | 788 | 0 | 0 | 107 | 894 | | |
| | | *capital payments* | | | | | | | |
| | | vehicle/equipment | 16000 | 0 | 0 | 0 | 16000 | | |
| | | loan principal | 889 | 889 | 889 | 889 | 3557 | | |
| | | total payments | 54028 | 12962 | 10402 | 9853 | 87246 | | |
| | | net cash flow | 51430 | -11862 | -9302 | 82805 | 113071 | | |
| | | opening bank blce | -35000 | 16430 | 4568 | -4734 | | | |
| | | closing bank blce | 16430 | 4568 | -4734 | 78071 | | | |

The opening bank balance at the beginning of the year is an overdraft of £35,000. Douglas therefore calculates an overdraft interest charge for the first quarter, using the expected interest rate of 9%, as:

$$£35,000 \times 0.09 \div 4 = £787.50$$

**Sum receipts and payments**

For quarter 1 Douglas can now add up the receipts, which total £105,458. Including the overdraft interest charge, the total payments figure is £54,028.

**Calculate net cash flow**

Subtracting £54,028 from £105,458 gives net cash flow of £51,430 for quarter 1.

**Calculate closing bank balance**

Adding the net cash flow figure (£51,430) to the opening bank balance (-£35,000) Douglas arrives at the closing bank balance for the first quarter, £16,430.

Douglas repeats this procedure for the other three quarters; the calculations are easier because there will be no further overdraft interest, given the high positive bank balance, until the final quarter. The bottom line of Table 6.7 shows the closing bank balance, which is predicted to reach £78,071 by the end of the year. Although Douglas is happy with that position, he might have been wiser to make plans to put surplus cash into productive use (an interest earning bank account or other investment) rather than leaving it as idle money. More on that later when we are able to look back at how the business actually performed during 2002.

The cash flow budget for the year 2002 is now ready. Douglas also constructed a less detailed budget for the years 2003-2006. He is now ready to move on to the next step.

# Appendix 6.1   Alternative Cash Flow Headings

As we will see in the next chapter, large companies calculate profits according to a number of headings (Dodge, 1993). Therefore, the cash flow budget (when we are 'looking forward') and cash flow statement (when we are 'looking back') should have a number of headings to reflect this. The five headings are:

*Operating*. This heading covers all of the normal costs and returns arising from the operation of the business: things like wages, contractor's costs and chemicals on the payments side, and harvesting revenues and grants on the receipts side.

This heading and the next one coincide with the 'trading' heading which we have used.

*Non-operating.* A more precise wording for this heading is given by Dodge as 'returns on investments and servicing of finance'. Interest and dividends are, in effect, payments for the use of someone else's money or receipts from allowing someone else to use your money. So a business may have to pay interest to banks and other financial institutions to 'service' loans and overdraft, and dividends to shareholders. On the other hand, the business may receive interest if it has a positive balance at the bank or if it has invested in shares in other businesses.

*Company taxation.* The income tax paid by the sole trader and partnerships does not come into the profit calculations since it is not directly a tax on the business. However, it still involves a cash flow, so it comes under the 'personal' heading. In the case of companies, the company or corporation tax is levied directly on the business so it is shown in the profit calculations and deserves a cash flow heading of its own.

*Investing.* There are medium- to long-term capital items which need to be purchased (and perhaps sold later too), but provide a service to the business over a number of years. Rather than include these within the operating payments and receipts these items are kept separate. Under this heading we include the purchase and sale of the various types of machinery and buildings, items for which there will be depreciation calculations when calculating profits.

This heading and the next one cover the same elements as our 'capital' heading.

*Financing.* The second heading, 'non-operating receipts and payments', dealt with the servicing of loans and shares. This heading deals with the loans and shares themselves, rather than the interest and dividend paid on them. Thus, when the business takes out a loan or issues shares these will give rise to positive cash flows. When repayments are made on loans and when shares are purchased, negative cash flows will result. Both positive and negative cash flows fall under the 'financing' heading. However, the payments and receipts of interest on loans and dividends on shares come under the 'non-operating receipts and payments' heading. So, for instance, if the business takes out a loan for £20,000, there will be a cash receipt under this 'financing' heading. In future years, when the loan is paid back, the repayments of the loan itself, the 'principal', will come under this heading too, but the interest charges will come under the 'non-operating' heading.

# Chapter 7

# Budgeting - Step 4 - Budgeted Profit and Loss Statement

The fourth budgeting step involves constructing another profit budget. This time the profit budget is in a different form. The Budgeted Profit and Loss Statement summarises, in a widely accepted format, the financial transactions and valuations for the business over a particular time period. But why do we have to calculate profit again, having already built the profit budget based on cost centres in step 2? The profit budget in step 2 was in a form that enabled its construction in sections (cost centres) in order to avoid errors, and to provide a means of fairly quickly comparing alternative options. That profit budget also provided a logical way of constructing the cash flow budget. However, the profit budget in step 2 did not present profit in the form in which accounts are normally portrayed, nor was it complete, since the overdraft interest charge was not calculated until step 3. Therefore, although it is not entirely necessary to carry out this fourth step to calculate profit, it is useful for presentation purposes. The reasons for this are threefold: it presents the profit forecast in the same way as the profit results are presented in the accounts at the end of the period; it allows direct comparison between budgeted and actual (accounts) figures; and it helps the reader to better understand the accounting logic. In fact, this extra step should not prove to be too onerous if we have computerised our budgeting process, as all of the information to construct this statement should have already been derived in earlier steps.

Two more points before we get on with the construction of the budgeted profit and loss statement. Firstly, when we looked at our earlier profit budget we were more concerned with splitting the costs and revenues into their various cost centres - this is termed **cost accounting**, and comes under the umbrella of the more general **management accounting** with which we are concerned in this book. In this profit step, however, instead of building up the profit picture from cost centres, we use aggregate figures and we take account of the form in which those amounts arise - cash, debtors, creditors, valuation changes, etc. - this is the way in which **financial accounts** are normally presented. Financial accounting is concerned with presenting a view of the performance of the business for outsiders, as distinct from our management accounting objective, which is here to produce accounts and budgets to assist our own management of the organisation. Nevertheless, it is something that we have to be concerned with as well, so it is important that we know how to produce and interpret such accounts.

Secondly, accountants present their financial statements in either horizontal or vertical format - generally, you will find that many small businesses and the accountants who deal with them will employ the former format, while larger businesses and their accountants will use the latter. In forestry, the vertical format is most common, so that is the way we will deal with the statements throughout the book. Since, however, you may come across accounts presented differently, it will be useful for you to understand the way in which the same information can be presented in horizontal format; this will be dealt with in Appendix 7.1.

Let us now proceed with the construction of our profit budget. When accountants in industry construct a **Profit and Loss** (or Income) **Account**, they effectively have two sections to the accounts (the first termed the Trading Account, the second, the Profit and Loss Account), but derive up to four measures of profit. These are illustrated in Fig. 7.1.

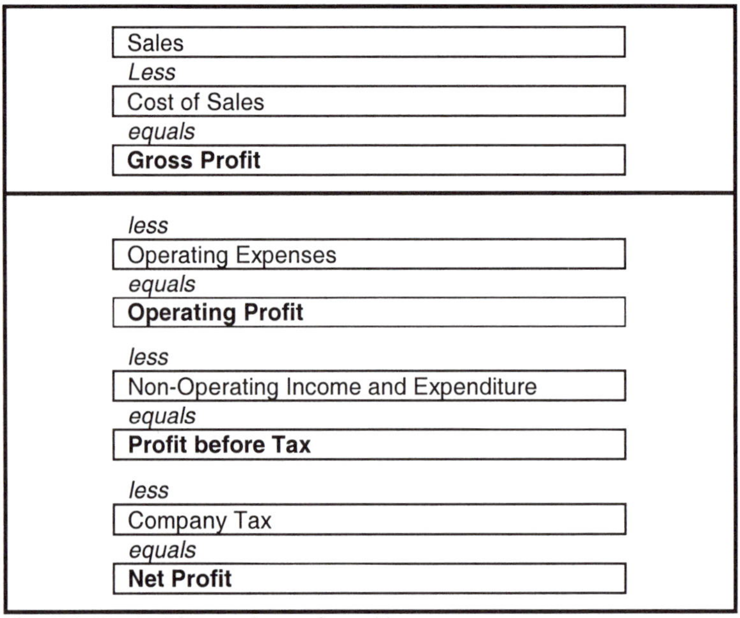

```
┌──────────────────────────────────────────────────────┐
│  ┌────────────────────────────────────────────┐       │
│  │ Sales                                        │       │
│  └────────────────────────────────────────────┘       │
│    Less                                                │
│  ┌────────────────────────────────────────────┐       │
│  │ Cost of Sales                                │       │
│  └────────────────────────────────────────────┘       │
│    equals                                              │
│  ┌────────────────────────────────────────────┐       │
│  │ Gross Profit                                 │       │
│  └────────────────────────────────────────────┘       │
├──────────────────────────────────────────────────────┤
│    less                                                │
│  ┌────────────────────────────────────────────┐       │
│  │ Operating Expenses                           │       │
│  └────────────────────────────────────────────┘       │
│    equals                                              │
│  ┌────────────────────────────────────────────┐       │
│  │ Operating Profit                             │       │
│  └────────────────────────────────────────────┘       │
│    less                                                │
│  ┌────────────────────────────────────────────┐       │
│  │ Non-Operating Income and Expenditure         │       │
│  └────────────────────────────────────────────┘       │
│    equals                                              │
│  ┌────────────────────────────────────────────┐       │
│  │ Profit before Tax                            │       │
│  └────────────────────────────────────────────┘       │
│    less                                                │
│  ┌────────────────────────────────────────────┐       │
│  │ Company Tax                                  │       │
│  └────────────────────────────────────────────┘       │
│    equals                                              │
│  ┌────────────────────────────────────────────┐       │
│  │ Net Profit                                   │       │
│  └────────────────────────────────────────────┘       │
└──────────────────────────────────────────────────────┘
```

**Fig. 7.1** Vertical format for profit and loss account.

Since this is the way in which we are likely to present our accounts, or have them presented to us, it is wise to produce our budgeted Profit and Loss Statement in the same way. We can now go through each section and insert all of the relevant figures. But first, before we do, let us consider which sorts of figures we should be looking for. In this regard there are three questions which need to be addressed - which figures, why do we need them, and where do we get them from?

The figures we need are:

- *Trading Cash Flows;*
- *Opening and Closing Stock Valuations;*
- *Opening and Closing Creditors;*
- *Opening and Closing Debtors;*
- *Depreciation; and*
- *Benefits in Kind.*

Why do we need each of these? Let us look at each in turn.

## Trading Cash Flows

If we sell something, such as timber or contract services, during the year and receive payment for it then it obviously contributes to profit. Conversely, if we pay for things, such as wages, fuel, sprays and even office inputs, needed directly or indirectly for the trading activities of the business to take place, then that cash flow detracts from profit. But not all cash flows should be included. If a machine is expected to be purchased during the year the cash flow arising from this payment should not be included in the profit statement. This is because we have already made a separate calculation for the amount of this machine 'used up' during the year and this depreciation charge is all that is needed. If we include the cash flow as well we will actually be double counting.

Also excluded are any loans taken out (which would appear as cash inflows since we would be likely to pay a loan into our bank current account) and any loan repayments expected to be made during the year. Such amounts are merely means of funding the business and do not themselves contribute to the trading activities of the business. They will be likely to be used to pay for inputs, but the cost of these will be included as cash flow items. However, the charge for the use of these funds in the business, namely interest, should be included as a trading payment. This is why we have separate categories of cash flow, as discussed in the last chapter: *trading cash flow* items (and interest is one of these) are included in the calculation of profit, but *capital cash flow* items, such as the machinery purchase and the loan repayments, are not. There is one other category of cash flows, but these only arise in the case of a 'sole trader' (sole proprietor) or partnership where the bank account is used for both business and personal or household transactions. In this case *personal cash flows*, such as payments for groceries or wages paid to a member of the family for work outside the business, should also be excluded from profit calculations, as they are nothing to do with the business.

Thus, only forecast **trading receipts** and **trading payments** should be included in the profit budget.

## Opening and Closing Stock Valuations

As we discussed in Chapter 3, there are likely to be stocks or *inventories* of inputs and products, finished or in process, at the end of the year, and these may well fluctuate between one year end and the next. Any valuation change over a period implies that we have produced more or less than we have sold, or purchased more or less than we have used up. Since we would wish our budgeted profit to show the surplus (or deficit) of the value of what is expected to be produced over the value of the resources used in that production, then it is important that we take account of changing values of stocks of inputs and produce over the year.  In order to get a clearer picture as to why this is so, consider the following examples.

### Example 1 - Change in valuation of products

Imagine that there are three compartments in a forest, 1, 2 and 3, valued today at £100,000, £10,000 and £250,000 respectively. Over the next year we expect to clear cut compartment 2, obtaining £10,300, whilst the other two compartments will grow in value. The results are tabulated in Table 7.1.

**Table 7.1** Growing stock valuation changes and profits.

| Compartment | 1 | 2 | 3 | total |
| --- | --- | --- | --- | --- |
| | £ | £ | £ | £ |
| Opening value (today) | 100,000 | 10,000 | 250,000 | 360,000 |
| Sales | 0 | 10,300 | 0 | 10,300 |
| Closing value (in a year's time) | 106,000 | 0 | 265,000 | 371,000 |
| Valuation change | 6,000 | -10,000 | 15,000 | 11,000 |
| Contribution to profit | 6,000 | 300 | 15,000 | 21,300 |

If we were to consider only the cash flow here then the figure would be £10,300. However, this would not take account, on the one hand, of the fact that compartment 2 will be empty at the end of the year and so have no value[1] (excluding of course the value of the land itself - we'll ignore this for simplicity)

---

[1] Assuming no replanting takes place before the end of the year.

and, on the other hand, the fact that the trees in compartments 1 and 2 can be expected to add increment and value during the year. Thus if we include the valuation change (closing minus opening valuation) of £11,000, the contribution to profit now becomes £21,300, more than double the figure based only on sales.

The inclusion of the change in the value of the growing stock won't always add to the sales figure; in the next example it has the opposite effect. Compartments 1, 2 and 3 have the same opening values, but this time it is compartment 1 which is clear felled. The sales revenue is forecast at £103,000, but because this compartment makes up such a large proportion of the total value, the total value of the growing stock is expected to fall to £275,600, a decline of £84,400. This then reduces the contribution to profit to only £18,600. This inclusion of valuation change does make sense when you think about it - otherwise we could fell a huge proportion of the forest and give the impression that we had made a huge profit in one year, when in fact we had eaten away at our asset base. Table 7.2 shows these results.

**Table 7.2** Growing stock valuation changes and profits.

| compartment | 1 | 2 | 3 | total |
| --- | --- | --- | --- | --- |
| | £ | £ | £ | £ |
| Opening value (today) | 100,000 | 10,000 | 250,000 | 360,000 |
| Sales | 103,000 | 0 | 0 | 103,000 |
| Closing value (in a year's time) | 0 | 10,600 | 265,000 | 275,600 |
| Valuation change | -100,000 | 600 | 15,000 | -84,400 |
| Contribution to profit | 3,000 | 600 | 15,000 | 18,600 |

**Example 2 - Change in valuation of inputs**

Now imagine that we have a stock of fertiliser valued at £3,000. During the year we expect to spend £6,000 on fertiliser purchases and at the end of the year we expect to have none left. The figure for purchases alone would suggest that the amount to be used as a cost in the profit calculation should be £6,000. But that is not the value of the quantity we expect to use. If I plan to spend £6,000 and use up the existing £3,000 worth, then the correct figure is £9,000. Thus we should take:

| | |
| --- | --- |
| purchases | £6,000 |
| *plus* | |
| opening valuation | £3,000 |
| *minus* | |
| closing valuation | £0 |
| *equals* | |
| expense figure in profit budget | £9,000 |

which is the same as saying (remembering that minus minus is equivalent to plus):

| | |
|---|---|
| purchases | £6,000 |
| *minus* | |
| valuation change (closing – opening valuation) | -£3,000 |
| *equals* | |
| expense figure in profit budget[2] | £9,000 |

On the other hand the valuation might go up: if I had only £1,000 worth in store at the start and planned to spend £11,000 so that I had £5,000 in store ready for use early in the following year the correct cost figure for the profit budget would be:

| | |
|---|---|
| purchases | £11,000 |
| *minus* | |
| valuation change | £4,000 |
| *equals* | |
| expense figure in profit budget | £7,000 |

This £7,000 figure ties in with our desire to show the value of the amount used this year since we expect to use the £1,000 worth in store plus £6,000 worth of that purchased, which will leave £5,000 worth in store at the end of the year.

So the rule for including valuation changes in the profit budget is *increase revenues* by the *change in value of product* and *reduce costs* by the *change in value of stocks of inputs*.

## Opening and Closing Creditors

The cash flow will not always indicate the value of inputs that are planned to be acquired during the coming year, because payments of debts may be delayed until the following year. Conversely, the cash flow for the coming year may contain payments of debts outstanding from the previous year. Therefore, if we are to obtain a proper picture of what is to be acquired during the year we must make adjustments for these outstanding amounts at the beginning and the end of the year. Another example will illustrate why this is necessary.

A contractor is owed £500 at the start of the year. During the year I plan to use him again and expect to use another £1,500 of his services. Unless I plan to leave some of the debt unpaid again at the end of the year, I would expect to pay him £2,000 during the year to pay for the services to be carried out this year (£1,500) and the outstanding debt at the start (£500), i.e. the cash flow during the year for contract work will be £2,000. However, if I want a clear picture of the

---

[2] The equation is £6000 minus minus £3000 which is the same as £6000 plus £3000.

value of the work carried out during the year I should take *payments* less *opening creditors*.

What will happen, though, if I delay paying for some of the work during the year? Imagine if the contractor carries out some work in the middle of the year and charges £700 for it, and then does £800 worth of work towards the end of the year. If I delay payment by a month, the £700 invoice might be paid in the third quarter while the £800 invoice might remain unpaid at the year end. Also, in quarter 1 I will pay the £500 from the previous year. Table 7.3 illustrates the possible scenario.

**Table 7.3** Creditors, cash flow and profit.

| | opening creditor | cash flow | | | | | closing creditors |
|---|---|---|---|---|---|---|---|
| | | q 1 | q 2 | q 3 | q 4 | total | |
| | £ | £ | £ | £ | £ | £ | £ |
| contract work | 500 | 500 | | 700 | | 1,200 | 800 |

With this further complication, not only do we have to adjust for the opening creditor, but also for the closing one: this time we add on closing creditors. Thus, the adjustments would be:

Trading payment (adjusted for creditors) =
   trading payment *minus* opening creditor *plus* closing creditor
i.e.
 Trading payment (adjusted for creditors) = £1,200 - £500 + £800 = £1,500

which is correct, isn't it, since it reflects the £1,500 worth of contract work which we expect to have done for us in the coming year?

We can put this formula slightly differently:

Trading payment (adjusted for creditors) =
   trading payment *plus* change in creditors

which gives the same answer:

£1,200 + £300 = £1,500

## Opening and Closing Debtors

Adjustments for debtors work in the same way as for creditors. Imagine, for example, that we are owed £33,000 for timber sold last year, and we expect to receive this in quarter 1. We also expect to sell £100,000 worth this year, but only to be paid for half of it. The figures are shown in Table 7.4.

**Table 7.4** Debtors, cash flow and profit.

|  | Opening debtor £ | Cash flow | | | | | Closing debtor £ |
|---|---|---|---|---|---|---|---|
|  |  | q 1 £ | q 2 £ | q 3 £ | q 4 £ | total £ |  |
| timber sales | 33,000 | 33,000 |  |  | 50,000 | 83,000 | 50,000 |

Thus, the figure which we wish to insert into our profit budget is £100,000, representing the value of timber sold during the coming year. If we apply the formula:

Trading receipts (adjusted for debtors) = trading receipt + change in debtors

we obtain the correct answer:

Trading receipts (adjusted for debtors) = £83,000 + £17,000 = £100,000

# Depreciation

In Chapter 5 we saw that for machinery, buildings and similar assets, the normal procedure of inserting, in the profit budget, cash flow figures adjusted for valuation changes is replaced by making a separate depreciation charge and using this only. It is important to reiterate that because of this, to avoid 'double counting', we must *not* also insert any associated capital payments or receipts, nor valuation changes.

# Benefits in Kind

This final item, which was touched upon briefly in Chapter 6, usually only occurs, like personal cash flows, with smaller businesses which are combined with the household. In this case the owner of the business may take, for personal use, some of the produce, such as firewood, or inputs, such as fuel for the family car. Often the amounts are negligible and may be ignored. Otherwise, if ignored, then either the value of production will be underestimated, or costs of production will be overestimated. Adjustment is quite straightforward: in the case of *produce*, the value should be *increased* by an estimate of the value of the amount consumed in the household, and for *inputs*, the amount should be *reduced* by the value of the benefit in kind.

Benefits in kind can occur for companies whereby staff are given firewood, use of a company vehicle, meals, and so on. These can either be ignored, because, as we shall see in a moment, their effects cancel out, or a rather laborious set of adjustments can be made. I know which I would prefer, and if the amounts are not large I would ignore them! Unfortunately you may feel that the amounts are too large to be ignored, in which case it is important that you understand, firstly, why adjustments need to be made, and secondly, how we make those adjustments.

If I give my staff firewood as well as wages, I am effectively paying them in two forms, money and goods. But by giving firewood to staff I am also foregoing the sales value of this produce and underestimating production if no account is taken of its value. If I were to make adjustments to the profit budget to account for the value of this benefit in kind, I would add its value to the wage cost, and also add its value to the value of production. The net effect would obviously be nil. Similarly, if a member of staff had the use of a company vehicle, I would need to estimate the cost of its use in terms of the share of fuel, tax, insurance, repairs and depreciation and subtract it from the machinery costs in the budget but also add it to labour costs. Again, the net effect would be nil. Why do it then? In order to be able to analyse the contribution of the different cost and revenue elements to profit.

One final point: in some situations, staff, including management, actually take benefits in kind without permission. A different term is applied to these amounts: theft. Although such embezzlement, or illicit felling or other theft by people who are not employees, is not subject to the adjustments which we have just described, it should be taken into account. How? By amending downward our predictions of production and sales and recognising that we may have to purchase greater amounts of inputs than expected. Furthermore, this problem should not be regarded as simply a matter for financial adjustment, but should also be a cause for concern and action on the part of management.

Now that we have seen what sorts of cash and non-cash items need to be included in the budgeted profit statement, we can turn to the question of where in the statement the various items of revenue and expense should be entered. In Fig. 7.1 the different categories or headings were listed; each of these will now be considered in turn.

## Sales

Sales, also referred to as *turnover*, generally means just what it says - it shows the value of sales during the year, adjusted for changes in debtors. But in forestry, we have already seen that much of the produce, in terms of growth increment, is not seen as sales in a particular year, but instead in a change in the valuation. How is this accounted for?

Some accountants might regard trees as semi-finished products (work in progress) while others might suggest that they constituted medium- to long-term capital assets. If trees come into the first category the change in their valuation would normally be used to adjust the *cost of sales* (although, as Appendix 7.2 shows, they would then only be valued in terms of accumulated net costs). If, on the other hand, trees are regarded as capital which appreciates instead of depreciates, then accountants would not bring the valuation change into the profit statement, but instead insert this value under the heading 'Revaluation

Reserve' in the Balance Sheet (Appendix 7.3 considers this further). However, forestry does not fit easily within the accountant's conventions and so special treatment is merited. Since the change in the valuation of growing stock is not some small amount which can be used to make a marginal adjustment to costs, and because it tends to make such a major contribution to profit, it is suggested here that it be included under the *Sales* heading. If this heading no longer seems appropriate you may prefer to use the term '*Output*'. If there are also stocks of harvested timber waiting at the roadside or in store, these too should be included under the 'output' heading.

So now, under the *Output* heading there would be two categories:

- sales (adjusted for opening and closing debtors), which would include sales of timber, timber products, shooting permits, etc., rents and planting grants; and
- change in value of growing and harvested stock.

## Cost of Sales

This heading is also known as '*Cost of Goods Sold*' and refers to those costs that are involved in the production process; we might prefer to use the term *Cost of Production*. In Chapter 3 you may remember that we looked at three cost categories in forestry: direct costs, on-costs and overheads. Under the **Cost of Sales** heading come the first two of these, which accountants term **prime costs**, plus those overhead costs known as **production** or **manufacturing overheads**. The sort of costs which we are referring to here are costs of plants, fertilisers and sprays, production and supervisory machinery and vehicle costs (including depreciation), direct and supervisory labour, and costs of, and within, buildings, such as sawmills, used for production purposes.

Although planting grants were mentioned earlier as coming under the 'Output' heading, you may (although I would not) prefer instead to bring them under this heading (subtracting them from costs) as they are associated with the costs and effectively serve to reduce them.

As explained earlier, these costs should not only include trading payments, but also any associated depreciation charges, changes in trade creditors, and changes in values of stocks of inputs and semi-finished, 'manufactured' products (such as may be found in the sawmill)[3].

## Gross Profit

*Sales* less *Cost of Sales*, gives the first measure of profit. Strictly speaking it is not a profit measure, because not all costs have been subtracted, but it is an

---

[3] If transfers out have been included in output, then transfers in should be included as a cost here.

indicator of the margin in the production or manufacturing part of the business. Hence, another name for it is **Gross Margin**.

## Operating Expenses

To operate the business, it is not enough simply to produce things; there are other activities involved, notably in getting the product to the purchaser, in administering the affairs of the organisation, and in keeping the site or estate clean, tidy, safe, secure and in good repair. Although not involved in the productive side of the business, these activities are nonetheless necessary for the operation of the organisation and so must be costed and brought in to the calculation of profit. **Operating Expenses** can be classified as selling/marketing/distribution costs, administrative expenses, and general costs. Examples of each are transport and advertising costs, office staff and equipment costs, and wages of security guards, respectively. Again such costs may be in the form of payments, changes in creditors and stock valuations, and depreciation.

This section may also include **Operating Receipts** which do not readily fit under the 'Output' heading. Thus, you might decide that rents and shooting permits should be included here.

## Operating Profit

This is the second profit figure, measured as Gross Profit less Operating Expenses plus Operating Receipts. It is the profit made from the trading activities of the business, but does not include quite everything, particularly interest.

## Non-Operating Income and Expenditure

There are certain other costs and revenues which are not really associated with the trading operations of the business, of which the most notable would be interest. Interest arises when we have insufficient cash available and so may have to borrow money, or when we have a surfeit and are able to lend to others, usually via the bank.

Another form of non-operating income may arise when a business sells assets whose valuation was not included in the earlier sections of the profit statement. In this category come machinery, buildings, land (if not included with the growing stock valuation) and investments, such as shares in other companies. If any of these are sold during the year at a value greater than their valuation (or *book value*) then a **profit on sale** arises. For example, if the business owns a plot of land valued in the accounts at £3,000 and sells it during the year for £3,400, then the surplus of £400 should be entered under *profit on sales of property and investments*. Such a gain is unlikely to be planned for so would not tend to appear in the budget, but it is found in accounts.

## Profit before Tax

This third profit measure, also known as **net profit before tax** or **profit on ordinary activities before taxation** is calculated simply as
*Profit before tax = Operating Profit - Non-Operating Income and Expenditure.*

## Company Tax

Although the rates, allowances and terminology may differ, all governments tax companies. **Company**, or **Corporation Tax**, is normally levied on companies other than those operating as sole traders, partnerships and, perhaps, co-operatives. Such taxes are often paid in arrears, that is, after the profits on which they are levied have been earned. Consequently, at the start of the year there may well be Corporation Tax owed, a form of creditor, which will then be paid during the year, and at the year end tax will be owed for this year. For our purposes, we wish to show the tax levied on the profits shown, so the tax figure should be the expected amount to be paid on the estimated profit, that is, the tax likely to be owing at the end of the year ahead.

## Net Profit

**Net profit**, **net income** or **earnings** is the 'bottom line', the surplus remaining to be distributed to shareholders or retained within the business, and it is calculated as:
*Net profit = Profit before Tax - Corporation Tax.*
We can now set out a more detailed illustration of the profit statement as in Fig. 7.2.
Finally, accountants often include an extra section in the profit statement showing what happens to the profits. In fact, this section is not really part of the profit calculation, but a bridge between the profit statement and the balance sheet, and is sometimes known as the **capital account**. The table may show the accumulated profits (or retained earnings) over the lifetime of the company, or simply the current year's figures, as in Fig. 7.3. The net profit of the company belongs to the shareholders, but the management does not necessarily pay all of it to the shareholders in the form of dividends. Instead profits can be ploughed back into the business or 'retained', which serves instead to increase the size of the shareholders' wealth tied up in the business.

Sales/Output
*less*
Cost of Sales/Cost of Production
                     direct costs
                     on-costs
                     production overheads
*equals*
**Gross Profit**

*less*
Operating Expenses
                     selling/marketing/distribution costs
                     administrative expenses
                     general costs
*plus*
Operating Receipts
                     other income
*equals*
**Operating Profit**

*less*
Non-Operating Income and Expenditure
                     interest paid and received
                     profit on sales of property and
                     investments
*equals*
**Profit before Tax**

*less*
Company/Corporation Tax
*equals*
**Net Profit**

**Fig. 7.2** Vertical format for budgeted profit and loss statement - detailed version.

**Net Profit**
*less*
Dividends
*equals*
**Retained Earnings**

**Fig. 7.3** Capital Account.

This brings us to the end of the fourth budgeting step in which budgeted profit is portrayed in the same manner as the accounts. The profit figure arrived at should match that calculated in step 2, except for the interest charge, which was missing in the latter.

## Menzies Example

Douglas begins construction of the 'Budgeted Profit and Loss Statement' for the year ahead by taking sales figures from the cash flow budget (Table 6.7). The clear cut (£95,058) and thinnings (£88,258) cash flows are summed to give £183,316. Sales of plants and transfers of plants also contribute to 'sales', as does the increase in the valuation of the nursery and the forest. The negative debtor change, which occurs because the business is owed money at the start for last year's clear cut, counteracts the cash flow for this amount which is expected in quarter 1. This is all shown in Table 7.5.

From the 'Sales' total is subtracted the total for the 'Cost of Sales'. The materials and labour figure is made up of all of the direct cost cash flows and the cost of the forest worker, as well as the £10,000 for the plants transferred into compartment 3 from the nursery. If some of this cash flow were being used to build up stocks of inputs for the following year this positive change in stock value would have to be subtracted, but the opposite is the case here; stocks are expected to be run down over the year by £80, so this amount should be added to the costs (which is what happens when we subtract a negative valuation change). Production overheads include the costs of machinery and non-office equipment and the store, both trading cash flow items and depreciation (See Table 3.4). Road maintenance costs and Douglas' salary are also included as they are deemed to be directly affecting the productive activities of the business.

The first profit figure, gross profit, is £208,717, but from this must be subtracted operating expenses, which here cover the secretarial costs, water, electricity and telephone, the costs of the office (including depreciation on the office building and equipment) and miscellaneous administration costs. Operating profit is therefore about £11,000 lower than gross profit, at £197,677.

The only other costs remaining are those for interest on the overdraft and the loan.

These reduce the third profit figure to £195,132, and because Douglas reckons the estate will not be liable to tax on this amount of profit, the after-tax net profit figure will also be £195,132.

Predicted profits therefore seem to be satisfactory, although, as we will see in Chapter 11, they do need to be measured against some scale in order to gauge quite how good they are.

How does our net profit figure compare to the profit estimate that we derived in Chapter 3? How would you expect it to compare; shouldn't it be the same?

If you turn back to Table 3.6 you will see that the figures are not, in fact, the same. The figure there is £196,026. The difference is £894, which, if you look back at Table 6.7, is equal to the overdraft interest charge. Apart from that the profit figures, arrived at by different routes, are in agreement.

**Table 7.5** Menzies Estate - budgeted profit and loss statement (£).

| | | | |
|---|---|---|---|
| Sales | thinnings & harvested timber | 183,316 | |
| | plants – sales | 11,000 | |
| | transfers | 10,000 | |
| | planting grant | 0 | |
| | change in value of forest and nursery | 170,614 | |
| | change in debtors | -95,058 | |
| | Sales | | 279,872 |
| Cost of Sales | *direct costs* | | |
| | materials & labour | 53,750 | |
| | *less* | | |
| | change in stocks of raw materials | -80 | |
| | prime costs | 53,830 | |
| | *production overheads* | | |
| | machinery costs | 6,240 | |
| | road maintenance | 1,925 | |
| | building costs | 1,160 | |
| | manager salary | 8,000 | |
| | production overheads | 17,325 | |
| | Cost of Sales | | 71,155 |
| GROSS PROFIT | | | 208,717 |
| Operating Expenses | salaries | 4,000 | |
| | services | 1,489 | |
| | office costs | 2,040 | |
| | miscellaneous administration costs | 3,500 | |
| | change in creditors | 11 | |
| | Operating Expenses | | 11,040 |
| OPERATING PROFIT | | | 197,677 |
| Non-operating Income and Expenditure | | | |
| | interest | 2,545 | |
| | Non-operating Income and Expenditure | | 2,545 |
| PROFIT BEFORE TAX | | | 195,132 |
| Company/Corporation Tax | | | 0 |
| NET PROFIT | | | 195,132 |

**Fig. 7.4** Douglas believes in prompt payment of creditors

## Appendix 7.1  Profit Statement in Horizontal Format

Exactly the same information as that presented above in vertical format can also be presented in horizontal format. Figure 7.5 shows the headings used for the latter.

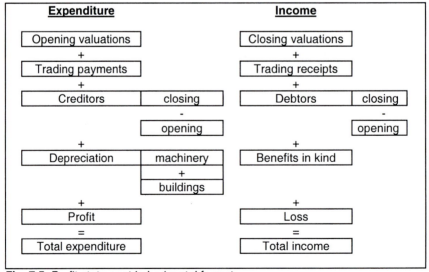

**Fig. 7.5** Profit statement in horizontal format.

The left-hand side can be considered as the 'minus' side and the right the 'plus' side. Both sides will be equal in total, with the profit or loss being the balancing item. Each of the headings will now be considered in turn.

## Expenditure

*Opening valuations*

With the statement in vertical form the stock valuation changes might be split between different sections, particularly sales and cost of sales. Here, however, although the opening and closing valuations are separated, all stock items are grouped under one main heading.

*Trading payments*

All trading payments appear here, although they may be broken down into direct and overhead costs, or even into the individual cost categories, such as wages, fuel, etc.

*Creditors*

Trading payments have to be adjusted for changes in trade creditors. This may be carried out by including the change in creditors as a separate item, as here, or adjusting trading payments for this change and putting just that figure in the statement.

*Depreciation*

Again, rather than splitting depreciation on different items between the different cost categories, when using the horizontal format, depreciation charges are grouped together, under one depreciation heading.

## Income

*Closing valuations*

On the 'plus' side we have closing valuations, mirroring the opening valuations on the 'minus' side. The effect of this, of course, when the left-hand side is subtracted from the right, is to derive the valuation change.

*Trading receipts*

These may be broken down under main headings, such as timber sales, grants, rents, etc.

*Debtors*

As with creditors on the left-hand side, the change in trade debtors can be calculated separately or included in trading payments as an adjustment.

*Benefits in kind*

As we mentioned earlier, benefits in kind to the proprietor or owner of the business only occur in the case of sole traders or partnerships. As they are part of the production of the business, but no payment will be received for them, they are added to the right-hand side.

Finally, how do we arrive at the profit or loss figure? First add the elements of the right-hand side together, then those on the left. The difference between the two is added to the side with the smallest total, as profit if on the left, or loss if on the right. Both sides will then sum to the same total. It should help to give an example: Table 7.6 has figures for the Menzies Estate inserted:

**Table 7.6** Profit statement in horizontal format.

| Expenditure | | £ | Income | | £ |
|---|---|---|---|---|---|
| Opening valuations | | 316,885 | Closing valuations | | 3,331,419 |
| Trading payments | | 67,689 | Trading receipts | | 194,316 |
| Creditors | | | Debtors | | |
| closing | 125 | | closing | 0 | |
| opening | 114 | 11 | opening | 95,058 | -95,058 |
| Depreciation | | | Benefits in kind | | |
| machinery & equip. | 4,640 | | | | |
| buildings & furniture | 2,320 | 6,960 | | | |
| *sub-total* | | *3,235,545* | *sub-total* | | *3,430,677* |
| Profit | | 195,132 | Loss | | - |
| | | 3,430,677 | | | 3,430,677 |

Notice that the Income sub-total is greater than the Expenditure sub-total (£3,430,677 compared to 3,235,545), indicating that a profit of 195,132 is forecast. To balance the two columns, this profit figure must go on the left-hand side.

# Appendix 7.2  Growing Stock Valuation Changes as Adjustments to Cost of Sales

As was mentioned earlier, accountants try to match 'efforts' with 'accomplishments', in other words, they try to match the value of the batch of things sold with the costs of producing them. In the forestry context this would mean matching the revenue from a particular stand of trees with the costs associated with that stand. This may seem to be an eminently sensible approach to take, but in the case of a production process taking a very long time the implications can be quite unexpected.

Consider the simple example of a single compartment forest (i.e. a single stand) with a rotation length of five years only. The costs and revenue associated with the compartment are shown in Table 7.7.

The profit for each year is shown along the bottom line and is calculated as sales less cost of sales, the latter being costs adjusted for changes in the growing stock valuation. Note that, in this context, accountants would normally value on the basis of accumulated net costs, because by doing so they are able to aggregate the costs associated with the production of that stand of trees.

**Table 7.7**  Single compartment lifetime costs and revenue - conventional valuations.

| | year | 1 | 2 | 3 | 4 | 5 |
| --- | --- | --- | --- | --- | --- | --- |
| | | £ | £ | £ | £ | £ |
| revenue | a | 0 | 0 | 0 | 0 | 380 |
| costs | b | 150 | 75 | 20 | 20 | 50 |
| opening valuation | c | 0 | 150 | 225 | 245 | 265 |
| closing valuation | d | 150 | 225 | 245 | 265 | 0 |
| change in valuation | e=d-c | 150 | 75 | 20 | 20 | -265 |
| sales (output) | f=a | 0 | 0 | 0 | 0 | 380 |
| cost of sales | g=b-e | 0 | 0 | 0 | 0 | 315 |
| profit | h=f-g | 0 | 0 | 0 | 0 | 65 |

For the first four years of the rotation there is no profit (or loss) at all because the costs are exactly compensated for by the change in the valuation. Only in the fifth, and final, year of the rotation does any profit show up - this is effectively the profit for the whole rotation - all five years' costs being subtracted (via the valuation change) from the revenue. Such a procedure does not seem to be very satisfactory since the growth in value of the trees each year is contributing to the profit. It would appear to be more appropriate to somehow show the contribution to profit of each year of the rotation.

This can be facilitated by using one of the other valuation methods discussed in Chapter 4: market, devastation or present value. And, as suggested above, this can be included in the sales, rather than the cost of sales section.

Table 7.8 illustrates the use of this proposed method - the valuation method used here is the expectation value, using a 6% discount rate[4].

Here the output is not only sales, but also growing stock valuation change: this gives rise to a profit figure each year, as opposed to the earlier method which

---

[4] The valuation refers to both trees and land (adjusted LEV).

gave a profit figure only in the final year. Note, nevertheless, that the total profit for all five years comes to the same figure[5] in both cases, namely £65.

To be fair to the accountancy profession, they do have a means of dealing with such a problem of sharing profits out over several years. This is done by treating the stock as *long term contract work in progress* (Chopping and Skerratt, 1998), which does enable the apportioning of a share of the profits over the lifetime of the asset. The method proposed above would therefore probably constitute a special case of this type of treatment.

**Table 7.8**   Single compartment lifetime costs and revenue - present value method.

| Year | | 1 £ | 2 £ | 3 £ | 4 £ | 5 £ |
|---|---|---|---|---|---|---|
| revenue | a | 0.00 | 0.00 | 0.00 | 0.00 | 380.00 |
| costs | b | 150.00 | 75.00 | 20.00 | 20.00 | 50.00 |
| opening valuation | c | 5.70 | 160.56 | 245.20 | 279.90 | 316.70 |
| closing valuation | d | 160.56 | 245.20 | 279.90 | 316.70 | 0.00 |
| change in valuation | e=d-c | 154.86 | 84.63 | 34.71 | 36.79 | -311.00 |
| sales (output) | f=a+e | 154.86 | 84.63 | 34.71 | 36.79 | 69.00 |
| cost of sales | g=b | 150.00 | 75.00 | 20.00 | 20.00 | 50.00 |
| profit | h=f-g | 4.86 | 9.63 | 14.71 | 16.79 | 19.00 |

# Appendix 7.3  Sales and Growing Stock Valuation Changes in the Profit Statement

There is some debate as to where growing stock valuation changes should go in the profit statement. Although the method of bringing this under the 'Sales' heading has been advocated here, since the growth in the value of the forest stock constitutes most, if not all, of the value of output for the period, and as such is a major contributor to profit, it can be criticised.

The profit figure is made up of two elements, that part which is expected to be received in the form of cash, i.e. **realised profit**, and that which, at the end of the year, will still be tied up in some form of assets, **unrealised profit**. The reason why it is considered important to know how much of the figure is to be realised is so that managers and shareholders may judge how much money is likely to be available for distribution to the latter as *dividends*.

In this chapter both realised and unrealised profit have been combined together. However, some managers and accountants prefer, in the budgeted profit and loss statement (and later in the profit and loss account), to present 'sales' as

---

[5] In Table 7.8 the profit figures sum to £64.99 due to the effect of rounding up.

and loss statement (and later in the profit and loss account), to present 'sales' as just that. If this is done then the profit figure represents only 'realised' profits. In fact, for accountants, it is not a matter of choice, since they should normally follow the conventions of their profession, one of which is the realisation convention. Glautier and Underdown (1986) explain how this convention applies to an asset, such as the growing stock,

> "...any change in its value may only be recognised at the moment the firm realises or disposes of that asset."
> To an accountant there is no certainty of profit until a sale has been made: hence, increases in value which have not been realized are not recorded as profit."           (Glautier and Underdown, 1986, p. 61)

However, because the whole profit (after distribution of dividends to shareholders) will expand the total value of the owners' stake in the business, the missing 'unrealised' amount, which is essentially the growing stock (and land) valuation change, has to be inserted as an extra item under a heading in the balance sheet entitled 'the **revaluation reserve**'. In this situation, proponents would claim, the profit figure gives a correct indication of the amount available for distribution.

Nevertheless, there are two criticisms of presenting profits in this way:

1. Presentation of realised profits only in the profit and loss statement implies that that figure represents the total profit, yet,

> "... The reported profit of a business is a part only of the total increases in value which accrue to a firm during an accounting period."
> (Glautier and Underdown 1986, p. 62)

Economists, especially, are highly critical of only stating realised profits,

> "They argue that if an asset has increased in value then it is irrelevant that it has not been sold. For economists, it is sufficient that the gain in value could be realised for that gain to be recognized."
> (Glautier and Underdown 1986, p. 61)

When presented in the traditional way, the total profit can be calculated from a complete budget or set of accounts, but it is not immediately obvious as the realised profit presented in the profit statement must be combined with the unrealised amount added to the revaluation reserve in the balance sheet.

2. The impression may be given that all realised profits are available for distribution, whereas this is not necessarily so. There are three possible causes of this: firstly, the net cash flow may be less than the realised profit because of capital payments such as machinery purchase or loan repayment; secondly, even

might not be a sufficient amount in the bank to cover the distribution; and thirdly, if the valuation change is negative, then if all realised profits are distributed this will effectively cause a decline in the owners' share of the business, an action which is unlikely to be acceptable because this is likely to lead to lower profits in the future.

As an illustration of these problems, consider the following example, with three scenarios, the details of which are given in Table 7.9. In Scenario A, as with the other two, it is assumed for the sake of simplicity that there are no debtors or creditors. In A the net cash flow of £50 suggests that there will be sufficient cash available to cover the realised profit of £41.20. Nevertheless, if the opening bank balance at the start of the year were to be, say, £20 overdrawn, then the closing bank position would be a positive balance of only £21.20; insufficient to enable all the realised profits to be distributed without further overdrawing. In Scenario B, because of the negative capital cash flow arising from the repayment of a loan of £4 and a machinery purchase of £15 (which increases the depreciation charge by £3), the net cash flow is less than the realised profit. Thus, again a problem of distribution of realised profits could ensue.

Finally, in Scenario C, there is a forecast decline in the value of the growing stock, which could arise if a substantial amount of clear cut were to take place. Consequently, because of this decline of £30, only £8.20 (which is the overall profit figure) of the realised profit of £38.20 could be distributed without longer term detriment to the business.

**Table 7.9**  Example of realised profits scenarios.

|  |  | Scenario A £ | Scenario B £ | Scenario C £ |
|---|---|---|---|---|
| trading cash flow | a | 50.0 | 50.0 | 50.0 |
| growing stock valuation change | b | 10.0 | 10.0 | -30.0 |
| depreciation | c | 8.8 | 11.8 | 11.8 |
| profit | d=a+b-c | 51.2 | 48.2 | 8.2 |
| of which: |  |  |  |  |
| realised | e=a-c | 41.2 | 38.2 | 38.2 |
| unrealised | f=b | 10.0 | 10.0 | -30.0 |
| capital cash flow | g | 0.0 | -19.0 | -19.0 |
| net cash flow | h=a+g | 50.0 | 31.0 | 31.0 |

What can be concluded from this? From a management accounting point of view, where we are not necessarily bound by accounting conventions, the profit statement should not show the realised profit figure only, but the overall profit figure. However, it might be helpful to also provide a breakdown of this figure between realised and unrealised profit, in much the same way as is done in Table 7.9. In fact, as part of financial reporting requirements, accountants are now normally expected to produce a note of reserve movements as well as a statement normally expected to produce a note of reserve movements as well as a statement of total recognised gains and losses, which includes unrealised gains on revaluation of fixed assets (Chopping and Skerratt, 1998).

Incidentally, another reason why accountants may take growing stock valuation changes out of the profit figure is because the growing stock is being treated as capital. From the accountant's point of view such a practice might normally be very sensible; capital assets such as land and office buildings are only likely to change in value because of inflation, and such changes are nothing to do with the production or trading activities of the business so should not be included in the profit figure. The revaluation reserve does seem an appropriate category in which to classify such changes. However, trees do contribute to the production activities of the business and their values change for reasons other than inflation[6] so their values do merit inclusion in the profit statement.

---

[6] It could be argued that, as with machinery and buildings, the change in value *purely* due to inflation should be separated out (as a holding gain or loss) and inserted in the revaluation reserve, but this is perhaps making things too complicated for most practitioners!

# Chapter 8

# Budgeting - Step 5 - Budgeted Balance Sheet

This is the fifth and final step of the budgeting process. So far we have budgeted for profit (twice!) and cash, but not for capital. Profit and cash are concerned with *flows* between two periods, whereas 'capital' (stability) relates to the *stock*[1] of things owned and things owed at a point in time, normally the beginning or end of the year. Why is this important?

As we saw in Chapter 1, we need to plan for and keep a check on whether the business is growing or contracting, and what is happening to the owners' share of the business, whether that is growing or contracting. To do this we need to construct a **balance sheet**, which is defined as:

> "a statement of the **assets** and **liabilities** of a business at a point in time."

But what are assets and liabilities? **Assets** are defined as:

> "anything of value in the possession of the business or claims on anything of value in the possession of others."

and **liabilities** are defined as

> "the total value of claims on the assets of a business by the various suppliers of funds to it."                    (MAFF, 1977, p. 16)

---

[1] This has nothing to do with 'stocks and shares' and 'the stock exchange'.

or you may prefer to simply think of **assets** as values of things *owned* by the business and **liabilities** as the values of things *owed* by the business.

Not only does the balance sheet show the assets and liabilities, but the difference between the two shows how much of the business belongs to the shareholders or owners. This amount is variously termed the net worth[2], net asset value, owners' equity, net capital, shareholders' funds or shareholders' equity. **Net worth** can be formally defined as:

> "the value of the assets left over to the owners of a business after all other claims have been met".

In order to see whether the size of the business and the size of the owners' share is growing a series of balance sheets need to be compared. To help in this, balance sheets normally show the capital position at the beginning and the end of the period. Thus, in this budgeting step it is suggested that the balance sheet position at the start of the budgeting year and that forecast for the end of the year be shown. To get a better picture, of course, this is not enough: we should compare balance sheets over a number of years so that trends can be discerned.

**Fig. 8.1**  Assets: trees, machinery, harvested timber and land. Kielder Forest, England (photo Colin Price)

---

[2] It can be argued that if the balance sheet does not reflect the true value of the assets, since 'book values' are not always close to the values that could be realised if sold, then neither will it reflect the true net worth (Hussey, 1995). However, because we are particularly concerned here with management accounts and realistic valuations, then our balance sheets should provide reasonable estimates.

Thus, the final budgeting step involves the construction of one balance sheet showing the current position and one showing the estimated position at the end of the period. Before we go into the procedure for doing this we need to have a look at what the balance sheet looks like and the classification of assets and liabilities contained within it.

Taking assets first, Fig. 8.2 illustrates the way in which assets can be classified in terms of their length of life, i.e. how long they will be in existence in the business before being used up or worn out. Thus Fig. 8.2 has the assets with the longest lifetimes on the left, land and immature trees for instance, and those with the shortest lifetimes on the right, cash being the most short term. Generally, **fixed assets** or *fixed capital* tend to have lifetimes of greater than a year to 18 months, with **long-term capital** items lasting for more than about 10 years. **Current assets**, also known as *short-term* or *circulating capital*, can be split between cash and near cash items - **liquid assets**, and **physical working capital** or *assets*, which are inputs, finished or harvested produce and work in progress which will be used up or sold within a year or so. The boxes at the bottom of Fig. 8.2 show the sorts of items that fit into these different categories.

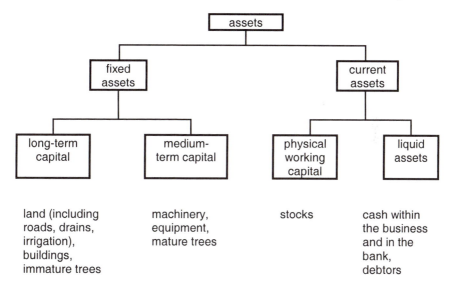

**Fig. 8.2**  Classification of assets.

Likewise, *liabilities* can be split into categories, although here we only tend to be concerned with two main groupings, namely **fixed** and **current liabilities**. Fixed liabilities, sometimes separated in a similar fashion to assets, into medium- and long-term liabilities consist generally of loans and mortgages, whilst current liabilities, which are those that will normally have to be paid off within 1 year to 18 months, consist of overdraft, creditors and short-term loans.

As with the profit statement the layout of the balance sheet can be in vertical or horizontal format. The former will be dealt with here, while the latter is discussed in Appendix 8.1; again, the vertical form is common for companies, while the horizontal is more typical of businesses run as sole traders or partnerships. Table 8.1 shows the typical format for the balance sheet in vertical format. Note that the closing, or end of year, figures are normally listed immediately to the right of the headings with the opening, or start of year, figures given on the extreme right-hand side.

**Table 8.1**  Balance sheet in vertical format.

| | |
|---|---|
| Fixed Assets | a |
| Current Assets | b |
| Current Liabilities | c |
| Net Current Assets | d=b-c |
| Fixed Liabilities | e |
| Balance | f=a+d-e |
| Shareholders' Funds and Capital Reserves | |
| Share Capital Issued | g |
| Capital Reserve | h |
| Earned Surplus | i |
| Balance | j=g+h+i |

The top half of the balance sheet lists the assets and liabilities, and the balance refers to the difference between them, which is the owners' share - the *net worth*. The items which go under each heading are much in line with those in Fig. 8.1. Under fixed assets come land, buildings, office fixtures and fittings, machinery and trees, all of which are termed **tangible fixed assets**, since they are things that can be touched[3].

Next, *current assets* (cash, debtors and stocks) are followed by *current liabilities* (overdraft, short-term loans and creditors). The difference between these two is known as **net current assets** or *working capital*, and gives a

---

[3]  One other item may also be listed here - an *intangible* known as **goodwill**, which is defined as: "the amount paid by one company for another over and above the value of its assets" (Vause, 1997, p. 1).

snapshot at that particular point in time showing whether sufficient funds are likely to be available to meet bills that have to be paid in the near future.

The final heading in the top half of the balance sheet is **fixed liabilities**, i.e. loans and mortgages. If current and fixed liabilities are subtracted from current and fixed assets, the resulting figure shows what would be left over if all of the liabilities were to be paid off. This is the figure that appears under the first 'balance' heading.

Now we come to the reason why this table is called the **balance sheet**.

Where does the owner's share come from and how is it built up or run down?

When a business is started the owners or shareholders provide money for the purchase of assets; in return they receive shares. Later they may provide some more money and receive more shares. Over the years, the company may make a profit. Some of this will be paid to shareholders as dividends[4], but the remainder will be retained within the business and so enhance the shareholders' wealth. On the other hand, if a loss is made, then the wealth of the shareholders will decline. Finally, there may be an increase in the value of an asset which has not been taken account of in the profit statement: for instance inflation may increase (or decrease) the value of buildings or goodwill might increase. In this case such assets will have to be revalued and again the extra amount is an addition to the wealth of the shareholders. If we calculate the total shareholders' stake in the business in this way we should come to the same figure as that arrived at by subtracting total liabilities from total assets - and this is precisely what we do in the balance sheet. The top half subtracts liabilities from assets and the bottom half adds the amount of money provided by shareholders, retained profits since the inception of the company and any asset revaluations. The balances arrived at by the two methods should balance; i.e. the balance calculated in the top half of the balance sheet should be the same as the balance calculated in the bottom half.

Thus, the bottom half of the balance sheet, which may be labelled **Shareholders' Funds and Capital Reserves** or *Capital and Reserves* or simply *Equity*, lists the three things we have just discussed. Firstly, **share capital** issued lists the original amount provided by shareholders in setting up the company plus any extra amounts which have been provided since then. Secondly, the **capital reserve**, also known as *capital surplus* or *revaluation reserve*, shows the revaluations of assets, not accounted for in the profit statements. Again, this is a cumulative figure, calculated from the date the company was formed. Any gains arising from the effects of inflation on depreciated items such as machinery and buildings (holding gains) will be included in the revaluation reserve. The third heading is **earned surplus**, which is the cumulative value of retained profits (and losses). It is sometimes termed *accumulated profits* or *retained earnings*. Each

---

[4] The payment of dividends is a means of supplying the owners of the business with a share of the profits. They will normally expect this, so if management fail to pay dividends for more than a limited period, they risk losing their jobs.

year, this figure is added to from the profit statement: do you remember at the end of the last chapter we mentioned a short table which may appear at the end of the profit statement showing retained earnings? Well, from this table we take the latest retained earnings figure and add it to the cumulative *earned surplus* figure in the balance sheet.

Incidentally, we mentioned earlier that the sole trader or partner would be likely to adopt the horizontal format for their profit and loss account and balance sheet. But what if they were to use the vertical format? The only problem that would arise would be in understanding the lower half of the balance sheet: what would 'Shareholder's Funds and Capital Reserves' be translated as when there are no shareholders? Since the sole trader or partners are effectively the shareholders, 'Shareholders Funds and Capital Reserves' could be rephrased 'Owner's Funds and Capital Reserves' or, simply, Net Worth. And within that section 'Share Capital Issued' would be the amount of money put into the business when it was set up, along with any further injections of money by the owner.

Constructing the budgeted balance sheet should now be reasonably straightforward. Remember that we are here budgeting for a *stock*, not a *flow*: a stock of assets and liabilities at a particular point in time. We will therefore probably be predicting the balance sheet position for 1 year ahead, but will also wish to present it alongside the current balance sheet as a means of comparison. Consequently, we will need to estimate the assets and liabilities for say 2 months ahead - the start of the budget year- and perhaps 14 months ahead - the end of the budget year. However, having already carried out the earlier steps in the budgeting process, the figures should be available. Thus, the opening and closing valuations were estimated for both profit budgets, and the liabilities information was set out in the first step, and any repayments of or additions to creditors and loans were dealt with in the cash flow budget.

Completion of step five brings us to the end of the budgeting process. Having completed all five steps means that we will have built up a picture of the expected financial performance in terms of the three elements with which we are particularly concerned, namely profit, cash and capital. However, before we meet up again with our friend Mr Hornbeam to finalise his budget, there is one final point. Cash, profit, and capital (or rather liquidity, profitability and stability) are separate aspects of the performance, but they are linked together. As a result of the stepwise process that we have followed so far, we should now be able to trace the linkages between these elements; Fig. 8.3 attempts to do this diagramatically.

In the diagram, the left-hand boxes denote the main indicator of the item with which we are concerned, the boxes on the right of those show the elements contributing to that figure, and the solid lines show the links between them. Thus, *cash*, as indicated by the net cash flow figure, is made up of trading, capital and, sometimes, personal cash flow. *Profit*, as indicated by the net profit figure, is linked to cash, but only by one part of the cash flow, and also includes other, non-cash elements, namely changes in debtors, creditors and stock valuations, depreciation and, sometimes, benefits in kind. In order to measure the capital, or stability, aspect of a business it is necessary to look at the *change* in the owners' share; hence the indicator used is 'change in net worth'. A rise (or fall) in net worth is linked to net profit, but only that part which is retained in the business (i.e. not distributed to shareholders as dividends). Furthermore, net worth can also change if shareholders inject more money into the business, via the issue of more shares, or if certain assets are revalued. One can conclude, therefore, that cash, profit, and capital are linked, but only loosely so. And this explains why one can have situations in which the indicators of the three aspects of performance are moving in different directions. For instance, the net cash flow may be negative, profit positive and net worth falling. How can this occur? It is worth thinking this one through with the help of Fig. 8.3.[5]

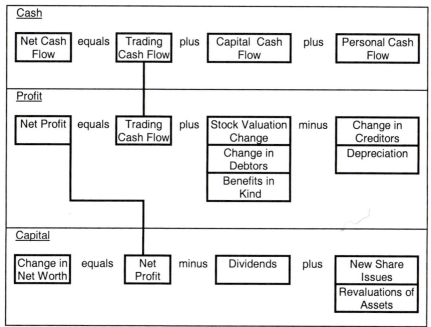

**Fig. 8.3** Profit, cash and capital linkage diagram.

## Menzies Example

For the balance sheet part of the budget, Douglas wants to produce a budgeted balance sheet showing the expected position in one year's time, and alongside

---

[5] Answer: the trading cash flow may be positive, counteracted by negative capital and personal cash flows. Even if trading cash flow is negative, profit can be positive if valuation change is positive, debtors increase, benefits in kind are high, or creditors fall. Net worth may fall despite positive profits if dividends exceed profits, or, again, benefits in kind are high.

this he wishes to show the balance sheet for the current position, that is at the start of the coming year. So one balance sheet is based on estimates, while the other uses actual information because it concerns the values of things today, or at least in a few days or weeks time. Table 8.2 shows the detailed balance sheet, or rather, balance sheets.

The first part of both balance sheets shows the values of the fixed assets. As we saw in Chapter 4, Douglas has already valued these, using the expectation value for the trees, land and nursery plants, a market value for the stocks of chemicals, and using depreciation for the buildings, machinery and other wasting assets. Having valued these items already, Douglas simply has to slot them into the right places in the balance sheets.

Note that some values are expected to go up over the year while others go down. Growth in value occurs because of growth in volume and/or quality, new purchases or plantings or increased prices. Can you think of what causes a decline in valuations over the year? There are three things which might happen and these are the counterpart of the factors we just mentioned. Firstly, there may be a decline in volume or quantity which can be caused by death, decay, disease or simply wearing out, becoming obsolescent or being used up. Secondly, items might be sold. And thirdly, prices might decline.

In the case of the fixed assets on the Menzies Estate, the values of most items decline, either because of depreciation or in the case of the stores of materials, some are used up. The two asset categories which show an increase over the year are growing stock and vehicles. In the first case, the rise is due to a growth in volume and value, whereas in the second, this is because an old vehicle is replaced by a newer one, which counteracts the depreciation.

The Current Assets consist of cash-in-hand (being the £50 petty cash which is maintained at that level each year), and cash in the bank - this is zero at the start, since the account is overdrawn, but rises to over £78,000 by the end of the year. Note that the closing bank balance figure is found at the bottom of the cash flow budget. There is one debtor at the start, the company that owes for the clear cut timber. This is expected to be paid off early in the coming year and no other debtor is expected to be outstanding at the end. Finally, the stores of chemicals are expected to be partly used up over the year, so the figure falls from £180 to £100.

Liabilities are listed the other way round, with current liabilities first. These are the overdraft, which, moving in the opposite direction to 'cash at bank', is £35,000 at the start, but is erased at the end, since the bank account is expected to move into a surplus position over the year. The small creditor, the telephone bill, which is paid in arrears, goes up over the year in line with an expected price increase.

There is only one fixed liability, namely the loan. We know what the opening amount outstanding is, but how do we calculate the closing figure? If you think about it, the amount owing at the end is the amount owing at the start less any amount that is expected to be paid back over the year. Where do we find this information? This latter amount should be found in the cash flow budget. If you go back to Chapter 6, Table 6.7, you will see a payment of £3,557 against the 'loan principal' heading.

So, if we take the opening loan outstanding £16,508 and subtract loan repayments of £3,557, we get a closing loan outstanding figure of £12,951.

**Table 8.2** Menzies Estate - actual and budgeted balance sheets.

| | | 1/12/01 £ | 1/12/02 £ |
|---|---|---|---|
| Fixed Assets | growing stock (including land) | 3,111,684 | 3,282,298 |
| | plants | 49,021 | 49,021 |
| | buildings: | | |
| | office | 25,600 | 24,320 |
| | store | 7,680 | 6,720 |
| | furniture | 560 | 480 |
| | office equipment | 1,500 | 1,000 |
| | vehicles | 9,000 | 15,200 |
| | machinery | 500 | 400 |
| | equipment | 800 | 560 |
| | Total Fixed Assets | 3,206,345 | 3,379,999 |
| Current Assets | cash in hand | 50 | 50 |
| | cash at bank | 0 | 78,071 |
| | debtors/receivables | 95,058 | 0 |
| | stocks/inventories: | | |
| | stores | 180 | 100 |
| | harvested timber | 0 | 0 |
| | Total Current Assets | 95,288 | 78,221 |
| Current Liabilities | overdraft | 35,000 | 0 |
| | creditors/accounts payable | 114 | 125 |
| | Total Current Liabilities | 35,114 | 125 |
| Net Current Assets | | 60,174 | 78,096 |
| Fixed Liabilities | lease | 0 | 0 |
| | loan | 16,508 | 12,951 |
| | Total Fixed Liabilities | 16,508 | 12,951 |
| BALANCE | | 3,250,011 | 3,445,143 |
| Shareholders' Funds (Capital and Reserves) | | | |
| Share Capital Issued | Share Capital Issued | 2,100,000 | 2,100,000 |
| Capital Reserve | land | 0 | 0 |
| | improvements | 0 | 0 |
| | buildings | 0 | 0 |
| | machinery | 0 | 0 |
| | Capital Reserve | 0 | 0 |
| Earned Surplus | Earned Surplus | 1,150,011 | 1,345,143 |
| BALANCE | | 3,250,011 | 3,445,143 |

Note that, although there is also a figure in the cash flow budget for loan interest this payment does not reduce the amount of the loan outstanding, so should not be used in the above calculation.

The figure for Net Current Assets gives an initial indicator of the liquidity of the business. Given the very high figure in this case, both at the start and the end of the year, there would appear to be no danger in terms of cash availability. It might, however, signal a possible waste of cash: if there is unneeded cash for certain periods then it might be worth putting some of it to more productive use, such as in a deposit account or other interest-earning facility. There will be more on indicators later in Chapter 11.

There is a space for lease payments, although Douglas has no leases at present. This is to highlight a problem with leases which we will deal with in Chapter 13. Briefly, leases are financial agreements much like loans, but which do not strictly pass ownership of the leased item onto the forest business. So accountants have in the past treated leases like hire charges, with the leased item not being an asset and so not appearing in the balance sheet. The suggestion is here that we should enter them into the balance sheet.

Subtracting the liabilities from the assets gives the 'balance' which is shown about half-way down the balance sheet. Thus for the start of the year we have:

Fixed Assets + Current Assets - Current Liabilities - Fixed Liabilities  = Balance

£3,206,345   +   £95,288    -    £35,114    -    £16,508   = £3,250,011

You might now like to check that Douglas has got his calculations right for the end-of-year balance figure of £3,445,143.

As we saw earlier, this balance figure shows the value of the owners' share of the business, often called *net worth* for small businesses or *shareholders' equity* for companies. The lower half of the balance sheet shows where this share has come from.

The first heading in the lower half is Share Capital Issued. Where does the £2.1 million come from?

When the Orffly-Porsh family decided, some years ago, to turn the Menzies Estate business into a company it was valued at £2.1 million at that point. Consequently £2.1 million worth of shares were issued in the names of the Orffly-Porsh family members who were the owners.

Without inflationary gains on holding the assets there has been no addition to the owners' share via the revaluation reserve, the second heading, but profits have been made, which are added to the third heading. The accumulated profits since the date of purchase and formation of the company, amount to £1,150,011.

The total of the amounts under the three headings of Share Capital Issued, Revaluation Reserve and Earned Surplus total £3,250,011 for the start of the year, the same as the balance for the top half of the balance sheet.

For the end of the year (right-hand side of Table 8.2), the only value that changes is that for Earned Surplus. To the opening amount of £1,150,011 are added the retained earnings for the year, which, as we saw in the last chapter, are expected to be £195,132. This gives a closing figure of £1,345,143 and then results in a final balance of £3,445,143.

These results look to be reasonably good: the shareholders own the bulk of the business and retained earnings are predicted to add substantially to this. How things actually turn out and how we decide what is good and bad performance will be considered shortly.

## Appendix 8.1  Balance Sheet in Horizontal Format

In horizontal format the balance sheet contains exactly the same information as that in vertical format, although it tends to be expressed in a simpler way. As Table 8.3 shows, all assets are listed on the right, with liabilities on the left, all generally ordered according to lifetimes, with those with the shortest lives first. Opening figures are listed to the left of the headings and closing figures to the right.

**Table 8.3**  Balance sheet in horizontal format.

| start of year | | end of year | start of year | | end of year |
|---|---|---|---|---|---|
| **Liabilities** | | | | **Assets** | |
| | Bank overdraft | | | Cash in hand | |
| | Trade creditors | | | Cash at bank | |
| | Short-term loans | | | Trade debtors | |
| | Medium-term loans | | | Stock valuation | |
| | Long-term loans | | | Machinery | |
| | and mortgages | | | Buildings | |
| | | | | Growing stock | |
| | Net worth | | | Land | |

Net worth is calculated in the same way as in the top half of the vertical balance sheet. The steps to arrive at net worth are:

a) assets, from cash-in-hand to land, are summed at the bottom of the right-hand side;
b) liabilities, from overdraft to mortgages, are summed on the right-hand side, but usually not entered;
c) net worth is calculated as a) - b);
d) liabilities and net worth are summed at the bottom of the left-hand side.

Now, again, as with the vertical balance sheet, there is another way of arriving at the net worth figure, or more accurately, another way of arriving at the closing net worth figure. However, whereas the vertical balance sheet shows this calculation in the lower half, in the horizontal balance sheet the calculation is either shown on the left-hand side next to the net worth heading or as a separate table called the **capital account**. The latter looks like that shown in Table 8.4 which illustrates the situation of a business not run as a company, but where the owner is trading as a sole trader or partnership. The calculation starts with the opening net worth, then adds any elements which enhance the owner's wealth, namely net profit, holding gain on assets such as buildings and machinery, and capital fed into the business from external sources, such as another business owned by the proprietor or a gift from granny. Then any 'leakages' are subtracted, i.e. things which would tend to drain wealth from the business, such as private drawings (which are the sole trader equivalent of shareholder's dividends) and benefits in kind, and we are left with the closing net worth. This figure should be the same as that obtained earlier in the balance sheet. The two figures being in agreement indicates that the calculations were correct, hence the construction of the capital account is known as 'proving' the accounts.

**Table 8.4**  Capital account.

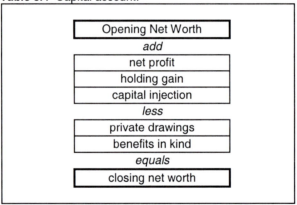

|  |
| --- |
| Opening Net Worth |
| *add* |
| net profit |
| holding gain |
| capital injection |
| *less* |
| private drawings |
| benefits in kind |
| *equals* |
| closing net worth |

The Menzies Estate budgeted balance sheet has been converted into horizontal format in Table 8.5. If you compare this with Table 8.2 you will see that, apart from the fact that some of the headings have been combined to save space, the individual figures are the same. However, the figures at the bottom of Table 8.5 refer to total assets, not the balance of assets minus liabilities. The figure for Shareholder's Funds, or Net Worth, is instead inserted within the liabilities section on the left. Nevertheless, you will note that these figures are the same as the 'Balance' figures in the vertical balance sheet.

The accounts are 'proved' in the capital account shown in Table 8.6. This form of account is more typically used for small business accounts so the headings for share capital issued, revaluation reserve and earned surplus are

**Table 8.5** Menzies Estate balance sheet in horizontal format[1].

| 31/12/01 £ | **Liabilities** | 31/12/02 £ | 31/12/01 £ | **Assets** | 31/12/02 £ |
|---|---|---|---|---|---|
| 35000 | Bank overdraft | 0 | 50 | Cash in hand | 50 |
| 114 | Trade creditors | 125 | 0 | Cash at bank | 78071 |
| 0 | Short term loans | 0 | 95058 | Trade debtors | 0 |
| 16508 | Med. term loans | 12951 | 180 | Stock valuation | 100 |
| 0 | Long term loans and mortgages | 0 | 9500 | Vehicles and machinery | 15600 |
| 51622 | | 13076 | 2300 | Equipment | 1560 |
| | | | 560 | Furniture | 480 |
| 3250011 | Net worth | 3445143 | 33280 | Buildings | 31040 |
| | | | 49021 | Plants | 49021 |
| | | | 3111684 | Growing stock | 3282298 |
| 3301633 | | 3458219 | 3301633 | | 3458219 |

termed capital injection, holding gain and net profit instead. Note also that retained earnings are effectively calculated within this capital account by adding net profit and subtracting dividends (or private drawings and benefits in kind).

Despite the procedural differences, we still arrive at the same closing net worth or shareholders' funds figure as in the right-hand column of the vertical balance sheet in Table 8.2.

**Table 8.6** Menzies Estate - capital account.

| | £ |
|---|---|
| Opening net worth | 3,250,011 |
| *add* | |
| net profit | 195,132 |
| holding gain | 0 |
| capital injection | 0 |
| *less* | |
| dividends | 0 |
| *equals* | |
| Closing net worth | 3,445,143 |

---

[1] Figures may not add exactly to totals because of the effects of rounding.

# Chapter 9

# Recording

The last seven chapters have considered the process of building up a physical and financial plan, which is known as budgeting. Planning, however, is only one of the aspects of management which form the management cycle, which was presented diagrammatically in Chapter 1. Once the budget has been calculated, approved and implementation has begun, over the period for which the budget applies the manager will need to *monitor*, to ensure that the business is performing according to the plan, and *control*, taking corrective action, if it is not. At the end of the period, the manager will *evaluate*, that is, calculate how the business actually performed over the period, and then *plan* again for the next cycle. In order to monitor and evaluate there must be measurement of what has happened - measurement of physical and financial aspects of performance. These measurements will then be noted or *recorded* and used to compare with the budget, to calculate profitability, liquidity and stability, and also to provide information for planning. Therefore, if the manager is to have the right information to carry out that management function efficiently, a suitable recording system needs to be put in place.

A useful way of covering the points that need to be considered when designing a recording system for a forestry business is to ask a number of questions; the most important are:

- Why?
- What?
- How?
- Who?
- Where?
- When?

These will now be dealt with in turn.

## Why record?

There are three, what might be called, 'efficiency' reasons for recording, and another three 'obligatory' reasons. The 'efficiency' reasons for recording are to enable the manager to:

1. *Monitor* short-term performance, which enables him to take steps to control the business, if necessary.
2. *Evaluate* performance periodically, allowing the manager and owners to judge how well the business has done, both in general and at a disaggregated level.
3. *Plan*, basing forecasts partly on previous performance. Although use can be made of published standards and expert forecasts, own data, adjusted according to the manager's judgement, usually provide the best basis for planning ahead.

The other three, 'obligatory', reasons are because they are required by:

4. Banks and other suppliers of credit: in order to obtain a loan or overdraft facility banks will normally require records of recent performance; a 'track record' over three or four years;
5. Government: there is a legal requirement on businesses to keep certain financial and physical records for tax, health and safety, information and other purposes.
6. Legal protection: if there are ever legal claims against or by the business or its investors or staff, records are likely to be required as evidence.

## What to record?

Records are needed, but records of what? This question can be further broken into three subsidiary questions, namely:

a)   What quantity of records should be kept;
b)   What features should they have, and;
c)   What specifically should we be recording?

a)   What quantity of records should be kept?

Different managers might have widely different responses to this question: some would say, "Records only add to the bureaucracy of the business, creating more paper and confusion. I know my business by keeping my finger on the pulse and being intimately involved with it. Records only serve to keep me in the office and off the ground." On the other hand, if you were to look at the records kept on a former Soviet collective or the record facility provided by some modern computer management software you would think that everything that could be recorded should be recorded! Both surely cannot be right, so how do I know what records should and should not be kept? The answer is quite simple - *only record if that record is worthwhile*. So, although the cynical manager speaking above has a point, in that a recording system is only an aid to better management and should be seen as a complement to, rather than a substitute for, the 'grassroots' involvement of the manager with the business, that business is likely to be too complex for the manager to be able to retain all information about it in his or her head. Records are needed, as the section above showed, and they should be available for others to see. On the other hand, there is no point to records if they are not useful, especially if obtaining and keeping them is too costly. For to every record there is likely to be a cost and a benefit - the cost is in terms of either the money that has to be paid for the record keeper, secretary, accountant and manager or the 'opportunity cost' of their time which might have been spent on other activities. Against this cost must be weighed the benefit of that record which, although difficult to measure is, nevertheless, real. Now, although you cannot accurately measure the marginal costs and benefits of gathering each and every piece of information, it is possible to weigh up, in a rough and ready way, whether or not it is worthwhile.

b)    What features should records have?

In response to this question, it is helpful to provide a checklist of the features that good records should have. Of course, it may not be possible to make our records ideal in every respect, and sometimes they might seem to be mutually exclusive, but the list below does indicate some key features towards which the manager might strive.

• *Records should have a definite purpose.* This follows from the point made above, that they should be worthwhile: measurements should be taken and recorded only to the extent that they help in achieving our objectives.
Records should also be:
• *Easily completed and stored.* Time and effort spent in writing or typing in information, and in filing it away needs to be minimised. The use of easily remembered codes and appropriately ruled sheets, which are then clipped into a file can be quicker than computer-based systems.
• *Easily retrieved and used.* Easy completion does not necessarily tie in with easy retrieval - a quicker way of completing records might be to put the information on any piece of paper that comes to hand and then stuffing it into a shoe box, but finding the required information later and understanding its meaning is then very difficult. On the other hand the coded and tabulated information mentioned above, can allow relatively speedy retrieval. Computers come into their own here, although there can be delay involved with starting the computer and loading software.

• *Up-to-date.* With information, there tends to be a swift decline in usefulness with age, especially if that information is meant for management use. If the records are to help in the regular monitoring of performance and in providing a realistic picture on which to base future forecasts, then there is little point if the manager is only able to see them late. And if those records highlighted a problem at an early stage, when still small, if only recognised some time later, the problem might have grown to mountainous proportions. There is also the question of accuracy here - if the records are actually filled-in long after the event, there is more chance of error occurring - you may, for instance, have faced the problem yourself of filling in a time sheet some weeks later!

• *Neat.* It may at times seem to be speedier to record information in a messy way, but for the person who wants to use the information later, time is wasted in understanding and sorting it. Untidy information can also mean that mistakes are made: "Is that a decimal point?" "Is that a seven or a one?" "What does that writing say?"

• *Complete.* There is nothing more frustrating for a manager than to find that one or two items of data are missing, because this can either render the whole body of information almost useless or involve a lot of time trying to discover the missing figures. You may have faced the problem, for instance, of missing amounts on cheque stubs, amounts which might range from 1 to 100 currency units.

• *Accurate.* A certain amount of inaccuracy has to be accepted, because again there are costs as well as benefits involved in increasing the level of precision. However, too much error can obviously lead to false conclusions about the performance of the business and must therefore be avoided. Causes of error might be poor enumeration methods, time delays, misunderstanding, ignorance, dishonesty, lack of motivation, or poor communication.

• *Checkable.* In order to be able to trace errors and to audit the recording system it should be designed to allow cross checking. This does not mean that the item should always be measured several times and recorded in different places - unnecessary, costly and demotivating duplication should be avoided. However, records of, for instance, what has been delivered according to the invoice should match what has been loaded into the store, what has been recorded as having gone out of the store should tally with what has been used on the ground, and the measuring tool should itself be measured to ensure its accuracy.

• *Permanent/Durable.* The author has witnessed the recording of production data using a pencil stub on paper towels - a quick and easy recording method perhaps, but not a durable one, particularly if there is water around! Yet even high-tech methods are not immune to this problem - unless backup copies are regularly made, computerised systems are vulnerable to loss of data - in fact, a large chunk of Chapter 6 was lost in this way. Rapid changes in computer technology can also cause problems as new systems may render data saved under older systems difficult, if not impossible, to retrieve. For example, data saved onto 5½ inch or single-sided 3¼ inch floppy disks could probably not be read by most modern computers.

Durability is important for a number of reasons: the information may not be used immediately, but stored for later use; the information may be re-used; the information may need to be checked later if an error is suspected or when strong and weak areas of performance are identified; and outside agents, such as auditors or government tax inspectors may require that records be retained.

c) What specifically should one be recording?

The last part of this section involves the question of what specific records need to be kept in a forestry context. Of course, what records we keep depends upon what we want to use them for. Some records we have to keep, to satisfy outsiders - this relates to points 4, 5 and 6 under 'why record'. Otherwise, the records we keep are for management purposes: for monitoring, evaluation and planning. For monitoring, we are particularly interested in cash flows as well as the physical and financial amounts which bring those about, and for evaluation and further planning, cash, profit and capital aggregates are needed. But if we want to be able to break down the figures further, to enable us to pinpoint strengths and weaknesses, then profitability and its physical and financial constituents, measured by cost centre, are also required.

Table 9.1 shows the specific types of records we are likely to require if we are to meet these needs.

Each of these records will now be looked at more closely. However, it must be emphasised that this chapter is not intended to show exactly how to carry out the keeping of specific records, but to explain the principles involved.

**Table 9.1** Record types.

| Cash | Profit and Capital | Supporting records (physical and financial) |
|---|---|---|
| Cash analysis book | Debtor and creditor records | Stock records: stocks of Inputs work in progress harvested timber |
| Petty cash book | Valuation records: stocks of inputs work in progress harvested timber growing stock machinery buildings land | Labour records - time sheets, etc. |
| | | Machinery records - log books |
| | | Cost centre/compartment records |
| | Loan records | |
| | Share issues record | |

It cannot be emphasised too strongly that, although we are only concerned here with records for management, you must be sure to keep 'obligatory' records as well, not just those for tax purposes.

# Recording for Cash

### Cash Analysis Book

Traditionally, the records of a business were kept in a series of 'books', such as the 'cash book', 'the journal', 'the sales day book', 'the purchases day book' and so on. Hence, the keeping of accounting records is known as '*book*-keeping'. Periodically these records were transferred to larger books known as the 'ledgers' where analysis for the construction of the accounts would be carried out. Although in some sectors and countries the keeping of accounting records has been computerised to a great extent, the 'books' are still there, albeit in electronic or 'virtual' form.

Normally nowadays book-keepers and accountants employ a '*double entry*' recording system. This means that every transaction has two entries - one a '*debit*', normally a positive amount, the other a '*credit*', normally a negative amount[4]. For instance, if I sell timber, the amount in the bank increases (a debit), while my stocks of timber decrease in value (a credit). These entries may go into different accounts or books, but because every transaction has a positive and a corresponding negative effect, the accounts must balance (Dodge, 1993).

One of the most important of the 'books' is the 'cash book' or **Cash Analysis Book** (CAB) wherein all cash flows during the year are recorded under various inflow and outflow headings. Traditionally, the CAB has been in the form of a large, bound or loose-leaf book of ruled sheets, but can now also be a part of a computerised accounting package or a home-designed spreadsheet.

In the CAB it is usual to have separate pages for inflows and outflows, but trading, capital and personal cash flows may well be entered on the same page. As seen in Fig. 9.1, columns show date, invoice number, supplier or purchaser details and any comment, followed by the cash flow categories and the total amount. Each transaction is then entered in one row, and figures can be totalled at the end of each month, quarter, or other appropriate period. It may help in deciding what headings are needed in this and other records to use Ellwood's (1998) 4Ds, namely: *date, dollars* (or 'dough' in the UK), *details* and *direction*, the latter referring to where further information relating to that item is to be found. Appendix A, towards the end of the book, has more explanation of the '4Ds' method.

The reason for breaking the information into the different sales or purchases categories and columns is so that we can dig deeper than a purely aggregate picture to identify areas of strong and weak performance. Specifically, with the

---

[4] Beware, however, because in certain types of account the signs may be reversed.

disaggregated cash book, information and comparison can be made with the cash flow budget to see every month or quarter whether or not the business is on the right track. This is simply done by adding up the columns for each period. However, in order to ensure that no errors have been made we will need to carry out a *'bank reconciliation'*. You see, entries should be made in the CAB when a payment or receipt has occurred, not when an invoice is sent or received - after all we are concerned with *cash flows*, not *invoice flows*. But even by doing things in this way our figures may not tie in with the bank account position because a cheque paid in may take several days to clear and a cheque sent out might not be received, paid in and cleared for even longer. Furthermore, there may be automated cash flows which we have not accounted for in the CAB - direct debits and standing orders which we have arranged with the bank to be taken out of our account on a regular, automatic basis. Therefore, periodically, when the figures are totalled, we need to compare the individual entries with our bank statement to reconcile the CAB with the latter.

| date | invoice No. | supplier | comment | material | wages | contract work | fuel | .. | total |
|------|---------|----------|---------|----------|-------|----------|------|----|-------|
| | | | **Cash Analysis Book – Outflows (£)** | | | | | | |
| | | | total brought forward from previous page | | | | | .. | *985.21* *b/f* |
| 19/9/02 | 1378/c | Choppit Ltd. | thinning 9b | | | 3,100.00 | | .. | 3,100.00 |
| 26/9/02 | 01151 | CanChem Supplies | sprays | 9.00 | | | 153.00 | .. | 162.00 |
| 28/9/02 | B004 | N. O'Fagus | nursery worker | | 831.25 | | | .. | 831.25 |
| ... | | | | | | | | | |
| ... | | | | | | | | | |

**Fig. 9.1** Example of cash analysis book page - expenses.

There are a few other hints which can be given concerning the filling-in of our CAB.

▪ *Numerous headings.* "It is all very well", you might say, "describing the CAB with only a few cost categories, but in reality there are tens, even hundreds, of categories - you surely can't deal with that situation on just one page?" It is true that some forestry businesses, particularly large, government or quasi-government organisations, do break costs into a host of different categories. If this is the case with our business, and remembering what we said in Chapter 3 about ensuring that it was worthwhile having so many categories, then it will be difficult dealing with cash recording on only one page for outflows and one for inflows. In this case there are a least three options:

1.    Use several pages to cover all of the cost (and income) categories.
2.    Use a computer. The computer comes into its own when you have large amounts of data to deal with - it can store, find and sort information very quickly whilst still allowing the user a relatively straightforward way of entering information.
3.    Continue to use the 'one page' format, but only use the main categories as column headings and then either note the sub-category details below each money entry or within the comments section. If there are not an awful lot of entries under each of the main headings every year then it need not be too difficult a task going through and calculating the sub-category totals later.

•    Record *net of discount* figures. Some companies will charge a certain amount for a good or service, but then offer a discount as long as payment is made before a certain date. Thus, the bill from CanChem Supplies in Fig. 9.1, might have been for a total of £180 (£10 for sprays and £170 for fuel), but with a discount of 10% if payment was made within 30 days[5]. Since the bill was paid early, it amounted to only £162 (see Fig. 9.2).

|  | sprays £ | fuel £ | total £ |
|---|---|---|---|
| original bill | 10 | 170 | 180 |
| *less* | | | |
| discount @ 10% | 1 | 17 | 18 |
| actual payment | 9 | 153 | 162 |

**Fig. 9.2**  Costs net of discount.

•    The CAB records *monetary* amounts only; other forms of records will be recommended later for keeping track of physical quantities. Nevertheless, you may find it useful to also record in the CAB (but only in pencil or another colour of pen) the amounts, but only where relevant. For instance, in the page of the CAB in Fig. 9.1, in the box recording £3,100 for contract work we might have noted which sub-compartment this referred to. And under the figure of £9 for materials we might have inserted the quantity and type of spray. However, if space allows, and the invoice does not include a lot of different items, then the information can be conveyed adequately in the 'comments' column.

•    *Purchase or sales tax.* If, as with value added tax (VAT) for instance, the business is charged tax on purchases of certain inputs and/or sales of its produce then this will affect the cash flow.
    Now it might be that tax can be reclaimed from the government or has to be paid over to it, but even in those circumstances there will be a delay between the

---

[5] Incidentally, if the bill were not paid within the 30 days, the annual percentage rate of interest represented by the loss of discount is extremely high; other credit options for financing this purchase might be much cheaper. Chapter 13 deals with such issues.

levying of tax and the counterbalancing transaction with the government. Therefore, a separate column must be kept in the CAB for tax, as Fig. 9.3 illustrates.

Amounts of tax paid on purchases and received on sales will be inserted in that column, and when the government refunds earlier tax paid or the business pays a cheque to government for tax received on sales, that too will be entered in that column. There will also be a legal obligation on the part of the business to keep a separate record of all VAT received and paid: this should be done using a book or account kept for that purpose.

| Cash Analysis Book – Outflows (£) | | | | | |
|------|------------|----------|-----------|-----|-------|
| Date | Invoice No. | Supplier | Materials | VAT | Total |
| 3/10/02 | 1471 | Noofence | 1,000 | 175 | 10,175 |

**Fig. 9.3** Example of Cash Analysis Book page – Outflows and VAT.

• *Contras*. Sometimes a transaction will involve both purchases and sales. For instance, a fencing contractor may carry out some work for our business, charged at say £2,000, but at the same time might have purchased some fencing posts from us, costing £600. If the contractor sends an invoice to us showing the charge for fencing less the cost of the posts supplied by us, the net amount payable, £1,400, does not reflect the cost of the services received. To properly account for this dual transaction in our CAB we have to have a **contra** entry. This is defined as:

"a book-keeping entry on the opposite side of an account to an earlier entry, with the object of cancelling the effect of the earlier entry."

(Hussey, 1995, p. 90)

The use of contras is best explained by following the contractor's example. There are two transactions here: an outflow item (the contract work) and an inflow item (the fencing posts) and both should be entered separately on the appropriate pages of the CAB. However, there should also be another entry in both cases under an extra, 'contras' column: Fig. 9.4 illustrates the pages of the CAB.

So the invoice information is inserted on the outflows page, with the contra being inserted to reconcile the contract work amount (£2,000) with the amount actually received (£1,400). Note that the contras are *subtracted* from the other amounts. On the inflows page the post sales are entered, but as there was no separate cheque received for them, there is a counterbalancing 'contra' entry of £600. Doing things in this way ensures that item columns reconcile with the total columns. Contras on the outflows pages should exactly match those on the inflows pages - checking that the sums of these columns match helps to ensure that errors are avoided.

| Cash Analysis Book – Outflows (£) | | | | | | | |
|---|---|---|---|---|---|---|---|
| Date | Invoice No. | Supplier | Comment | Contract work | .... .. | Contras | Total |
| . . . . | . . . . | . . . . | . . . . | | | | |
| 5/11/02 | 1821 | Sawfel Brothers | fencing in cpts 6&7. contra | 2000.00 | | 600.00 | 1400.00 |
| | | | | | | | |

| Cash Analysis Book – Inflows (£) | | | | | | | |
|---|---|---|---|---|---|---|---|
| Date | Invoice No. | Customer | Comment | Posts & poles | .... .. | Contras | Total |
| . . . . | . . . . | . . . . | . . . . | | | | |
| 5/11/02 | - | Sawfel Brothers | fence posts. contra | 600.00 | | 600.00 | 0.00 |
| | | | | | | | |

Fig. 9.4  Example of the use of 'contras' in the Cash Analysis Book.

### Petty Cash Book

Ideally all transactions would be carried out by cheque, thus ensuring that everything goes through the bank account. As a result, checking on accuracy is relatively straightforward and we would not have to go to the bank to draw out or deposit cash. In the real world, however, some transactions have to be carried out using cash rather than cheque - some pens are needed urgently, the forester travels away and needs to buy petrol, a passing trader offers to buy some scrap metal or a neighbour wishes to purchase some firewood. How is this dealt with? To withdraw and deposit small amounts every time such transactions are carried out can be frustrating and a waste of time. Instead, businesses tend to adopt a more pragmatic system for dealing with such 'petty cash' items.

On the purchase side we will always need to have some cash readily available; it need not be a great deal, and in fact, for security reasons it is wise not to have much cash kept on site. When we first withdraw an amount from the bank for this purpose, the amount of this 'float' will be entered under capital expenses in the CAB - it is considered as capital as the initial amount is simply a change of location of the cash asset from the bank to the business, rather than payment for an input. This initial withdrawal of a 'float' from the bank must be recorded in a small 'petty cash book' as 'money in'. Subsequently, when petty cash is paid out of the 'petty cash' tin, box or whatever container in which it is kept, the date, details, cash flow category and amount must be recorded.

Periodically the 'float' will need to be replenished, a cheque being drawn for exactly the amount to bring the float back up to its original level. Note that the amount of this replenishment cheque will exactly match the sum of the amounts paid out for petty cash items. Consequently, we can, at this point, transfer the transaction information from the 'petty cash' book to the outflows page of the CAB. This all sounds terribly complicated, but in practice it isn't. Imagine, for example, that we initiate our 'petty cash' system with a £50 withdrawal from the bank, entering the £50 in the CAB as a capital expense. Over the next few months we make only three payments - £5.50 for nails, £3.20 for coffee for visitors and £26.00 for wellington boots - a total of £34.70, leaving £15.30 in the 'petty cash' box. I go to the bank and write a cheque for £34.70 and then put the cash into the box to bring the 'float' back up to £50. The three 'petty cash' payments are now entered in the CAB under one line giving details of the cheque number and the three amounts under the appropriate outflows categories. Figures 9.5 and 9.6 respectively show what the petty cash book and CAB pages would show.

| Petty Cash Book | | | | | | |
|---|---|---|---|---|---|---|
| Date | Receipt/ cheque number | Supplier | Details | Money In (£) | Money out (£) | Balance (£) |
| . . . . | . . . . | . . . . | . . . . | | | |
| 1/4/02 | 404063 | Kwikbuk Bank | petty cash float | 50.00 | | 50.00 |
| 8/4/02 | 1014701 | Hard-wear | nails | | 5.50 | 44.50 |
| 29/5/02 | - | Buy-it-all | coffee, dried milk, sugar | | 3.20 | 41.30 |
| 16/6/02 | 1016782 | Hard-wear | wellies for D. Beckham | | 26.00 | 15.30 |
| 30/6/02 | 404113 | Kwikbuk Bank | petty cash float refill | 34.70 | | 50.00 |
| | | | | | | |

**Fig. 9.0** Example page of 'Petty Cash' Book.

| Cash Analysis Book – Outflows (£) | | | | | | | | |
|---|---|---|---|---|---|---|---|---|
| Date | Invoice No. | Supplier | Comment | Office expenses | Fence repairs | Misc. labour costs | Capital items | Total |
| . . . . | . . . . | . . . . | . . . . | | | | | |
| 1/4/99 | 404063 | Kwikbuk Bank | petty cash float from bank | | | | 50.00 | 50.00 |
| . . . . | . . . . | . . . . | | | | | | |
| . . . . | . . . . | . . . . | | | | | | |
| 30/6/99 | 404113 | Kwikbuk Bank | petty cash details - nails, coffee, wellies | 3.20 | 5.50 | £26.00 | | 34.70 |
| | | | | | | | | |

**Fig. 9.6** Example 'petty cash' entries in the Cash Analysis Book.

As far as 'petty cash' receipts are concerned it is best if they are paid straight into the bank when they occur and recorded in the CAB accordingly. If this is not feasible then another book can be kept for 'petty cash' receipts, mirroring that for payments, except that, in this case, no 'float' is needed. It is important, to avoid confusion, that 'petty cash' payments and receipts are not allowed to mix.

# Recording for Profit and Capital

### Debtor and creditor records

Outstanding debtors and creditors arise because of the delay between the supply of inputs and produce and the transfer of money to pay for them. If a careful track is not kept of these outstanding amounts then debts can be left unpaid for long periods or even missed completely, with the consequent adverse effects on cash flow, on accounting calculations and on relationships between organisations and individuals; it can even lead to legal action being taken. The CAB is inadequate for this since it only records amounts that have actually been paid or received; we need something else to record transfers of goods and services prior to payment. This can be done using what is termed the *sales/purchases daybook*. In this book purchases and sales are recorded when the input enters the premises, the service is carried out or the product is delivered. As with the CAB, details of date, invoice number, categories and amounts are recorded (the 4Ds again), although separate category columns may not be required. When the invoice is paid the entry can be crossed off, ticked, or an extra column might be used to indicate details of payment.

The daybook may take the form of a diary, divided up into days or weeks. This enables the book-keeper, when the transaction is recorded, to enter a note for the day or week when payment is expected to be made or by which time payment must be made under the terms of the transaction. This practice helps to ensure that payments are not missed.

### Valuation records

At the end of each accounting period valuations of all items in stock are needed for profit and loss account and balance sheet purposes. However, records of the values, and the physical amounts which those values reflect, need to be kept for other reasons as well, and not just on a year-end basis. Stock records should also be kept, in order to:

1.   allocate costs and revenues to cost centres;
2.   calculate and assess physical as well as financial performance; and
3.   check the accuracy of our records by reconciling closing amounts with opening amounts, inflows and outflows.

In fact, the records of financial values and physical amounts are frequently difficult to separate: to derive financial valuations we need physical records first. So here we are not just considering the valuations, but the physical records which support them and which themselves are used for other purposes. For what sorts of things do we need, then, to keep physical and financial records? The following categories can be singled out:

- stocks of inputs
- stocks of semi-finished produce
- harvested produce
- growing stock
- machinery
- buildings
- land.

These will now be looked at in turn.

**Stocks of inputs**, also known as '*stores and materials*', includes fertilisers, pesticides, fencing materials, plants in store, fuel, lubricants and other materials used in the business. Besides needing to value these for the accounts at the start and end of the year we need to keep a check on what comes in and where it goes out to. Such records are best kept in the place where the materials are stored, so as to facilitate timely recording, and would again take the form of a book (or computer). For each category a record should be kept of amount and value of material coming into the store and then amounts and destination (cost centre) when any is issued from the store. If there are several stores then record books should be kept in each.

Recording is fairly straightforward, although amounts need to be able to be accurately recorded and there is a problem of determining the value of what goes out. The problem with value is that the existing stores may include several batches of the same material, but which may have come in at different times with different prices attached to them. There are a number of ways of dealing with this, perhaps the most straightforward is to assume that material goes out of the store in order of age (i.e. first in first out) and consequently is charged to the cost centres in that way. Fortunately for the stores recorder, this problem should be identified and calculations made in the office rather than the store - the recorder should deal with quantities rather than values, but this will necessitate an 'office-based stores record book' which is regularly updated from the record book in the stores and will then involve calculation of financial values.

**Stocks of semi-finished produce**, or what accountants call '*work in progress*', should include growing seedlings in the nursery, the growing stock of trees and timber awaiting further processing in the sawmill. However, the first two are often put into categories in their own right, so here we only consider the timber 'in process', and this will only be pertinent if we have a sawmilling enterprise. In this case, if the effectiveness of this enterprise is to be properly monitored simply valuing at the year end will not suffice. We also need a record of what comes in, what happens to it, and where it goes afterwards. Thus, another book or account is required to keep track of the different categories of 'work in progress' and again this book is best kept in the place where this produce is stored. At the end of the year, a value will be put onto each amount in the 'current stocks account'.

**Harvested produce**. Unless we are using standing sales for harvesting and marketing of our trees, then we not only need records of year-end valuations of harvested timber, but also records of production quantities, movements and prices. Some of this information will be available in the CAB, but we do also need to keep a record of all of this information in one book in a convenient, and safe, place. This will then be analysed in what is known as the 'felled crop account'.

The **growing stock** of trees should be valued at the end of each year, although a formal valuation may only take place every three or five years; in between will be some form of interpolation. Whatever the means of valuing the growing stock a record must be kept of each compartment and sub-compartment to show the opening value, thinnings or harvesting output, inputs over the year, and possibly a calculation of the growth increment.

**Fig. 9.7** Measuring acacia woodlot plots in Bangladesh (photo: Shakil Akhter).

Details of how the figures were calculated must also be recorded. Perhaps the appropriate place for the recording of this information is the cost centre or compartment records with which we will deal later. This information will, at each year-end, be brought together and calculations made in the 'growing stock account'.

Individual **machinery** details can be recorded in a log book kept in the cab or store. However, for valuation and costing purposes it is worth keeping a book in the office in which the values, purchases, sales and depreciation are recorded and calculated for all items of machinery.

Similarly for **buildings** a record should be kept in the office covering all buildings, detailing original costs, depreciation and possibly repairs and maintenance.

Finally, a record should be kept of **land** acquisitions (both freehold and leasehold) along with any calculations of changes in value.

Note that for some of the records a good deal of support material will have been used to derive the figures - invoices for the CAB, yield tables for the growing stock valuation and aerial photographs and legal documents to support the land valuation, for example. Such records need to be stored and referenced in the main record documents. This is where Ellwood's fourth 'D', *direction*, applies.

## Loan records

A record should be kept of all other liabilities apart from overdraft and creditors which will be covered by the Cash Analysis Book and the Creditor Records. This will include loans, short-, medium- and long-term, mortgages and other credit arrangements such as hire purchase and leasing. If these are not too numerous then all records can be kept in one book.

Although the Cash Analysis Book will record when loans are received and payments made, the Loan Record Book will show when each loan or other was taken out along with the repayment terms, including interest rate, instalments and date when the loan will be fully paid off. At the end of the year it will be possible to calculate (or enter from the statement from the financial institution) how much of the interest has been paid, how much of the loan has been paid off and therefore, how much is still outstanding.

## Share issues record

As with loan records, the Share Issues Record is kept to facilitate the construction of the Balance Sheet at the end of the year. Any new issues of shares during the year are inserted and added to the total accumulated from when the company was started.

# Support Records

Some records do not feed directly in to overall accounting calculations, but are nevertheless needed to enable such calculations to be made, and to allow cost-centre accounts to be constructed.

## Stock records

As mentioned above, many of the records kept for valuation purposes are also needed for monitoring, control and evaluation of performance. In fact, it is really the other way round - we need to keep records of stocks and flows of inputs, of semi-finished produce, of growing stocks and of harvested or finished produce and these can then be used to provide the numbers for year-end or periodic valuations. These records have been dealt with under 'valuation records' and need not be discussed further here.

## Labour records

Labour is a hugely important component of forestry costs so if an accurate picture of the cost of operations and cost-centre performance is to be gained, then accurate labour records need to be maintained. Besides, records are needed simply to ensure that workers are paid the right amount. If workers are paid by the hour (a 'time rate' system) then records need to be kept of the number of hours worked.

The primary recording might be done by the supervisor or, in a large organisation, could be mechanised so that workers 'clock in'. If a system is adopted whereby workers are paid according to how much work they do or how much they produce ('a payment by results' or 'piece work' system), then the amount of work (seedlings planted, area sprayed, etc.) or production (cubic metres felled, metres planed, etc.) must be measured. Again, the task can be carried out by the supervisor or manager.

However, if operations are to be costed or labour attributed to cost centres more detail is needed. In this case time sheets should record hours spent on what and where. Besides time spent on the job, time travelling to the job, waiting for the job to begin and slack time caused by breakdown, inclement weather or other event, as well as training, sickness and holidays should also be recorded. As with all records, staff should not be required to fill in any more detail than is going to be put to worthwhile use and should be encouraged to fill the sheets in while the events are still fresh in their minds. The supervisor should then check them for accuracy before handing them on to secretarial or administrative staff.

Other labour-related records will need to be kept in the office: staff personal details, contracts of employment, training undergone, equipment and clothing issued, payment and pensions, and health and safety assessments, many of which will be legally required anyway. This will relate to all categories of staff.

Note that production workers may not be the only ones who have to fill in time sheets. The forester's time, for instance, might be recorded so that his salary and associated costs can be allocated to cost centres. Although this might not be the case for other staff, and although regular recording may not be necessary, occasionally their use of time might be surveyed in order to identify where efficiency gains might be made.

## Machinery records

Machinery has been dealt with under 'valuation records', but again, for more detailed monitoring and analysis, further information is necessary. A log book should be kept with each machine and the operator should record time spent on different operations and relating to different cost centres, fuel usage, breakdown, repair and maintenance details (although this may be filled in by the mechanic). Besides enabling machinery costs to be allocated to cost centres, such recording can allow efficiency of usage of machines to be gauged as well as the calculation of charges if machines are hired out.

## Cost centre/sub-compartment records

Once all the other records have been set up, there scarcely seems a need to have records for cost centres, after all, most of the information need will now be dealt with elsewhere. However, at some point, the various pieces of information relating to each cost centre will have to be drawn together to obtain a picture of cost-centre performance, although this can take place in the office of the administrative staff at regular intervals. Furthermore, these records will contain 'primary' data not recorded elsewhere - details of growing stock for instance, may first be recorded in cost centre or sub-compartment records. Other information recorded here might be amounts and timings of material, labour and machinery inputs, tree measurements, production quantities and events.

# How to Record?

The previous section answering the question, "what to record?" has, to some extent, answered the question of, "how to record?" in a general way. When it comes to deciding in more detail exactly how it should be done in your organisation, you should keep in mind the points listed under the previous question on features of good records. It is also wise to seek advice from others in the field, always remembering that someone else's system must be adapted to fit the peculiarities of your own case.

## Who Should Record?

Some managers and foresters might take the view that they personally have to undertake just about all of the recording, because they cannot trust their staff to do the job. However, there are a number of reasons for doing otherwise.

- Your time is expensive: if you leave recording to other, less well-paid staff, you will have more time to devote to more important matters;
- Other staff may be in a better position to carry out the recording: they are in the right place at the right time;
- Delegation of responsibility to your staff can improve motivation, as long as it is real delegation and they do not feel that you are not constantly checking up on them or telling them what to do. Apart from delegation of recording, you might also involve staff in the design of the recording system itself. However, if you delegate recording tasks you must ensure that they are able to carry them out - this involves careful choice of personnel and, possibly, informal or formal training and clear instruction from the outset exactly as to what is expected of them, who has the responsibility and right to record, and who does not. Further, delegation should be done wisely - there have to be 'checks and balances': if the task is open to corruption then there are ways of minimising the opportunities for this to occur, records must be checkable and consequences of misdemeanour must be clear. Finally, if you delegate responsibility, then you must be prepared to adequately reward the person who takes it on.

## Where to Record?

Normally, records should be kept where the event occurs: the machine's operations should be recorded in the log book kept in the machine; fertiliser delivered to and issued from the store should be recorded there; and cash flows should be recorded in the same office or building from which the cheques are issued and to which bank statements delivered. However, because we are dealing here with an 'outdoor' industry, recording on-site may not be appropriate. Physical work and Nature's ways often interfere with durable and neat recording. Thus, production, operations and labour information may best be recorded in the office or mess room. If recording does take place 'on site' then the recording materials will need to be suitably robust!

## When to Record?

As was mentioned earlier, recording should be carried out while the recorded event is still clearly remembered, otherwise inaccuracy can easily creep in.

However, the timing must be convenient and it is, therefore, helpful to try to allow time for recording in the work schedule of the member of staff responsible.

## Conclusion

Looking back at the discussion in this chapter you may come to the conclusion that this all sounds rather a lot of recording which may hardly seem worthwhile. The answer to this is, "If it doesn't seem worthwhile, then don't do it!" This is precisely the point that was made at the start - you have to weigh up, in the light of your objectives (what you are aiming to monitor, analyse and control), what records you need to help you to achieve those objectives and whether the benefit of those records outweighs their cost. If your aims are limited, then so will your recording needs be limited; if your aims are ambitious, then it is likely that your recording needs will be also.  In Hart's words:

> "Foresters sometimes are opposed to analysis forms, multiple columns and the like, asserting that the cost of account books and the amount of 'dead' paper work are considerable, that there is always some expenditure that does not find a ready place in any column provided, that if there are sufficient columns to allow full analysis and direct costing from them, the books and their constant writing up or posting are expensive beyond the value of the result, and that if the books are kept simple with few columns further working up of the figures is required and there is no advantage over the unanalysed account...
> The numerous figures obtainable from woodland detailed accountancy may entail so much extra booking that the analysis may be too expensive and may in the long run obscure the main account that the extra work fails to fulfil its chief purposes. The detailed costing of *every* operation and of *every* product can be tedious, and may not be worthwhile if only a few of the numerous facts and figures obtained are acted upon. Calculators and computers have greatly eased the burden, but it may still be desirable to select and set only the most worthwhile objectives and to reduce the number of analyses as far as is reasonably possible. The least to be aimed at may be the ascertainment of either the profit or the loss on each principal product, and determination of the cost of each major operation. Whatever the view, some form of accountancy and costing is a necessary adjunct to successful management."
>
> (Hart, 1991, pp. 597-8)

The question of what to record is perhaps the most important, but that is not all. You must then ask yourself or your team the associated questions of how, who, where and when, bearing in mind the list of features of 'good' records which we listed above (amended in the light of your own experience).

## Menzies Example

Douglas implements the budget which was developed in the earlier chapters and uses a recording system similar to the one outlined here. He uses the results to monitor performance during the year and at the year end he totals the information ready for the construction of the accounts. The following tables show summaries of the information from some of the key records.

Figures 9.8 and 9.9 show parts of the end-of-year pages for the cash analysis book. For outflows, at the year end, each of the different cost category columns is summed to give the year total. As would happen at the end of each quarter or month there would, prior to this, have to be a reconciliation with the latest bank statement so as to check that no money has gone astray or not been accounted for.

| | | | Cash Analysis Book – Outflows (£) | | | | | |
|---|---|---|---|---|---|---|---|---|
| Date | Invoice No. | Supplier | Comment | Fencing | Pre-plant weeding | Scarify | ... | ... |
| 31/12/02 | - | - | Year totals | £11,500 | £2,900 | £3,780 | | |

**Fig. 9.8** Cash Analysis Book - outflows summary.

The same process occurs for inflows so that Douglas will have end-of-year cash flow totals for all categories of outflows and inflows.

| | | | Cash Analysis Book – Inflows (£) | | | | | |
|---|---|---|---|---|---|---|---|---|
| Date | Invoice No. | Pur-chaser | Comment | Clear felling | Thinning | Plants | Vehicle sales | ... |
| 31/12/02 | - | - | Year totals | £95,058 | £70,607 | £8,800 | £6,000 | |

**Fig. 9.9** Cash Analysis Book – inflows summary.

The daybook will contain information on items coming onto the estate and items leaving the estate. Figure 9.10 shows two pages together: sales and purchases. To avoid confusion only some of the transactions have been included and the pages have also been concertina'd so that we can see the start and the end of the financial year at the same time.

In the sales section note that Humpin Wood Ltd purchased and felled the standing timber in November 2001 - before the start of the 2002 financial year. They still owed the money at the start of the financial year, so this was noted as a debtor at that point. The information was transferred into the section for the 2002 year, since the money was still owing, and the date was inserted when the money was received (10/1/02). At the end of that year, the page was ruled off and again information on debtors at that point (none in this case) written below the line.

Unlike the clear fell, the thinnings had been extracted and paid for within the financial year.

**Day Book**

**Sales**

| Date | Delivery note | Purchaser | Comment | Invoice No. | Invoice date | Amount (£) | Received |
|------|---------|-----------|---------|-------------|--------------|------------|----------|
| 27/11/01 | CF101 | Humpin Wood Ltd. | Clear fell | CF101-04 | | 95,058 | |
| debtors owing @ 31/12/01 | | Humpin Wood Ltd. | Clear fell | CF101-04 | | 95,058 | |
| | CF101 | Humpin Wood Ltd. | Clear fell | CF101-04 | 4/12/01 | 95,058 | 10/01/02 |
| ....... | | | | | | | |
| 13/09/02 | TH991 | Timber Fellas Ltd. | Thinnings | TH991-01 | 18/09/02 | 70,607 | 12/10/02 |
| ....... | | | | | | | |
| debtors owing @ 31/12/02 | | | | | | 0 | |

**Purchases**

| Date | Delivery note | Supplier | Comment | Invoice No. | Invoice date | Amount (£) | Paid |
|------|---------|----------|---------|-------------|--------------|------------|------|
| | | | | | | | |
| creditors owing @ 31/12/01 | | CalTel | accrual | | | 114 | |
| ....... | | | | | | | |
| 5/01/02 | | CalTel | telephone bill | CT20056 | 3/01/02 | 114 | 4/02/02 |
| ....... | | | | | | | |
| 13/04/02 | 1321 | Weedit Co. | sprays | IN1321 | 13/04/02 | 662 | 13/04/02 |
| ....... | | | | | | | |
| creditors owing @ 31/12/02 | | CalTel | accrual | | | 103.75 | |
| | | | | | | | |

**Fig. 9.10** Sales/Purchases day book - summary.

Similarly with purchases. Although, at the end of the previous year there were no bills unpaid, the estate was due a bill from CalTel for telephone services during the previous three months. So this would be considered a special type of creditor termed an *accrual*. Thus a creditor amount of £114 was effectively owing at the start of the 2002 financial year. The bill arrived on 5 January and was paid about one month later.

In the same way, by the end of the financial year telephone charges of £103.75 had accrued.

Note also that in March Douglas had purchased £662 worth of sprays from Weedit; he had paid for these when he went to their depot to pick up the chemicals.

Because of the importance of the valuations of the land and growing stock, a summary of the valuation record is shown in Fig. 9.11. How the opening figure for Compartment 1 was arrived at was explained in Chapter 4. The opening figures for all other compartments and the nursery were calculated in the same way. The closing figures are not those estimated in the budget at the start of the year, but those taking account of Douglas' revised view at the end of the year.

| cpt. | area ha. | Opening (31/12/01) | | Closing (31/12/02) | |
|------|----------|-----------|---------|-----------|-----------|
|      |          | per ha. £ | total £ | per ha. £ | total (£) £ |
| 1 | 35 | 3,166 | 110,816 | 3,404 | 119,150 |
| 2 | 40 | 1,946 | 77,856 | 2,111 | 84,453 |
| 3 | 40 | 305 | 12,214 | 1,305 | 52,184 |
| 4 | 20 | 17,567 | 351,337 | 18,669 | 373,380 |
| 5 | 35 | 15,452 | 540,814 | 16,427 | 574,948 |
| 6 | 35 | 12,140 | 424,908 | 12,917 | 452,088 |
| 7 | 30 | 13,846 | 415,378 | 14,725 | 441,745 |
| 8 | 45 | 8,437 | 379,663 | 8,991 | 404,609 |
| 9 | 30 | 9,685 | 290,548 | 10,314 | 309,425 |
| 10 | 40 | 12,704 | 508,149 | 11,308 | 452,305 |
| nursery | 3 | 16,340 | 49,021 | 15,512 | 46,537 |
| estate | 353 | 8,954 | 3,160,705 | 9,379 | 3,310,823 |

**Fig. 9.11** Valuation record - summary.

# Chapter 10

# Accounts - Construction

The part of the management cycle which involves looking forward and planning we termed budgeting. Then when the events take place we do the actual recording. After the events take place we need periodically to look back and assess or evaluate performance: was it good or bad? What aspects were good and what aspects were bad? Why was this the case? This we can term accounts analysis which is the subject of Chapter 11. Before we can appraise, however, we have to construct the accounts, which is the subject of this chapter.

As with budgeting, the key aspects of performance with which we should be concerned in accounting are *'profit'*, *'cash'* and *'capital'*. And just as with budgeting we constructed a budgeted profit and loss statement to provide a *'profit'* picture and a budgeted balance sheet to provide a *'capital'* picture, so with accounting we construct a Profit and Loss Account and a Balance Sheet, but this time rather than *looking forward* in terms of what we *expect* to happen, we are *looking back* at what *actually* did happen. With *'cash'* there are several ways of looking at it in retrospect: during the year we can construct a monthly or quarterly and a cumulative cash flow statement which can be compared with the cash flow budget, and at the end of the year, as well as having the cash flow statement for the whole year we can also construct a flow of funds statement to trace where the money has come from and gone to. Besides these 'macro' or aggregate accounts, if our recording permits, we can also dig deeper - constructing accounts which measure cost-centre performance and cost of operations.

We can only construct these accounts, however, if we have the appropriate records - so you see how important the topic of the previous chapter is.

Let us now go through the process of construction of the various accounts in turn. Because we spent a lot of the earlier part of the book going through the budgeting steps, we won't need to take as long explaining how accounts are constructed, since we are essentially looking at the same process in reverse.

## Profit

To account for 'profit' we need a 'Profit and Loss Account'. To see what recorded information we need for its construction let us take a look at Fig. 10.1: the left-hand section, which you have seen before in Fig. 7.2, shows the form of the account; the right-hand side of the figure shows the types of data needed to construct the account.

The headings for the P&L Account in the left-hand section of the figure should be familiar from Chapter 7; this format, or the horizontal one shown in Appendix 7.1, is how the account is normally presented. But where does the information come from to calculate this account? There are two steps to deciding where to find the information we need: first, we need to decide what types of data we need - cash flows, debtors, valuations, depreciation, etc. Secondly, we need to decide where that data will be held. Figure 10.1 helps us to answer the first question: what types of data we need under each heading within the account. Note that the abbreviations used in Fig. 10.1 are shown in Table 10.1.

In Fig. 10.1 for each heading in the account on the left-hand side, ticks are inserted on the right-hand side to show which types of data to consult. Let us look into this in more detail.

Sales are derived from trading cash receipts, changes in money owing and changes in the values of the growing and felled stocks: the data for these three elements come within the trading receipts, changes in debtors and change in valuations categories respectively. For instance, sales for the year might consist of £50,000 of timber sales for which payment has been received, another £30,000 of sales which is still owing at the end of the year, and an increase in the value of the growing stock[4] of £200,000. There might possibly also have been some benefits in kind given to staff, in which case the output figures will need adjusting for the values of these benefits. You will therefore see on the right-hand side of Fig. 10.1, across from the Sales/Output heading, that ticks have been inserted under TR, $\Delta$D, $\Delta$V and BiK.

The data for the different cost categories within the account, under the headings Cost of Sales, Operating Expenses and Receipts and Non-Operating Expenses and Receipts, come again, not just from the cash flow records, but also from non-cash records. Costs which have been paid over the year will come from trading payments, changes in money owed come from changes in creditors information and changes in the values of inputs or semi-finished produce come from the valuation changes information. Machinery and buildings depreciation figures will also be brought in under the costs headings and if any inputs, such as

---

[4] Whether or not you include growing stock valuation changes in your profit calculation depends upon the approach you take to 'unrealised' profits - Appendix 7.3 dealt with this issue.

fuel, have been given as benefits in kind to staff, then again costs will have to be adjusted for these.

Besides the Sales heading, profits might be boosted elsewhere in the P&L Account: Operating Expenses are adjusted for 'other income' and Non-Operating Expenses and Receipts may include a **profit on sales** of machinery or equipment. Information for the first of these will be also be found under trading receipts and changes in debtors. For the second, profit on sales is the difference between its selling price (shown under capital receipts) and its 'book value' at the time of sale. The latter is derived within the depreciation calculations (hence the asterisk against the tick in the 'Dep' column) since it is not actually the depreciation figure that we want.

| Account heading | types of data | | | | | | | | |
|---|---|---|---|---|---|---|---|---|---|
| | TR | TP | CR | CP | ΔD | ΔC | ΔV | Dep | BiK |
| Sales/Output | ✔ | | | | ✔ | | ✔ | | ✔ |
| *less* | | | | | | | | | |
| Cost of Sales/Cost of Production | | | | | | | | | |
|   direct costs | | ✔ | | | | ✔ | ✔ | | ✔ |
|   on-costs | | ✔ | | | | ✔ | | | |
|   production overheads | | ✔ | | | | ✔ | | ✔ | ✔ |
| *equals* | | | | | | | | | |
| **Gross Profit** | | | | | | | | | |
| *less* | | | | | | | | | |
| Operating Expenses & Receipts | | | | | | | | | |
|   selling/distribution costs | | ✔ | | | | ✔ | | ✔ | |
|   administrative expenses | | ✔ | | | | ✔ | | ✔ | |
|   general costs | | ✔ | | | | ✔ | | ✔ | |
|   *less* | | | | | | | | | |
|   other income | ✔ | | | | ✔ | | | | |
| *equals* | | | | | | | | | |
| **Operating Profit** | | | | | | | | | |
| *less* | | | | | | | | | |
| Non-Operating Expenses & Receipts | | | | | | | | | |
|   interest paid and received | ✔ | ✔ | | | | | | | |
|   profit on sales of property and investments | | | ✔ | | | | | ✔* | |
| *equals* | | | | | | | | | |
| **Profit before Tax** | | | | | | | | | |
| *less* | | | | | | | | | |
| Company/Corporation Tax | | | | ✔ | | | | | |
| *equals* | | | | | | | | | |
| **Net Profit** | | | | | | | | | |

See Table 10.1 for explanation of the abbreviations.

**Fig. 10.1** Profit and Loss Account - vertical format, with types of data.

The last item is tax. Any tax paid will be found in the capital payments section of the cash flow statement.

Following on from the first question concerning what type of data we need for the construction of the account, the second question concerns where we can find that data, i.e. where the data are held. Table 10.1 links the types of data (which were shown in Fig. 10.1) required for the 'Profit and Loss Account', to the records where they can be found. However, in between the record and the data item there is often an intermediate step, which occurs because the raw data is not usually in the form required for the accounts. Thus, in the right-hand column of Table 10.1 are shown the intermediate accounts wherein the raw data from the records is aggregated under various headings or converted ready for further use. For example, at the end of the year a 'Cash Flow Statement' can be prepared from the Cash Analysis Book to show the aggregate amounts under the different payments and receipts headings. The trading receipts and trading payments figures can then be extracted directly from the Cash Flow Statement. Similarly, in the Machinery and Equipment Account machinery depreciation is calculated using machinery stocks, purchases and sales information taken from the machinery records. These intermediate accounts may sound as if they are rather complex, but in practice all we may need is one sheet of paper which we use to draw together the bits of raw data recorded during the year in the particular record.

Using Fig. 10.1 to learn which data we need and Table 10.1 to see where to find it, we should now be able to construct the Profit and Loss Account and calculate the several measures of profit.

**Table 10.1** Sources of data for construction of the Profit and Loss Account.

| data item | abbrev* | record | via Intermediate Accounts |
|---|---|---|---|
| Trading Receipts | TR | Cash Analysis Book | Cash Flow Statement |
| Trading Payments | TP | ditto | ditto |
| Capital Receipts | CR | ditto | ditto |
| Captial Payments | CP | ditto | ditto |
| Change in Debtors | ΔD | Daybook or debtor records | Debtors A/c* |
| Change in Creditors | ΔC | Daybook or creditor records | Creditors A/c |
| Change in Valuations | ΔV | Records of stores & materials, work in progress, growing stock, and harvested produce | Current Stocks A/c ditto Growing Stock A/c Felled Crop A/c |
| Depreciation | Dep | Machinery and buildings records | Machinery & Equipment A/c Buildings & Fixed Plant A/c |
| Benefits in Kind | BiK | Daybook, stocks records | Benefits in Kind Summary |

*abbrev. = abbreviation; A/c= account.

There is, however, another way of presenting our profit information. Remember in the budgeting process, we calculated profit in two different ways: in Step 4 (Chapter 7), we produced a budgeted profit and loss statement, following the pattern that we have just used for the profit and loss account. But in Step 2 (Chapter 3) we produced a disaggregated picture of profit which was called by the snappy title 'the Profit Budget based on Cost Centres'. By working up from individual cost and revenue elements at cost-centre level to the level of the whole business, we were able to follow a logical, and hopefully more accurate, procedure than if we had tried to work out the whole business profit picture in one go.

Now that we are looking back over events (accounting rather than budgeting), it also makes sense to produce a profit and loss account based on cost centres. Why? Because, it will enable us to look below the surface (at the micro as opposed to the macro level) in order to see the contribution to profit of the various elements of the business. In the next chapter we look at how we can analyse the accounts at the macro and micro levels. However, the disaggregated, Cost Centre Profit Account can only be constructed if sufficiently detailed records have been kept, i.e. if records have been kept for this purpose.

If the records allow, then the Cost Centre Profit Account can be constructed according to the pattern illustrated in Fig. 10.2. Each of the output items - timber sales, growing and harvested stock valuation changes, rents, etc. will be listed on a separate line and allocated within the cost centres according to the records.

| | | Business | | | | | | | |
|---|---|---|---|---|---|---|---|---|---|
| | Nursery | Forest | | | | | Sawmill | | Business |
| Output | | cpt 1 | cpt 2a | cpt 2b | cpt | Forest | | | |
| - | - | - | - | - | - | - | - | - | - |
| - | - | - | - | - | - | - | - | - | - |
| - | - | - | - | - | - | - | - | - | - |
| total output | | | | | | | | | |
| Costs direct | | | | | | | | | |
| - | - | - | - | - | - | - | - | - | - |
| - | - | - | - | - | - | - | - | - | - |
| on-costs | | | | | | | | | |
| - | - | - | - | - | - | - | - | - | - |
| - | - | - | - | - | - | - | - | - | - |
| overheads | | | | | | | | | |
| - | - | - | - | - | - | - | - | - | - |
| - | - | - | - | - | - | - | - | - | - |
| total costs | | | | | | | | | |
| profit | | | | | | | | | |

**Fig. 10.2** Cost Centre Profit Account.

Sales should be calculated from receipts, adjusted for debtors. The separate cost items, direct and on-costs first, followed by overhead costs, should also be calculated as payments, adjusted for creditors and stock changes. Thus, for instance, if payments for sprays amounted to £3,200, opening and closing creditors were £1,100 and £1,350 respectively, and opening and closing stocks were valued at £1,000 and £920, then the calculation would be:

| | | |
|---|---|---|
| payments | | £3,200 |
| *plus* | | |
| change in creditors | | |
| closing creditors | £1,350 | |
| *minus* | | |
| opening creditors | £1,100 | £250 |
| *minus* | | |
| change in stocks | | |
| closing stocks | £920 | |
| *minus* | | |
| opening stocks | £1,000 | -£80 |
| *equals* | | |
| spray cost[5] | | £3,530 |

The only costs which would not be calculated in such a way would be the depreciation on machinery and buildings, which would be calculated according to the procedure explained in Chapter 5.

For overhead costs, the same calculations would have to be made, but these would be totals rather than amounts for each cost centre. As we discussed in Chapter 3, these can be allocated to cost centres according to weights or proportions. Allocations can be based on the cost centres' shares of area, direct costs, sales, or whatever measure is deemed most appropriate, using the two-step calculation:

*step 1*
proportion of total area, direct cost or whatever measure used =
amount in cost centre ÷ total amount
*step 2*
cost centre cost share = proportion of total amount × total overhead cost item

For instance, if depreciation on the office building is £1,200 and the forest manager has decided to share such costs between the cost centres according to productive area, then if the total productive area is 300 hectares and the four cost centres (compartments in this case) are 180, 10, 30 and 80 hectares in size, then the share of the office building depreciation charge for the first cost centre would be worked out as follows:

---

[5] The -£80 means an addition to costs of £80 as the calculation is *minus minus*

*step 1*
proportion of total area in compartment 1 = 180 ÷ 300 = 0.6

*step 2*
compartment 1 office building depreciation charge = 0.6 × £1,200 = £720

For the other three cost centres the figures would be £40, £120 and £320 as Table 10.2 shows.

**Table 10.2** Sharing overhead costs between cost centres - by productive area.

| cost centre | cpt. 1 | cpt. 2 | cpt. 3 | cpt. 4 | total |
|---|---|---|---|---|---|
| size (ha) | 180 | 10 | 30 | 80 | 300 |
| proportion of area | 0.60 | 0.03 | 0.10 | 0.27 | 1.00 |
| cost centre cost | £720 | £40 | £120 | £320 | £1,200 |

You can cross check the accuracy of your calculations by adding the four values together - they should of course total £1,200!

It is worth going through this calculation process again, this time assuming that the costs are to be shared according to proportions of the total direct costs. Before calculating the proportions you would first need to add up the various direct costs for each cost centre and then in total. If the overall direct cost total was £94,800 with the totals for each cost centre as shown in Table 10.3[6] then, because of differing proportions, the cost-centre shares of the £1,200 would be very different from those in Table 10.2. This suggests that choosing an appropriate weighting measure is very important if we are seeking to obtain a fair estimation of cost-centre performance.

**Table 10.3** Sharing overhead costs between cost centres - by proportion of direct cost.

| cost centre | cpt. 1 | cpt. 2 | cpt. 3 | cpt. 4 | total |
|---|---|---|---|---|---|
| direct costs | £39,100 | £6,400 | £17,600 | £31,700 | £94,800 |
| proportion of d.c. | 0.412 | 0.068 | 0.186 | 0.334 | 1.00 |
| cost centre cost | £495 | £82 | £223 | £401 | £1,200 |

Once the figures for each of the overhead costs have been shared between cost centres, the cost-centre profits can be calculated. The total profit figure will be the same as that shown in the earlier Profit and Loss Account as *profit before tax*. The advantage of producing the Cost Centre Profit Account as well is in its presentation of profit, cost and sales information by cost centre. This comes in useful when we look at the micro aspects of performance; we will return to this in the next chapter.

---

[6] Note that the figures total to £1,201 due to rounding. In this case you would need to reduce one of the figures by £1, perhaps the biggest - which is compartment 1.

## Capital

The Balance Sheet presents the 'capital' picture of the business; the way it is presented in vertical form is shown on the left-hand side of Table 10.4. On the right-hand side of the table are listed the sources of information for each section of the Balance Sheet. Nearly all of the data items required are actually valuations that will be available in the intermediate accounts which themselves will have been calculated from the corresponding records.

The Balance Sheet first lists the assets in their various forms, both those with a long to medium life[7] (Fixed Assets) and those with a short life (Current Assets). Each of these values is simply a valuation at a particular date. The short-term counterpart of 'Current Assets' is the group of short-term liabilities known as 'Current Liabilities' which are amounts owing in the form of overdraft, creditors and short-term loans[8]. The difference between Current Assets and Current Liabilities is known as Net Current Assets. The final heading in the top half of the Balance Sheet is Fixed Liabilities, the details of which are derived from the Loans Record. The Balance of all assets and liabilities, for the end of the current year and the previous year is shown by the small letter f, and is the effectively the owners' (the shareholders') share of the business.

The lower half of the Balance Sheet shows how this share has come about - via shares being issued in return for an injection of funds by the shareholders, via an increase in the value of machinery, buildings or growing stock (if not included as part of profit) or via retention of profits within the business. These pieces of information come from the Share Issues record in the first case, from the holding gains figures in the Machinery and Buildings Accounts (and possibly the valuation change from the Growing Stock Account) in the second, and in the third case, from the Profit and Loss Account. This latter case deserves some clarification. The Earned Surplus shows how much of the profits of the business have been ploughed back into, or retained within the business since its inception. Each year this cumulative figure will be added to (or taken away from in the case of losses) by the amount of the retained earnings, which, as we saw in Chapter 7 and Fig. 7.3, can be calculated at the end of the Profit and Loss Account. Retained Earnings, you will remember, are calculated as net profit less dividends distributed to shareholders. So the earned surplus at the end of this year is calculated as the earned surplus at the end of last year plus the retained earnings for this year.

---

[7] Remember too from Chapter 8 that 'goodwill' can also be included here. How do we calculate it? There is not the space here to go into this issue, particularly as in the case of a forestry estate we may deem there to be no 'goodwill' element. However, for some businesses with a 'good name' or well-known products, it can be important - in which case you should consult a good accounting text, such as Chopping and Skerratt (1998) or Dodge (1993).

[8]Some accountants and bankers also prefer to include under 'Current Liabilities' the part of longer term liabilities falling due within the next year.

**Table 10.4** Balance Sheet in vertical format and data sources.

| Account Format | this year | last year | Intermediate Account/Record |
|---|---|---|---|
| Fixed Assets | | | |
|   land | | | Land Records |
|   buildings & fixed plant | | | Buildings & Fixed Plant a/c |
|   growing stock | | | Growing Stock a/c |
|   machinery & equipment | | | Machinery & Equipment a/c |
| Fixed Assets | **a** | a | |
| Current Assets | | | |
|   cash in hand | | | Petty Cash Book |
|   cash at bank | | | Cash Flow Statement |
|   debtors | | | Debtors Account |
|   stores & materials | | | Current Stocks a/c |
|   work in progress | | | *ditto* |
|   harvested produce | | | Felled Crop a/c |
| Current Assets | **b** | b | |
| Current Liabilities | | | |
|   overdraft | | | Cash Flow Statement |
|   creditors | | | Creditors a/c |
|   short term loans | **c** | c | Loans Record |
| Net Current Assets | **d=b-c** | d=b-c | |
| | | | |
| Fixed Liabilities | | | |
|   hire purchase & leasing | | | Loans Record |
|   medium- & long-term loans | | | *ditto* |
|   mortgages | | | *ditto* |
| Fixed liabilities | **e** | e | |
| | | | |
| Balance | **f=a+d-e** | f=a+d-e | |
| | | | |
| Shareholders' Funds and Capital Reserves | | | |
| Share Capital Issued | **g** | g | Share Issues Record |
| | | | |
| Capital Reserve | | | Buildings & Fixed Plant a/c |
| | | | Machinery & Equipment a/c |
| | **h** | h | (Growing Stock a/c) |
| Earned Surplus | **i** | i | Profit and Loss a/c |
| Balance | **j=g+h+i** | j=g+h+i | |

The Balance (j) at the bottom of the Balance Sheet should exactly match the Balance figure (f) at the end of the upper part since they are simply showing the same thing derived in different ways.

# Cash

The two main tables used for summarising the financial performance of the business are the Profit and Loss Account and the Balance Sheet. Some aspects of the 'cash' side of the business can be appraised from the Balance Sheet - we will look at how this is done in the next chapter. However, there are ways of presenting the cash performance information of the business separate from these other accounts: the first we are going to look at is the Cash Flow Statement. This is really one of those intermediate accounts and is simply a summary, or bringing together, of the information from the Cash Analysis Book under particular headings, and will tend to be presented in the same sort of form as the Cash Flow Budget which was covered in Chapter 6 - a cut-down version is shown in Table 10.5. As mentioned in the introduction to this chapter, we can present this information on a whole year basis, showing the totals for the year and the ensuing bank balance, or we can also give the within-year data on a monthly or quarterly basis. The latter enables us to see the pattern of cash flows and a profile of the bank balance over the year as well as the year-end figures.

**Table 10.5** Cash Flow Statement format.

|  | Year 1 | | | | |
|  | quarter 1 | quarter 2 | quarter 3 | quarter 4 | Total |
|---|---|---|---|---|---|
| **Receipts** | | | | | |
| Trading Receipts | | | | | |
| .. | | | | | |
| .. | | | | | |
| Capital Receipts | | | | | |
| .. | | | | | |
| .. | | | | | |
| Total Receipts | | | | | |
| **Payments** | | | | | |
| Trading Payments | | | | | |
| *sprays* | | | | | |
| .. | | | | | |
| *overdraft interest* | | | | | |
| .. | | | | | |
| Capital Payments | | | | | |
| *loan principal* | | | | | |
| .. | | | | | |
| Total Payments | | | | | |
| Net Cash Flow | | | | | |
| Opening Bank Balance | | | | | |
| Closing Bank Balance | | | | | |

Besides being used in its own right, the Cash Flow Statement is also used to provide information to feed into the two main accounts, as we saw above.

Another way of presenting the year's cash information which links in to profit and capital as well, is in the form of the **Flow of Funds Statement**, otherwise known as the *Source and Application of Funds Statement* or the *Sources and Uses of Funds Statement* (Arnold *et al.*, 1985). This shows where funds (not just cash) come from and where they have gone to and what has happened to the liquidity position of the business as a result. Production of this statement helps us to better understand what has happened to the money in the business. Even though you may have understood the links between profit, cash and capital illustrated in Fig. 8.2, you may still wonder to yourself, "If we made a profit, then what has happened to it - why isn't it mirrored in the cash position of the business?" If so, the Flow of Funds Statement (FFS) may help to make things clearer. This process is, in fact, a way of 'digging deeper' into how funds have been employed by the business over the year.

**Table 10.6** Flow of Funds Statement.

| Sources of cash - inflows | Uses of cash - outflows |
|---|---|
| Trading | Trading |
| net profit (loss) | |
| *plus* depreciation | |
| *minus* benefits in kind* | |
| External injections | External withdrawals |
| new shares issued | private drawings/dividends |
| private gifts* | income tax* |
| Increase in Liabilities | Reduction in Liabilities |
| increase in: | reduction in: |
| creditors | creditors |
| loans, lease, etc. | loans, lease, etc. |
| Reduction in Assets | Increase in Assets |
| reduction in value of: | increase in value of: |
| debtors | debtors |
| stores & materials, | stores & materials, |
| work in progress, | work in progress, |
| harvested produce | harvested produce |
| growing stock | growing stock |
| sale of: | purchase of: |
| machinery | machinery |
| buildings | buildings |
| land | land |
| other investments | other investments |
| Total inflow | Total outflow |
| Net inflow | Net outflow |
| Balance | Balance |
| reduction in cash balance | increase in cash balance |
| increase in overdraft | reduction in overdraft |

* in the case of sole traders or partnerships only

Table 10.6, based on Warren (1998), shows the headings used in the FFS; here it is presented in 'horizontal' format, but it can instead be presented in vertical format (Arnold *et al.*, 1985). Note that all of the information needed comes from the two main accounts. In summary, to construct this statement we are saying, "List all the ways in which funds came into the business over the year and add them up, then list all the ways in which funds were used and add them up. If inflows were greater than outflows then the surplus must have been used to either increase the cash balance or reduce the overdraft and *vice versa*".

It is worth going through Table 10.6 in more detail. We start at the top left-hand side by inserting the profit (or loss as a negative figure). We then adjust for items which have not involved actual movements of cash: depreciation is a notional charge so should be added back and benefits in kind, in the case of a business not trading as a company, have contributed to profits so should now be subtracted. This gives the net amount of cash from trading; if it is a negative figure we should really take off the minus sign and insert it on the right-hand side - since it would, in fact, be a use of funds rather than a source.

Proceeding down the left-hand side, note that we have four main headings, the first of which is 'Trading'. Next comes 'External'. Funds can be obtained from outside the business, in the case of a company, generally through some form of share issue. For the sole trader or partnership there is also the possibility of a private injection of funds in the form of a gift, from a close relative perhaps. Unfortunately for companies, they do not usually have a kind uncle or granny to help them out!

Thirdly, the business can obtain funds by increasing its liabilities. This is obvious in the case of loans - the company takes out a loan and in return the bank issues a cheque or transfers the amount into the account of the business. In the case of creditors the process is different - how can increasing the amount owing to creditors provide more cash? To understand this we need to go back to the profit figure which was fed into the statement as a source of cash. Suppose the profit and loss account of the business was as pictured in the left-hand side of Table 10.7 (Example 1). Profit for the year would be £25, which exactly mirrors the amount of extra cash made available as a result of trading, which would be cash receipts minus cash payments, i.e. £100 - £75 = £25.

**Table 10.7** Effect of increases in creditors on availability of cash.

| Example 1 | | Example 2 | |
|---|---|---|---|
| Profit and Loss Account | £ | Profit and Loss Account | £ |
| sales | | sales | |
| cash receipts | 100 | cash receipts | 100 |
| cost of sales | | cost of sales | |
| cash payment | 75 | cash payment | 45 |
| increase in creditors | 0 | increase in creditors | 30 |
| | 75 | | 75 |
| gross profit | 25 | gross profit | 25 |
| net profit | 25 | net profit | 25 |

On the right-hand side (Example 2), however, although exactly the same profit performance is shown, namely a profit of £25, this is arrived at in a different way. Instead of paying for all its purchases during the year, the business has paid only for £45 of these, but has not yet paid for £30 worth of them[9]. The amount of cash available as a result of trading in this case is £100 - £45 = £55, which is £30 more than if the creditors had been paid. In the FFS, if profits of £25 were shown as a source of cash, there would have to be a further addition of £30 under the heading 'increase in creditors' to allow for the effect of this on cash availability.

The fourth heading in Table 10.7 is 'Reduction in Assets'. Again, selling off assets not appearing in the Profit and Loss Account (except in terms of depreciation), such as machinery, would generate cash. On the other hand, as far as debtors and valuations of stocks included in the Profit and Loss Account are concerned, the principle is the same as for the 'increases in creditors', but in reverse. Table 10.8 shows the effect of a reduction in debtors and Table 10.9 the effect of a reduction in the stocks of materials. In the case of a reduction in debtors, as the right-hand side (Example 2) of Table 10.8 shows, imagine that opening debtors had been £13 and closing debtors were £0, then this extra £13 would have been paid into the business over the year, inflating the cash flow. The profit would still show £25, but more cash had been generated by running down the debtors: net cash flow would be £113 - £75 = £38 (Example 2) instead of £25 (Example 1).

With stocks of materials, Table 10.9 shows that if £8 of materials had been used from stocks, this would reduce the need for spending on such items by the same amount. Thus the cash outflow would be £67 (Example 2) instead of £75 (Example 1), and net cash flow would be £8 higher than the profit figure implied (£33 instead of £25).

**Table 10.8** Effect of a reduction in debtors on availability of cash.

| Example 1 | | Example 2 | |
|---|---|---|---|
| Profit and Loss Account | £ | Profit and Loss Account | £ |
| sales | | sales | |
|     cash receipts | 100 |     cash receipts | 113 |
|     *less* | |     *less* | |
|     reduction in debtors | 0 |     reduction in debtors | 13 |
| | 100 | | 100 |
| cost of sales | | cost of sales | |
|     cash payment | 75 |     cash payment | 75 |
| gross profit | 25 | gross profit | 25 |
| net profit | 25 | net profit | 25 |

[9] Assuming for simplicity that there were no creditors at the start of the year.

**Table 10.9** Effect of a reduction in stocks of materials on availability of cash.

| Example 1 | | Example 2 | |
|---|---|---|---|
| Profit and Loss Account | £ | Profit and Loss Account | £ |
| sales | | sales | |
| cash receipts | 100 | cash receipts | 100 |
| cost of sales | | cost of sales | |
| cash payment | 75 | cash payment | 67 |
| reduction in stocks | 0 | reduction in stocks | 8 |
| | 75 | | 75 |
| gross profit | 25 | gross profit | 25 |
| net profit | 25 | net profit | 25 |

Those four categories show the sources of cash and these can be totalled to show the total inflow. We then turn to more or less the same categories on the right-hand side of Table 10.6 to see where the cash went to.

Under 'Uses of Cash' a figure only appears under the first, 'Trading' category if the adjusted profit figure is negative. Otherwise that section is left blank. Withdrawals of funds from the business, the second category, occur in the case of the sole trader or partnership where the owner will draw money from the shared bank account for personal expenses, to pay income tax, or, in the case of a company, when dividends are paid. Thirdly, funds might be used to pay off loans and, as such payments are deemed to be 'capital payments' rather than 'trading payments', they do not appear in the Profit and Loss Account' so will not have come into the calculation of profit. Reductions in creditors, however, will have been included in the profit calculations, but as creditor changes will be reflected in cash flow they should be accounted for under 'Reduction in Liabilities'.

The fourth category, 'Increases in Assets' again effectively has two sections: increases in asset values which appear in the P&L Account and those which do not. Increases in stocks of inputs, work in progress, harvested produce and growing stock affect profit, but indicate that the profit figure will overestimate the amount of cash available. So, just as reductions in stocks meant more cash available, so with increases in stock less cash is available.

The amounts shown under the four 'Uses of cash' categories are summed to give the 'cash outflow'. The cash outflow is then subtracted from the inflow to show whether more cash came into the business over the year than went out, or *vice versa*. If more funds came in (a net inflow), this figure is entered on the right-hand side; if there was a net outflow, the figure is entered on the left. Finally, since a net inflow, or surplus, of cash must have gone somewhere, or a net outflow, a deficit, must have been financed somehow, we have the balancing item at the bottom. A net inflow, shown on the right-hand side, will have either[10] increased the cash balance or reduced the overdraft between the beginning and end of the year. Conversely, a net outflow, shown on the left, will have been met by running down the cash reserves or increasing the overdraft.

## Review

In constructing the accounts we are aiming to obtain, for ourselves and others, a picture of the profit, capital and cash performance of the business over the year. This is primarily presented in the Profit and Loss Account, the Balance Sheet and the Cash Flow Statement, although we may also wish to produce a Flow of Funds Statement to provide a clearer picture.

We have seen that the process of constructing the accounts involves two stages: first, intermediate accounts are produced in order to bring together or aggregate the raw data entered in the record books - this will include completion of the Cash Flow Statement; secondly, these intermediate accounts are used to build the Profit and Loss Account and the Balance Sheet.

Because these main accounts are essentially summaries of the information contained in the primary records and the intermediate accounts, it is helpful to provide a set of the relevant intermediate accounts, such as growing stock account, machinery and equipment account, etc. along with the main accounts. To help the reader of the accounts further, you can number these intermediate accounts and insert the number in the main records where reference should be made to the source of the information.

## Menzies Example

Douglas has constructed the Profit and Loss Account, the Balance Sheet and the Flow of Funds Statement and we are now going to go through each of them to see how they were arrived at.

As we saw in Table 10.1, to construct the Profit and Loss Account we take data from the Cash Flow Statement along with other pieces of information from the other accounts which summarise the records concerning debtors, creditors, valuations and so on. Therefore, in order to show some of the calculations the cash flow statement for the year is presented in Table 10.10.

Table 10.11 shows the Profit and Loss Account for the past year. Under the Sales heading, the first item, thinnings and harvested timber, is derived from the first two totals in the Cash Flow Statement - the clear felling total is £95,058 and that for thinnings is £70,607; together these total £165,665. Similarly, the next item, 'plants - sales', comes from the third item in Table 10.10.

---

[10] It could have done both if there are several places where cash is held - such as two accounts or the bank and the office.

**Table 10.10** Cash Flow Statement.

| | q. 1 £ | q. 2 £ | q. 3 £ | q. 4 £ | total £ |
|---|---|---|---|---|---|
| RECEIPTS | | | | | |
| Trading receipts | | | | | |
| clear felling | 95058 | 0 | 0 | 0 | 95058 |
| thinning | 0 | 0 | 0 | 70607 | 70607 |
| plants | 3520 | 880 | 880 | 3520 | 8800 |
| planting grants | 0 | 0 | 0 | 0 | 0 |
| Capital receipts | | | | | |
| vehicle sales | 6000 | 0 | 0 | 0 | 6000 |
| Total receipts | 104578 | 880 | 880 | 74127 | 180465 |
| PAYMENTS | | | | | |
| Trading payments | | | | | |
| clear Felling | 0 | 0 | 0 | 0 | 0 |
| thinning | 0 | 0 | 0 | 0 | 0 |
| fencing | 11500 | 0 | 0 | 0 | 11500 |
| pre-plant weed | 2900 | 0 | 0 | 0 | 2900 |
| scarify | 3780 | 0 | 0 | 0 | 3780 |
| planting | 9320 | 0 | 0 | 0 | 9320 |
| planting material | 2520 | 0 | 0 | 0 | 2520 |
| fertilisers and sprays | | 662 | 0 | 0 | 662 |
| other materials | 0 | 200 | 0 | 0 | 200 |
| casual labour | 1404 | 4212 | 1404 | 0 | 7020 |
| roads maintenance | 0 | 0 | 0 | 2800 | 2800 |
| crop insurance | 0 | 0 | 1625 | 0 | 1625 |
| salaries – forest manager | 2000 | 2000 | 2000 | 2000 | 8000 |
| secretarial | 995 | 995 | 995 | 995 | 3980 |
| forest worker | 2480 | 2535 | 2145 | 1945 | 9105 |
| tax & insurance | 0 | 890 | 0 | 0 | 890 |
| fuel & oil | 290 | 239 | 187 | 160 | 876 |
| vehicle repairs | 367 | 285 | 100 | 27 | 779 |
| building repairs | 0 | 375 | 15 | 0 | 390 |
| office repairs | 0 | 103 | 0 | 0 | 103 |
| water | 105 | 105 | 105 | 105 | 420 |
| electricity | 125 | 125 | 125 | 125 | 500 |
| telephone | 114 | 105 | 98 | 104 | 421 |
| misc. admin. costs | 320 | 544 | 180 | 751 | 1795 |
| loan interest | 413 | 413 | 413 | 413 | 1651 |
| overdraft interest | 788 | 0 | 12 | 224 | 1023 |
| Capital payments | | | | | |
| vehicle/equipment purchase | 16000 | 0 | 0 | 0 | 16000 |
| loan principal | 889 | 889 | 889 | 889 | 3557 |
| Personal payments | | | | | |
| dividends | 0 | 0 | 0 | 45000 | 45000 |
| Total payments | 56309 | 14677 | 10293 | 55537 | 136817 |
| Net cash flow | 48269 | -13797 | -9413 | 18589 | 43648 |
| Opening bank balance | -35000 | 13269 | -528 | -9941 | |
| Closing bank balance | 13269 | -528 | -9941 | 8648 | |

Transfers of plants, however, do not give rise to a cash flow, since they are internal to the business. Nevertheless, as was mentioned in Chapter 7, it is useful to show these since this is part of production. The source of recorded information for transfers was not shown in Table 10.1 because many practitioners might prefer to omit transfers from the accounts as the transfers-out exactly balance transfers-in giving a net effect of zero. Nevertheless, you may wish to follow the practice of including them as has been done in this example. If so, the information could be found in the Growing Crop Account, in the section relating to the nursery. In this record Douglas has noted the numbers of plants transferred out of the nursery into compartment 3, where planting took place during the year. Note that, although the number of plants was the same as predicted in the budget, the price was lower, in line with the lower price which was received for those plants which were actually sold.

The change in the value of the forest and the nursery was also derived from the Growing Crop Account. The opening figure for the forest is £3,111,684 and for the nursery is £49,021, which together total £3,160,705. The closing figure, after recalculations were made at the end of the year in the light of revised expectations, is £3,310,824, which is the sum of the figures for the forest and the land (£3,264,287 and £46,537). The difference between the closing and the opening value, £150,118, is entered as the valuation change.

Finally, under 'Sales', comes the change in debtors. Since there are no debtors at the year end, whereas £95,058 was owing at the start of the year for felled timber, the figure is a decline of exactly the latter amount.

Under 'Cost of Sales', the cost of materials and labour figure comes from the Cash Flow Statement. Included in this are all payments from clear felling down to casual labour (totalling £37,902) plus the forest worker's wage (£9,105). Added to these is the notional value of the plants transferred into compartment 3 from the nursery (£8,000). Together these three sums total £55,007. However, this figure has to be adjusted to take account of any change in the stocks of the materials used. In this case the Current Stocks Account shows that the stocks of materials and chemicals has been run down over the year - from £180 at the start to £100 at the end. This means that £80 worth of materials have been used in production on top of those materials which were actually paid for over the year. Thus the decline in stocks has been added to the prime costs.

Production overheads also come under 'Cost of Sales', and here again most of the information comes from the Cash Flow Statement. The first of these items, machinery costs, consists of the cash flows for tax and insurance (£890), fuel and oil (£876) and vehicle repairs (£779). However, one other machinery cost is the depreciation charge. Budgeted depreciation was calculated in Table 5.5, and since Douglas did not change the figures during the year, those calculations still stand for the accounts. To save you having to go back to Chapter 5 to check the figures Table 5.5 is reproduced here as Table 10.12. The depreciation charges to be used under the machinery costs heading are all those under the Vehicles & equipment heading in Table 10.12; these total £4,140. Adding this last figure to the three cash flow items already mentioned gives the £6,685 which appears in the Profit and Loss Account.

The road maintenance costs are those that appear in the Cash Flow Statement while the building costs of £1,350 include the £390 building repairs cash flow and the store depreciation charge of £960. Finally, the manager's salary is again derived from the Cash Flow Statement.

**Table 10.11**  Menzies Estate - Trading and Profit and Loss Account.

| | | £ | £ |
|---|---|---|---|
| Sales | | | |
| | thinnings & harvested timber | 165665 | |
| | plants - sales | 8800 | |
| | transfers | 8000 | |
| | planting grant | 0 | |
| | change in value of forest and nursery | 150118 | |
| | change in debtors | -95058 | |
| | Sales | | 237525 |
| Cost of Sales | | | |
| | prime costs | | |
| | materials & labour | 55007 | |
| | less | | |
| | change in stocks of raw materials | -80 | |
| | prime costs | 55087 | |
| | production overheads | | |
| | machinery costs | 6685 | |
| | road maintenance | 2800 | |
| | building costs | 1350 | |
| | manager | 8000 | |
| | production overheads | 18835 | |
| | Cost of Sales | | 73922 |
| GROSS PROFIT | | | 163603 |
| | | | |
| Operating Expenses and Receipts | | | |
| | salaries | 3980 | |
| | services | 1341 | |
| | office costs | 1963 | |
| | miscellaneous administration costs | 3420 | |
| | change in creditors | -10 | |
| | Operating Expenses | | 10694 |
| OPERATING PROFIT | | | 152909 |
| | | | |
| Non-Operating Expenses and Receipts | | | |
| | interest | 2674 | |
| | Non Operating Expenses and Receipts | | 2674 |
| PROFIT BEFORE TAX | | | 150236 |
| | | | |
| Company/Corporation Tax | | | 0 |
| NET PROFIT | | | 150236 |
| dividends | | | 45000 |
| Retained Earnings | | | 105236 |

**Table 10.12** Menzies Estate machinery, equipment and building depreciation.

| item description | dep. rate | date acquired | original value | opening valuation | purchases | sales | deprec. | closing value |
|---|---|---|---|---|---|---|---|---|
| | % | | £ | £ | £ | £ | £ | £ |
| Vehicles & equipment | | | | | | | | |
| Tractor | 20 | | | 3,000 | | | 600 | 2,400 |
| 4WD -1 | 20 | | | 6,000 | | 6,000 | 0 | 0 |
| 4WD -2 | 20 | | | | 16,000 | | 3,200 | 12,800 |
| Trailer | 20 | | | 500 | | | 100 | 400 |
| Equipment | 30 | | | 800 | | | 240 | 560 |
| Office | | | | | | | | |
| Office equipment | 25 | 2000 | 2,000 | 1,500 | | | 500 | 1,000 |
| Furniture | 10 | 1998 | 800 | 560 | | | 80 | 480 |
| Buildings | | | | | | | | |
| Store | 4 | 1984 | 24,000 | 7,680 | | | 960 | 6,720 |
| Office | 4 | 1996 | 32,000 | 25,600 | | | 1,280 | 24,320 |

Under Operating Expenses come the wages of the cleaner, under 'salaries', and 'services', which are the charges for water, electricity and telephone. Office costs include office repairs of £103 and depreciation on the office equipment, furniture and the building itself. Miscellaneous administration costs are derived from the cash flows entitled 'misc. admin. costs' and 'crop insurance'. You may wish to check each of these figures to see if you agree.

One of the items included within 'Operating Expenses and Receipts' is the cost of the telephone. Since this is paid in arrears there was an opening *accrual* (a form of creditor, remember?) of £114. Similarly, at the year-end there was another accrual of £103.75. Because the cash payments for the telephone service during the past year included the £114 effectively owing at the start of the year, but do not include the amount accrued at the end of the year, adjustment needs to be made. The change in creditors, in this case -£10.25, should, therefore, be added to the expenses.

The only charges under 'Non-Operating Expenses and Receipts' are for interest on the loan and on the overdraft. In the Cash Flow Statement you will see that these amounts are £1,651 and £1,023, totalling £2,674.

In Caledonia forest businesses are treated favourably for tax purposes[11], so no Corporation Tax is payable by the Menzies Estate. The Net Profit therefore remains the same as the Profit Before Tax at £150,236.

Finally, we have an extra calculation after the Net Profit has been worked out. This is to show how much of the profit has been retained or 'ploughed back' into the business. This year the *retained earnings* of the Menzies Estate were somewhat less than Net Profit. This came about because Lord Jake and Lady Jody Orffly-Porsh, with their son Nigel the sole shareholders, instructed

---

[11] Some cynical observers would say that this is because close relatives of Prime Minister Smug have recently invested heavily in forestry, but this is obviously unwarranted.

Douglas, just before the year-end, to make a dividend payout of £45,000. This came as rather a surprise to Douglas since it had not been budgeted for. The retained earnings figure, which is carried forward to the Balance Sheet, is therefore £105,236.

**Fig. 10.3** Some shareholders take a close interest in the forest business.

Apart from constructing the P&L Account for the whole business, Douglas also wished to break the figures down by cost centre. Since he had recorded with this in mind he was able to extract the figures from the records. Table 10.13 shows the resulting account, although for brevity only the main headings, some of the individual items and a sample of cost centres are shown.

Although the main headings differ from the P&L Account, the individual items are the same: clear felling, valuation change, fencing, insurance, machinery costs, etc. Unlike the main account, however, the changes in debtors, creditors and stocks are incorporated into each item total, along with the cash flow figure, before sharing between cost centres using the same method as for the budget. For instance, although there was a cash receipt of £95,058 for clear felling during the year, the figure entered into the Cost Centre P&L Account is zero since the opening debtor figure exactly matched this. For the fertilisers, sprays and other materials the cash payment was £862, but because stocks were run down over the year from £180 to £100, the figure which Douglas entered into Table 10.13 was £942 (i.e. £862 + £180 - £100). Since all of this material was used on the nursery, the cost was all charged to that cost centre. The telephone payment of £420.75 was adjusted for opening and closing creditors, thus:

£420.75 + £103.75 - £114 = £410.50

This was then shared between cost centres on the basis of proportion of area. So compartment 1, which constituted 35 ha out of a total of 353 ha, or 9.9%, was allotted £410.50 × 0.099 = £40.64 of the total telephone charge. You might now like to check the other cost-centre figures for telephone charges and machinery costs in Table 10.13 to see if you agree - if you don't, contact the author.

**Table 10.13** Menzies Estate - Cost Centre Profit and Loss Account.

|  | | compartment/sub-compartment | | | | | | |
|---|---|---|---|---|---|---|---|---|
|  | Nursery | 1 | 2 | 3 | .... | 10 | Forest | **Estate** |
|  | 3 ha | 35 ha | 40 ha | 40 ha | ha | 40 ha | 350 ha | **353 ha** |
| Output valuation change | -2485 | 8334 | 6597 | 39970 | | -55844 | 152603 | **150118** |
| - - - - | | | | | | | | |
| Total output | 14315 | 8334 | 6597 | 39970 | | 14763 | 223209 | **237525** |
| Costs | | | | | | | | |
| Direct costs | | | | | | | | |
| fertilisers, etc. | 942 | 0 | 0 | 0 | | 0 | 0 | **942** |
| - - - - | | | | | | | | |
| Total direct costs | 10482 | 0 | 0 | 35500 | | 0 | 35500 | **45982** |
| Overhead costs | | | | | | | | |
| - - - - | | | | | | | | |
| machinery costs | 57 | 663 | 758 | 758 | | 758 | 6628 | **6685** |
| - - - - | | | | | | | | |
| telephone | 3 | 41 | 47 | 47 | | 47 | 407 | **411** |
| - - - - | | | | | | | | |
| Total overhead costs | 4353 | 3695 | 4223 | 4223 | | 4223 | 36954 | **41307** |
| Total costs | 14835 | 3695 | 4223 | 39723 | | 4223 | 72454 | **87292** |
| Profit | -520 | 4638 | 2373 | 247 | | 10539 | 150755 | **150236** |

Douglas' next step was to construct the Balance Sheet; this is shown in Table 10.14. Most of the information needed to complete the Balance Sheet has already been covered, but we will go through the figures to show where Douglas got them from. We do not need to go through the figures for the start of the year because these will have been known from the end of the previous year and even when the budget was produced these figures were known. Thus we will concentrate on the right-hand set of figures in the table, that is, the Balance Sheet at the present time - the end of the year.

The first two items of Fixed Assets are valuations of stocks of trees (and the land on which they stand), young and old - we mentioned these earlier on in this chapter when discussing the valuation change which was needed for the P&L Account. All of the remaining fixed asset values are derived from the depreciation calculations. So if you refer back to Table 10.12 you will see all of these values calculated in the final column.

The values for the Current Assets section of the Balance Sheet are taken from a number of sources. The cash in hand refers to the petty cash, so the petty cash book should be consulted. Following good practice, Douglas made sure that he maintained the figure at £50 by drawing sufficient cash from the bank before the year end. 'Cash at bank' refers to the closing bank balance. To obtain this Douglas could simply 'phone the bank or consult the latest bank statement. However, this should be adjusted to take account of any outstanding cheques which had not been presented or cleared by the bank at the end of the year - you may remember from the previous chapter that this is called a '*bank reconciliation*'. Where, instead, should Douglas look to find the end result of this process - i.e. what account or statement shows the closing bank balance? The answer is, the Cash Flow Statement; to check the accuracy of this Douglas will have had to carry out a bank reconciliation. If you look back to the bottom of Table 10.10 you will see that the bank balance at the end of the year was £8,648, which coincides with the figure in the Balance Sheet.

Next come debtors which have also already been mentioned - they were zero at the year end - Douglas obtained this information from the Debtor's Account. There were no stores of harvested timber, but, as we saw above, the stores of fertilisers and other materials were run down from a value of £180 at the start of the year to £100 at the end.

On the liabilities side, the first item is the overdraft. Given that an overdraft is a negative current account balance, any evidence of an overdraft will be shown in the Cash Flow Statement. And, clearly, since Douglas has already entered a figure for 'Cash at bank', there cannot also be an overdraft[12]. The other current liability is the creditor category. Douglas has already used the creditor figures for the P&L Account; the only creditor was the telephone company which was owed £114 at the start and £103.75 at the end of the year.

Finally, in the top half of the Balance Sheet the only Fixed Liability is the outstanding loan. The opening figure is known and the closing figure will simply be the opening figure, plus any new loans which have been taken out during the year, less any amounts repaid over the year. Where might we find this information? In the Cash Flow Statement again! Refer back to Table 10.10 and there you will see that there were no loan receipts under Capital Receipts, but there was a loan principal repayment of £3,557 which is shown under Capital Payments. The closing amount outstanding is therefore £16,508 less £3,557 = £12,951.

Subtracting all of the liabilities from the assets gives the balance at the year end of £3,355,246, which is £105,235 higher (or £105,236 if the rounding effects are removed) than the opening figure of £3,250,011. You have seen this figure of £105,235 before. What does it show? The rise in the owners' share of the business between one year and the next depends upon how much of the profits has been ploughed back into the business (as well as other external injections, of

---

[12] Unless there were several bank accounts, rather than one. This may be the case in larger businesses, where special care must be taken to bring together all of the bank account information when constructing the accounts.

which, however, there are none in this case). This figure, which we saw earlier, is called *'retained earnings'* and is shown at the bottom of Table 10.11.

Moving down to the lower half of the Balance Sheet we can trace this change in the owners' share of the business, looking at how the different

**Table 10.14** Menzies Estate - Balance Sheets.

|  | 31/12/01 | 31/12/02 |
|---|---|---|
|  | £ | £ |
| Fixed Assets |  |  |
| growing stock (including land) | 3111684 | 3264287 |
| plants | 49021 | 46537 |
| buildings: office | 25600 | 24320 |
| store | 7680 | 6720 |
| furniture | 560 | 480 |
| office equipment | 1500 | 1000 |
| vehicles | 9000 | 15200 |
| machinery | 500 | 400 |
| equipment | 800 | 560 |
| Total Fixed Assets | 3206345 | 3359503 |
| Current Assets |  |  |
| cash in hand | 50 | 50 |
| cash at bank | 0 | 8648 |
| debtors/receivables | 95058 | 0 |
| stocks/inventories: stores | 180 | 100 |
| harvested timber | 0 | 0 |
| Total Current Assets | 95288 | 8798 |
| Current Liabilities |  |  |
| overdraft | 35000 | 0 |
| creditors/accounts payable | 114 | 104 |
| Current Liabilities | 35114 | 104 |
| Net Current Assets | 60174 | 8694 |
|  |  |  |
| Fixed Liabilities |  |  |
| lease | 0 | 0 |
| loan | 16508 | 12951 |
| Total Fixed Liabilities | 16508 | 12951 |
| BALANCE | 3250011 | 3355246 |
|  |  |  |
| Shareholders' Funds (Capital and Reserves) |  |  |
| Share Capital Issued |  |  |
| Share Capital Issued | 2100000 | 2100000 |
| Capital Reserve |  |  |
| land | 0 | 0 |
| improvements | 0 | 0 |
| buildings | 0 | 0 |
| machinery | 0 | 0 |
| Capital Reserve | 0 | 0 |
| Earned Surplus |  |  |
| Earned Surplus | 1150011 | 1255246 |
| BALANCE | 3250011 | 3355246 |

elements of that share have changed. In this case, the amount of share capital which the shareholders have contributed to the business has not changed over the year, nor have there been any inflationary changes in the value of the assets. The only change is in the cumulative total of 'ploughed back profits' called *Earned Surplus*. Over the year this figure moved from £1,150,011 to £1,255,246 - a rise of £105,235 which constitutes the *'retained earnings'* for the year again (with the effect of rounding).

Douglas has now constructed the main Cash-Profit-Capital statements: the Cash Flow Statement, the P&L Account and the Balance Sheet, as well as a more detailed profit statement. To provide a little more insight he decides to construct a Flow of Funds Statement too. This is presented in Table 10.15.

**Table 10.15**  Menzies Estate - Flow of Funds Statement.

| Sources of cash | £ | Uses of cash | £ |
|---|---|---|---|
| Trading | | Trading | |
| net profit (loss) | 150,236 | | |
| plus depreciation | 6,960 | | |
| External injections | | External withdrawals | |
| | | dividends | 45,000 |
| Increase in Liabilities | | Reduction in Liabilities | |
| increase in: | | reduction in: | |
| creditors | | creditors | |
| loans, lease, etc. | | loans, lease, etc. | |
| Reduction in Assets | | Increase in Assets | |
| reduction in value of: | | increase in value of: | |
| debtors | 95,058 | debtors | |
| stores & materials, | 80 | stores & materials, | |
| growing stock | | growing stock | 150,118 |
| sale of: machinery | | purchase of: | |
| | 6,000 | machinery | 16,000 |
| Total inflow | 258,334 | Total outflow | 214,686 |
| Net inflow | 43,648 | Net outflow | |
| Balance | | Balance | |
| reduction in cash balance | | increase in cash balance | 8,648 |
| increase in overdraft | | reduction in overdraft | 35,000 |

All of the information for the Flow of Funds Statement has already been presented, so Douglas simply has to pick it out from the accounts. Remember here that what we are doing is moving from profit to cash, in a sense, the reverse of the earlier process of moving from cash (the Cash Flow Statement) to profit (the P&L Account). One way of looking at the procedure is to say to ourselves, "Assume firstly that profits are all in cash. Then adjust this for any costs or benefits which are not in the form of cash and any other cash flows which do not come into the profit calculation."

On the 'Sources' side, depreciation (a non-cash charge) is added back to profit. For the Menzies Estate there have been three other sources of cash over the year. The decline in debtors from £95,058 to £0 has meant that an extra

£95,058 cash has been paid into the bank over the year, the use of £80 worth of stores has meant that their cost has not involved a cash payment over the year, and the sale of machinery has meant an extra £6,000 cash received during the year, which was not included in the profit calculations. The total inflow over the year was the sum of these amounts, which comes to £258,334.

The total outflow was only £214,686. This consisted of only three items: the dividends paid to the three shareholders, the growth in the value of the stock of trees and land, which was included in the profit, but did not involve any cash receipt, and the purchase of machinery, again an expense which was not included in the profit calculations.

The difference between the Sources and Uses of cash was a net inflow of £43,648. This is, in fact, the net cash flow; you may wish to check this in the Cash Flow Statement in Table 10.10. The bottom part of the Sources and Uses table shows where this net inflow went. Although all of this money went into the bank, it was, in effect, used in two ways: £35,000 was used to pay off the overdraft and the remaining £8,648 boosted the bank balance.

Douglas now has the accounting information in a format which allows him to analyse the performance of the business. Let us move on to the next chapter to see how this is done.

# Chapter 11

# Accounts - Analysis

Construction of the accounts on its own is not enough. If the accounts are to be used as an aid to management then the figures which they contain must be analysed. But before we begin the analysis we need to decide what we want to know!

At the macro, or whole business, level we want to know how well or badly the business is or has been performing in terms of those three key aspects of 'profitability', 'liquidity' and 'stability'. However, if we want to improve performance in the future we need to know which parts of the business performed well and which did not, and why. To do this we have to 'dig down' to the 'micro' level - looking at and within cost centres, and this time assessing physical as well as financial aspects.

Some of the figures in the accounts can be used for analysis as they stand, whilst others must undergo some transformation to obtain more meaning from them. But whatever the figure we ultimately obtain it is still of little use unless we have a standard against which we compare it. How do we know whether a net profit figure of £30,000 or a yield of 60 cubic metres is good or bad unless we have something to compare it against - some objective measure of what is good or bad performance? The standard against which our business should be compared should be that of other businesses or that of alternative investments. So we might compare our profitability with levels achieved by industry in general, by forest businesses in particular or even forest businesses in our region. To give a fair comparison of how the business might be expected to perform it is probably best to compare with those in a similar situation. Where do we obtain these comparative figures? For the macro measures some of the large financial analysis companies produce performance statistics for the economy and also by sector (Investment Property Databank, 1997; Dunn and Bradstreet, 1998). Governments also produce data on certain measures such as return on capital. If we wish to compare with individual companies it is possible to obtain sets of published accounts. However, you should remember that many of these performance measures come from the accounts which have not been produced for management purposes and so may not be strictly comparable with our management accounting figures. This is a very important point because when making comparisons, we need to be sure that the businesses with which we are making comparison have employed similar accounting procedures to our own - and that includes how things like depreciation and valuations are dealt with, as well as how the final profit calculations are made.

When it comes to more micro aspects of performance, such as timber yields and costs of operations, government, quasi-government, timber growers associations and academic institutions sometimes produce survey results, although these may not be on a regular basis, may be rather out of date and may relate to dissimilar businesses to our own. There is one other organisation which we can use for comparison: our own! Not only should we have records of the past performance of the business, but we may also have budgeted for this year. This then enables us to compare this period's performance with recent trends, as well as with what we expected to happen. And if our budgets were built up in the way suggested earlier in the book, we should then be able to compare 'budget' versus 'actual' at the micro level to help find out where the strengths and weaknesses lie.

This chapter, then, takes the reader through some of the key measures of performance both at the macro and the micro level. There are, in fact, a whole host of performance measures available, but only those likely to be most useful in a forestry context will be considered here.

## Macro Analysis

Chapter 1 explained the importance of the three aspects of financial performance: profit, cash and capital or profitability, liquidity and stability. Therefore, when analysing accounts, performance needs to be satisfactory on all three fronts otherwise there is cause for concern. As will be seen below (and as summarised in Table 11.1), there are a number of measures of each of the three aspects of performance, often viewing them from slightly different angles. Consequently, it may be useful to employ several measures so that a more complete picture can be obtained. However, it is important that we know not only how to calculate these measures but also what they mean and how they should be used.

Before the measures of the three aspects are considered in this way two points need to be made: firstly, it is often more helpful to look at a series of measures rather than one in isolation, for instance, the last three years' net profit figures; and secondly, when comparing with standards we need to be sure that we are comparing like with like - other people may not be measuring things in the same way as us.

**Table 11.1** Profitability, liquidity and stability indicators.

| Type of measure | Specific measure |
|---|---|
| **Profitability** | |
| Direct measures | Gross Profit |
| | Operating Profit |
| | Profit Before Tax |
| | Net Profit |
| Return measures | Return on capital employed |
| | Return on equity |
| **Liquidity** | |
| Tracing flows | Cash Flow Budget |
| | Flow of Funds Statement |
| Ratios | Current Ratio |
| | Liquidity Ratio |
| **Stability** | |
| Direct measures | Total Assets |
| | Net Assets |
| | Equity |
| Ratios | Percent Equity |
| | Solvency Ratio |
| | Gearing Ratio |

**Profitability**

*Profit*

How do we measure profitability? Surely there is only one way - profit, after all, is profit. But if you go back to the last chapter you will see in Fig. 10.1 that there are four different measures of profit - Gross Profit, Operating Profit, Profit before Tax and Net Profit. Which is profit? The answer is that, in a sense, they all are, although most people would go for the last one, Net Profit, because that is truly the 'bottom line' - after all costs or charges have been subtracted. Nevertheless, the others do also provide us with some extra information: Gross Profit shows what surplus the business is generating over the more specific production costs; Operating Profit is the surplus taking account of only those costs involved in operating the business; and Profit before Tax shows what surplus the business is making after all costs, including those involved in financing the business, and revenues, including non-trading receipts, have been included. Given that Corporation Tax can vary according to government policy and is really outside the control of the manager, one could suggest that this profit measure, Profit before Tax, is, in fact, the one to be used in assessing profitability. However, if one is concerned with measuring the ultimate surplus left over then the Net Profit figure is the right one to use[4].

---

[4] But is it? If unrealised gains, such as growing stock valuation change, have been included in the profit figure, then net profits will overestimate the amount available for distribution. But if it does not include unrealised gains, then, as we saw in Appendix 7.3, it can be argued that all of the profit

*Change in profit*

Rather than using the profit measures as stand-alone figures, you may wish to compare them to previous figures for the business and to the budgeted figure. It is also sometimes helpful to look at the change from the previous years in percentage terms. This can be calculated as:

$$\text{Percentage change in profit } = \frac{\text{change in profit}}{\text{previous profit}} \times 100\%$$

For example, if this year's profit figure is £18,000, while last year's figure was £15,000, then the calculation would be:

$$\text{Percentage change in profit} = \frac{£3,000}{£15,000} \times 100\% = 0.2 \times 100\% = 20\%$$

But what if profit went down from one year to the next? The formula remains the same; for instance, if the previous year's figure was £15,000 and this year's profit was £10,500 then the calculation would be:

$$\text{Percentage change in profit} = \frac{\text{- }£4,500}{£15,000} \times 100\% = -0.3 \times 100\% = -30\%$$

Thus, in the first example, profits went up by 20% between one year and the next, whilst in the second example profits fell by 30%.

*Return on capital*

Although the various measures of profit can be compared with previous year's figures as well as with the budgeted figure, they cannot be directly compared with any other business or industry standard. Why not?

Well, ask yourself this question, "Would a profit of £30,000 be good or bad?"

"Presumably," you would say, "it all depends on how big the business is," and that is correct. A profit of £30,000 might be extremely pleasing for the small shopkeeper, but for IBM or Ford it would be disturbingly small. Thus, profit needs to be gauged against the amount of resources tied up in producing it. OK, but how would you measure this?

"Simple," you might say, "divide profit by the size of the business."

---

figures underestimate profitability. If unrealised gains have been included, then when assessing the amount available for distribution we should subtract the unrealised gains. The latter case does pose problems - if you want a full measure of profit then unrealised gains must be added to profit - in which case you might as well have included them in the first place!

But how do we measure the size of the business?

"My goodness," says the reader, "this writer is asking the obvious."

"The size of the business," you patiently reply, "is the value of all of the assets tied up in it, which is termed 'total assets'."

And this is correct in a general sense: to compare profitability between businesses, profit can be divided by total assets.

However, there are many variations on this theme, with different authors suggesting different names, different numerators and different denominators. Nevertheless, there are really only two main 'return on capital' measures which we are likely to need: the return on *all* of the capital employed in the business, and the return on *owners'* capital - the capital belonging to the owners of the business, usually the shareholders.

The rate of return calculated by dividing profits by assets is most commonly known as **return on capital employed** (ROCE), and is measured as:

ROCE = Profit before interest and tax ÷ Opening Net Assets × 100%

where

Net Assets = Total Assets - Current Liabilities

So, for instance, if the business were to make a pre-tax profit of £55,000, interest charges were £33,000 and the opening Net Assets figure was £1,225,000, then the ROCE figure would be:

ROCE = £88,000 ÷ £1,225,000 × 100% = 7.2%

You may come across other terms or their acronyms: *return on assets* (ROA), *the primary ratio*, *accounting rate of return* (ARR), *accounting rate of profit* (ARP), *return on all capital* (ROAC), *return on investment* and *return on net assets*. These all mean more or less the same thing; we will stick with ROCE.

However, there is some variation in precisely what numerator and denominator is used. Generally, the profit measure is 'profit before interest and tax'. The reason for this is that firstly, analysts are interested in what profit the business made before tax was levied. Secondly, interest should not be charged since we are concerned with the return on all of the assets, by whomever they are owned.[5] As far as the denominator is concerned you might think that 'total assets' would be used, but this is not common. Instead, accountants prefer 'net assets' which are measured as 'total assets' minus 'current liabilities'. The reason for this seems to be that accountants deem that part of current assets should be excluded

---

[5] The assets are owned by the shareholders as well as those to whom the business owes money (in the form of liabilities). The business effectively pays these 'owners' for supplying funds to the business in the form of dividends and interest respectively. But we want to know what the return is before these are paid, so interest must be excluded from the numerator (dividends would not be included anyway).

from the total because they will be used up very soon to pay off current liabilities. Finally, before we settle on an agreed definition, we must ask the question, "To which time period should 'assets' refer, the start or the end of the accounting period?" There does not seem to be a great deal of clarity in the literature about this, although the theoretical treatment by Edwards *et al.* (1987) would support the use of the opening value. Here, despite the fact that the use of the average of the opening and closing values can be shown to be superior when investment takes place within the year, the more straightforward use of the opening value will be adopted.

As with the more straightforward profit measures above, the ROCE figure is not very useful on its own; it must be compared with something. Comparison can be made with the previous performance figures of the business and the budgeted figure if one is available. This ROCE percentage can also be compared with the performance of other individual companies of groups, and since governments and some analysts do publish them, figures are fairly readily available. You may also wish to do what many analysts would do with a return on capital figure, namely, compare it with the *opportunity cost of capital*, i.e. the return in the next best alternative use of the funds tied up in the business. This might be the best return you could obtain by investing in the shares of another company or in bonds or bills issued by government.[6]

There is one final problem, namely the effects of inflation. As Appendix 11.1 indicates, if the accounts have been constructed so as to deal appropriately with inflation, then making adjustments to the ROCE is quite straightforward. If not, then you have a problem!

Turning now to the other return on capital measure, besides considering the return on all of the assets in the business, we should also be interested in the return on the share of the business belonging to its owners, the shareholders. After all, the shareholders will be especially concerned with what return is left to them after interest has been paid to the creditors of the business. Again there are various terms for this measure: *return on owners' capital employed*, *shareholders' return*, *return on own capital* and **return on equity**. We will employ the latter and its acronym ROE. This we will calculate as profit before tax, but not before interest, divided by 'equity' (total assets minus total liabilities) at the start of the accounting period, thus:

ROE = profit before tax ÷ opening equity

---

[6]Although economists might point out that it is not strictly accurate to do this using the ROCE measure which we are employing (see, for example, Edwards *et al.*, 1987), it is widely done and does not necessarily lead to erroneous judgements.

This figure can be compared, in the same way as ROCE, with previous and budgeted figures, other business figures and other earning opportunities elsewhere.

There are other profitability ratios, some of which are known as 'secondary ratios' because they can be used to build up to the ROCE figure. In a forestry context these indicators are not as useful as in other industries and we will not delve into them here, although some are listed in Appendix 11.2. If you do want to pursue the analysis further it is best to consult a good accounting text.

## Liquidity

Liquidity, for the manager of the forestry business, concerns the short-term availability of cash, in terms of both having enough to pay bills as they fall due, and not having too much idle capital. Perhaps the best way of assessing liquidity is to study the cash flow statement for the previous period as well as the cash flow budget. Another means is via the Flow of Funds Statement which we encountered in the previous chapter. However, there are also a couple of balance sheet ratios which give a useful 'snapshot' indication of liquidity - these are known as the 'Current Ratio' and the 'Liquidity Ratio'.

The **Current Ratio** is the more blunt of the two measures, and is measured as:

Current Ratio = Current Assets ÷ Current Liabilities

where Current Assets include cash in hand and at the bank, debtors, and stocks of materials and harvested or near-harvest produce, and Current Liabilities are overdraft, creditors and short-term loans.

The measure can be presented as a ratio or as a percentage. Thus, if current assets were £180,000 and current liabilities £100,000 the current ratio could be presented as

Current Ratio = £180,000 ÷ £100,000 = 1.8:1 or 180%

As with profitability measures, the current ratio can be compared with own or others' performance. Additionally, analysts have a rule of thumb that a figure below 1.5:1 or 2:1 (150% or 200%) is too low and one much over 2:1 (200%) is too high. The rationale for this is supposedly that current liabilities could all be payable within a fairly short time and to ensure that the business would have enough cash or near cash assets to pay for them, without having to turn all current assets into cash at an inconvenient time, then a ratio of 1:1 would not be sufficient. Instead a safety margin is needed, hence the figures of 1.5 or 2. So, if the figure was, say 1.4, then this might signal that the business could get into difficulties with regard to paying its bills on time. The outcome might merely mean having to sell off certain assets at a time when prices were low or could be so serious that bills could not be paid, a situation known as 'insolvency', which could lead to legal proceedings and the 'liquidation' (selling of the assets to pay the debts) of the business, even if it were potentially profitable.

The Current Ratio should be used alongside the **Liquidity Ratio** which is a sharper instrument in that it is concerned with cash and assets which will be turned into cash very soon. This ratio, also known as the 'Quick Ratio' or the 'Acid Test', is measured as:

Liquidity Ratio = Liquid Assets ÷ Current Liabilities

where Liquid Assets include only cash and debtors, although some analysts would also include any items which are to be sold within a short period, perhaps 1 to 2 months.

Again the measure can be expressed as a ratio or a percentage. In the above example, if, out of the £180,000 of current assets, liquid assets were £90,000, the liquidity ratio would be:

Liquidity Ratio = £90,000 ÷ £100,000 = 0.9:1 or 90%

Analysts would be concerned if this ratio were much below 1:1, especially if the Current Ratio was also low. So in this example, with a current ratio of 1.4:1 and a Liquidity Ratio of 0.9:1 there would be some cause for concern and managers would be advised to implement changes in order to put the business in a safer position.

As well as the present levels of the Current and Liquidity Ratios, it may also be helpful to compare with the values for previous years, particularly the start of the period, to see if the position appears to be changing for the better or worse.

## Stability

The management and shareholders of a business are likely to wish to ensure, as far as they can, that the business is stable over the medium to long term. That is, that the size of the business, its ability to generate profits and its equity (the shareholders' wealth tied up in the business) are likely to grow or are at least to be maintained over the next 5, 10 or even 20 years. To measure whether this is likely to be the case we should look at some of the current figures of business size and structure, and the trends in them.

It is important to understand before we proceed, that, although a stable business has to be a profitable one, we cannot gauge stability solely on the basis of current profitability. Why not? Firstly, current profitability is not future profitability and secondly, the beneficial impact of favourable profits can be negated if all or most is paid out as dividends to shareholders. Therefore, although it is important to study levels and trends in profitability, other measures are also needed to gauge stability.

As with profitability and liquidity it is useful to look at the current levels of certain indicators, but because stability is concerned with the future, trends are particularly important. The first value which might tell us something about stability is the size of the business. This is measured by the figures for Total Assets and Net Assets. On their own, however, these figures do not tell us very much - just that the business is worth a certain amount of money. If, on the other hand, we look at the trend in total or net assets we can see whether the business seems to be growing or contracting. To obtain a more objective picture we can also measure the percentage changes in these trend figures. This is done in the same way as for the percentage change in profit:

Percentage change in Total Assets = Change in Total Assets ÷ Total Assets × 100%

where the Total Assets figure is normally the value at the *start* of the year or period.

So, for instance, the current level of total assets might be £1,225,000, the previous year's was £1,263,900, and the year before that was £1,202,700. What can we say about total assets then? Firstly, we discuss the actual values: the current figure is nearly £1¼ million, which would have to be compared with other businesses to mean much. We can go on to say, however, that total assets declined over the past year by nearly £39,000, after a rise of about £61,000 the year before. Nevertheless, the current figure is still well above that of two years ago.

In percentage terms, total assets changed over the past year by:

$$-£38,900 ÷ £1,263,900 × 100\% = -3.08\%$$

that is, a decline of about 3%, whereas during the previous year total assets rose by

$$£61,200 ÷ £1,202,700 × 100\% = 5.09\%$$

or approximately 5%. We could also add that, despite the decline over the latest year, the current figure was still above the figure of two years ago by

$$£22,300 ÷ £1,202,700 × 100\% = 1.85\%$$

Total or net assets give an indication of the overall size of the business, but they can give a deceptive picture, since total assets may grow simply as a result of heavy borrowing from banks or other financial institutions. For instance, by borrowing £100,000 I could buy a harvesting machine. This would initially add £100,000 to my total assets, increasing the apparent size of the business. But £100,000 would also be added to liabilities. Such actions may not leave the owners of the business (the shareholders) any better off. It is, therefore, important to also consider the shareholders' equity position. This can be looked at in the same way as with total or net assets - we can consider current level, trends and percentage change.

Analysts also like to measure the proportion of the business which the shareholders own. There are two ways of doing this, the first produces a figure called **Percent Equity** and the second, the **Solvency Ratio**. The formulae for each are:

Percent Equity = Equity ÷ Total Assets × 100%

and

Solvency Ratio = Total Assets ÷ Total Liabilities

Since equity is total assets minus total liabilities, the two measures are directly correlated. There is, therefore, no point in using both - they both tell you the same thing. To illustrate this link, a series of Percent Equity figures are listed below, and below them are the associated Solvency Ratio figures:

| Percent Equity | 0% | 50% | 66.7% | 75% | 80% | 90% |
|---|---|---|---|---|---|---|
| Solvency Ratio | 1:1 | 2:1 | 3:1 | 4:1 | 5:1 | 10:1 |

You should, therefore, choose the measure which you, and your audience, best understand. As an illustration of how these measures are calculated, let us take the total assets values from the example above, and suppose equity is currently £918,750. This means that total liabilities must be the difference between the two, i.e. £1,225,000 - £918,750 = £306,250. Calculating the two indicators we get:

Percent Equity = £918,750 ÷ £1,225,000 × 100% = 75%

and

Solvency Ratio = £1,225,000 ÷ £306,250 = 4:1

These figures show that the shareholders own a large proportion of the business, three-quarters in fact. But what is a 'good' figure and what is a 'bad' one? If a business has a Percent Equity below 50% or a Solvency Ratio below 2:1, then the majority share of the business is owned by its creditors - a situation which would have serious cost (high interest payments) and control (the banks owning more than the shareholders) implications. But even Solvency Ratio figures below 3:1 or perhaps even 4:1, would spell danger, because that would imply that liabilities were so great that there was a high risk in the near future of interest payments being too high for profitability to be maintained. We will return to this when we look at 'gearing' in a moment, but suffice it to say that if the figures signalled equity below about two-thirds, particularly if this was also declining, then there would be a cause for concern (Turner and Taylor, 1998; Warren, 1998).

Risk is a most important aspect to consider when appraising the business, because risk implies danger that things could go wrong, and if they go wrong it means that profitability, business size and equity might all decline. Thus a high-risk business might be unstable. On the other hand, a business that does not take risks may lose out on profitable opportunities that could lead to future growth. Consequently, we need measures which give some indication of the degree of risk faced by the business. To do this properly we would have to look at the business in detail, but at the moment we are interested in 'macro' indicators.

The per cent equity and solvency ratio figures have already given some indication of risk, as was mentioned above, but a more refined tool is needed here. The measure in most common use is known variously as the *gearing ratio*, **capital gearing**, *the debt ratio*, *the debt:equity ratio* or, in North America and increasingly elsewhere, simply as *leverage*. The way in which gearing is calculated varies; here we will use:

Gearing Ratio = Long-term Debt ÷ Equity

where 'long-term debt' (loan capital) includes all liabilities that incur interest charges and have lifetimes of more than a year or so. Although overdraft is, strictly speaking, meant to be a short-term means of finance, because many businesses remain overdrawn for long periods, it is probably wise to include it as part of the long-term loan capital here[7].

Thus, for a business with long-term loan capital of £370,000 and equity of £1,230,000, the gearing ratio would be:

Gearing Ratio = £370,000 ÷ £1,230,000 = 0.3:1

As was suggested above, a business with too much of an interest burden, as indicated by a high gearing ratio, can be exposed to a substantial level of risk, but one with a low level of borrowing may be missing out on profitable opportunities. Therefore, what levels of gearing are about right? Warren (1998) suggests that,

> "In most rural businesses a ratio of 40% is probably the highest that can be tolerated, and then only if the business is specialising in high-margin products."                                  (Warren, 1998, p. 38)

There probably wouldn't be consensus on an exact figure indicating the upper limit for safe gearing levels, but Warren's suggested 40% or 0.4:1 would seem to be about right. At the lower end, a figure of 0.1:1 might be reasonable, although many family-owned businesses would have lower gearing than this,

---

[7] Why short-term loans are not generally included is not clear. The arguments that such amounts are not likely to be a longer term drain on the business, that they can vary considerably from year to year, and that they are likely to be covered by current assets do not seem very convincing. Nevertheless, here we will follow convention and stick to long-term loan capital (plus overdraft).

probably because they prefer independence to indebtedness, even if that might mean foregone profits.

But why is low and high gearing of concern? This can best be illustrated by way of an example. Consider three forestry businesses - one low geared, one moderately geared and one high geared. Their respective financial positions are shown in Table 11.2. Assuming an interest rate of 10% and that profits are proportional to the amount of assets (which are equal to the sum of long-term loan capital plus equity), the lower part of the table shows the effects of a 'good' year and a 'bad' year.

**Table 11.2** Effects of different levels of gearing.

|  | L<br>low gearing | M<br>moderate gearing | H<br>high gearing |
|---|---|---|---|
| *opening position* |  |  |  |
| long-term loan capital | £50 | £250 | £600 |
| equity | £1000 | £1000 | £1000 |
| gearing | 0.05:1 | 0.25:1 | 0.60:1 |
| good year (20% return on capital) |  |  |  |
| profits (before interest) | £210 | £250 | £320 |
| interest | £5 | £25 | £60 |
| net profit | £205 | £225 | £260 |
| *closing position* |  |  |  |
| long-term loan capital | £50 | £250 | £600 |
| equity | £1205 | £1225 | £1260 |
| gearing | 0.04:1 | 0.20:1 | 0.48:1 |
| bad year (2% return on capital) |  |  |  |
| profits (before interest) | £21 | £25 | £32 |
| interest | £5 | £25 | £60 |
| net profit | £16 | £0 | -£28 |
| *closing position* |  |  |  |
| long-term loan capital | £50 | £250 | £600 |
| equity | £1016 | £1000 | £972 |
| gearing | 0.05:1 | 0.25:1 | 0.62:1 |

Now let us work through what happens. The opening gearing levels for forestry businesses L, M and H are 0.05, 0.25 and 0.6:1, respectively. If the following year is a 'good' year then L makes a profit before interest of £210, this being a 20% return on the total assets of £1,050. Because of their larger borrowing and consequently greater asset values, companies M and H make correspondingly more. Interest charges are low compared to profits across the board, so net profits available for distribution or retention in this business are substantial. Assuming no distribution to shareholders, all of the profits are ploughed back into the business and consequently the closing equity position is higher than that at the start. Notice that the biggest gain is made by the highly geared company H. Notice too that gearing ratios improve as well.

If, instead, the forestry companies had a 'bad' year in which the return on capital was only 2%, then profit would be lower for all three companies. However, interest charges remain the same, and although these are not high enough to produce net losses in the cases of companies L and M, for company H high interest charges do produce a net loss. This then means that equity and gearing improve slightly for L, remain the same for M, and deteriorate for H. The effect over one year was not disastrous, but you can envisage what would happen if there was a run of several bad years.

## Macro measures reviewed

We have covered some of the key indicators of profitability, liquidity and stability; Table 11.3 summarises them again.

**Table 11.3** Profitability, liquidity and stability indicators.

| Type of measure | Specific measure | Trend measures change | percentage change |
|---|---|:---:|:---:|
| **Profitability** | | | |
| Direct measures | Gross Profit | ✔ | ✔ |
| | Operating Profit | ✔ | ✔ |
| | Profit Before Tax | ✔ | ✔ |
| | Net Profit | ✔ | ✔ |
| Return measures | Return on Capital Employed | ✔ | |
| | Return on Equity | ✔ | |
| **Liquidity** | | | |
| Tracing flows | Cash Flow Budget | | |
| | Flow of Funds Statement | | |
| Ratios | Current Ratio | ✔ | |
| | Liquidity Ratio | ✔ | |
| **Stability** | | | |
| Direct measures | Total Assets | ✔ | ✔ |
| | Net Assets | ✔ | ✔ |
| | Equity | ✔ | ✔ |
| Ratios | Percent Equity | ✔ | |
| | Solvency Ratio | ✔ | |
| | Gearing Ratio | ✔ | |

Remember that some of the indicators are direct measures, whereas some are derived as ratios of some sort. Remember too that it is often useful to study a series of figures so that one can see if latest figures are part of a trend or are anomalies. Percentage changes can also be helpful to gauge the relative size of any changes; notice in the table that there are two columns on the right-hand side showing with ticks where comparing absolute and percentage changes are appropriate. Comparison should also be made with other, similar businesses and with industry and economy standards.

Apart from these key indicators there are many others in use; some of these, along with their calculation formulae, are tabulated in Appendix 11.2. These further measures help us to identify more closely the strong and weak points of the performance of the business - whether, for instance, the profit per unit sold is low or perhaps number of units sold is the problem, whether the level of debtors might be too high in relation to sales, or whether high dividend payments to shareholders are limiting the growth of the business.

## Micro Analysis - Digging Down

It is, of course, necessary to look first at the 'big picture' in order to assess overall performance and to identify which aspects, profitability, liquidity or stability, are strong or weak. If there are problems identified it might be possible, even at the macro level, to devise solutions. These are macro solutions to macro problems. However, very often, the solutions to the macro problems lie at the micro level, because many of the macro problems might, in fact, arise at the micro level. For example, a macro problem might be one of insufficient liquidity. If the solution is seen as generally tightening up on the time allowed for payment by debtors, this can be seen as a whole-business or macro solution. If, however, the liquidity problem is found to stem from the sawmill cost centre which is losing money, and the decision is made to close it down, then the macro problems (lack of liquidity and profitability) have micro causes (sawmill generating losses) and micro solutions (closure of sawmill).

The implications of this are that a macro, or whole-business, appraisal should be undertaken first, but this should be followed by the tracing of causes at the micro level. Thus, after looking at the surface picture we need to 'dig down'. Following on from this, macro or micro solutions will need to be found, whichever is appropriate.

Pinpointing strong and weak sections of the business involves moving from the macro level down to specific elements of the business in a logical way. Figure 11.1 shows the how profit can be disaggregated to see the physical and financial components from which it is built, as well as the factors affecting those components. Thus, we might trace low profitability to a particular cost centre and from there discover that direct costs seem to be rather high. Within the direct costs, those for chemical sprays might have been much higher than expected, and on checking this was found to be because of a disease problem and a particularly expensive chemical having been used. Although, the problem might be over and so nothing can be done to ameliorate it now, it should lead the manager to consider how such a problem might be avoided in the future. Looking at Fig. 11.1, we see that reducing costs may sometimes reduce outputs, so we must beware of the wider effects of micro changes - not attacking the pest at this time might have lead to greater losses of output in the future. Nevertheless, the manager might decide that a more vigilant policy of early disease identification should be pursued from now on, and/or that an alternative, cheaper spray or

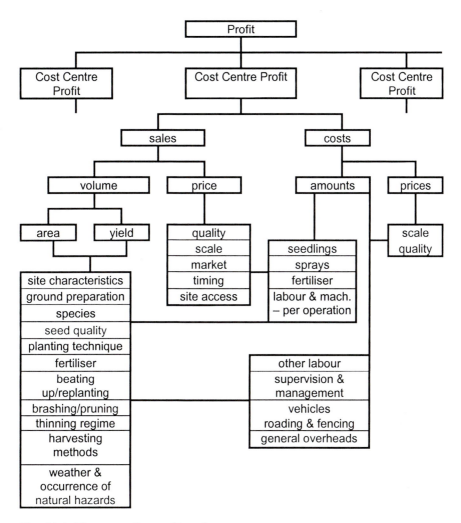

**Fig. 11.1** Disaggregating profit performance.

disease control method should be used.

Problems may not arise solely at the cost centre level. Perhaps the problem is with overhead costs, although these again might affect performance at the cost-centre level. So, for instance, the manager may consider that office costs are too high, or that they are too low, and the lack of office staff is giving rise to delays in pursuing debtors and ordering supplies of materials. Alternatively, the manager might decide that high machinery depreciation and repair costs are partly resulting from inadequate roading, in which case greater expenditure on this area might be cost effective. It is not always so easy, of course, and the causes of problems may be largely outside the manager's control - natural and market factors have a major influence on forestry. Nevertheless, such micro analysis needs to be done if the causes and their extent are to be identified and solutions sought.

Such 'digging down' can be carried out by starting with the Cost Centre Profit Account as this will have been constructed for this purpose. Another approach, which also helps to highlight causes of liquidity problems, is via the cash flow statement. Again, unexpected levels, especially in comparison with the cash flow budget, can be identified and then causes of those levels traced.

As with the macro analysis we can make use of certain ratios at the micro level. In fact, some of those 'macro' ratios can also be utilised at the cost centre level. In particular, some of the profit measures that we might use at the aggregate level can also be used at the cost centre level. For instance, one might measure the percentage change in profit, profit per hectare or even return on capital, although for the latter you would have to decide how to proportionally allocate those assets which are not readily allocated to a particular cost centre.

To analyse performance at the micro level in a logical way, we should start with the general and go down to the specific. Thus, as Fig. 11.1 suggests, we might start by assessing profit for the cost centre, then move down to a consideration of sales and costs. Then within those areas we can look at individual elements, such as different categories of timber or labour, materials and machinery costs. Even deeper, we might start to look at financial and physical aspects separately: prices received and volumes produced, hours spent and kilograms applied, for instance. But, as with the macro measures, measuring these features as ratios (per £ or per unit) gives a measure that tells us more than the absolute figure alone. In other words, what do we divide these figures by? Initially, we might divide profit, costs, and individual cost elements, by sales. Thus we can have cost centre profit per £ of sales, cost centre direct labour per £ of sales, and so on. But then we might also want to look at amounts expressed per unit of the size of the cost centre or per unit of a limiting factor: profit per hectare, cubic metres per hectare, labour hours or costs per hectare, or sales per £ spent on labour. The choice of numerators and denominators can be shown like this:

- profit
- sales
     and categories of sales
- costs          } per { - sales
     and categories of costs          - cost centre size unit
- physical production          - limiting factor
- input amounts

But which we use depends upon how far down we wish to dig and whether we have any figures available to compare with. As at the macro level, we may wish to compare with other businesses, with published standards or with our own past or budgeted performance or with other cost centres within the business. Notice, however, that analysis of overheads might be better conducted at the whole business or enterprise level. Thus, we might look at overheads per hectare or per unit of sales, at administration costs per unit of sales, fencing costs per hectare, or overheads per £ of labour costs.

The nature of forestry, however, does mean that some analysis is not relevant or possible over the short term. For instance, each compartment cost centre might be at a different stage and contain differing species. Is there anything to be gained by comparing profits, sales or costs of each cost centre with each other or with other businesses? One compartment might have heavy planting costs this year while another might have no costs, except its share of overheads. Comparison would mean little since we are not comparing like with like. What might be useful though, is to compare the costs or physical amounts of inputs used for particular operations, or to compare yields or prices. Given the different stages of the various compartments, however, we are unlikely to be able to compare current compartments within the business.

What we can do is compare with standards: what yields might have been expected for such a compartment? What prices have people been getting elsewhere? What is the average cost of this operation across the industry? How many worker-hours does it typically take for planting? And so on.

To compare within the business, we need to have kept records of performance over a number of years, so that we might compare planting costs for compartment 1, for instance, with those for compartment 20, which might have occurred last year, and compartment 19 the year before (suitably adjusted for inflation of course!). Keeping such records will also enable us to periodically look back at a complete rotation or part of it, to assess its overall profitability, as well as providing useful figures for budgeting.

Once we have decided where the strengths and weaknesses lie, we need to ascertain why this is so and, if necessary, do something about it. Again, towards the bottom of Fig. 11.1 are listed some of the factors which might influence performance; you may be able to think of others. Note, however, that there are interlinkages, so if you take steps to change one element it may have knock-on effects elsewhere. So, for instance, you may think that weeding costs are too high, but if you reduce them, this may ultimately affect yield. On the other hand, you may feel that harvesting costs are too high because of poor roading. A decision to improve certain of the forest roads may lower harvesting costs, but will of course increase other costs. However, it may also have effects on other compartments in the future by reducing costs of access to them. Obviously, this last decision is quite complex and should not be taken without carefully weighing up the extra costs and benefits. How this might be done is part of the subject matter of the next chapter.

Much of this digging down involves profitability aspects and these will, in turn, affect other aspects. However, we should also be trying to ascertain where the strengths and weaknesses lie from liquidity and long-term stability points of view.

For liquidity details we need to start at the level of the Cash Flow Statement. Within the statement we can look at which flows most influenced the bank position and then discover whether this can be attributed to a particular cost centre or is more general. But, as with the tracing of profit strengths and weaknesses, we must be careful in altering policies, lest the knock-on effects are deleterious.

For the longer-term stability considerations we can start with a series of balance sheets, perhaps making use of the flow of funds statements too. Here we need to look at the asset and liability structure and where change is occurring. Then the reasons for this structure and the changes can be traced - perhaps to cost centres or to a general policy. So, for instance, liabilities may have risen recently because of heavy planting costs in a number of compartments or due to the use of a loan to finance purchase of more land or machinery, or there might have been a steady decline in equity, traceable to a series of unprofitable years. The former two will have arisen because of policy decisions implemented earlier and these should have been properly evaluated beforehand. The latter is a matter of profitability, which ties back in with our earlier discussion on that aspect.

## Menzies Example

Having constructed the accounts Douglas now wishes to understand what the results tell him about the performance of the Menzies Estate and the cost centres within it. He therefore decides to look at the aggregate level first, considering profitability, liquidity and stability in order, then he disaggregates the profitability performance.

### Profitability

The business has made a profit of £150,236 over the past year which certainly seems a large amount. However, this is only just over three-quarters of the figure of £195,132 predicted in the budget. Douglas will come back to this when he disaggregates the results so that he can pinpoint the sources of this shortfall. To obtain a clearer picture of quite how good this profit figure is, Douglas calculates the ROCE and ROE for the year. For the return on capital employed, profit before tax and interest is required - this is the Operating Profit figure of £152,909 in Table 10.11, and for ROE the profit before tax figure is £150,236, again found in Table 10.11. These numbers are divided, respectively, by opening net assets and opening equity: Table 10.14 has these. The calculations are therefore:

$$\text{ROCE} = 152{,}909 \div 3{,}266{,}519 \times 100 = 4.68\%$$
and
$$\text{ROE} = 150{,}236 \div 3{,}250{,}011 \times 100 = 4.62\%$$

Both return on capital measures are positive, which is a step in the right direction, but to decide whether these are sufficiently high Douglas wishes to compare them with something. The first comparison can be with what he expected to obtain. The comparable calculations for the budget would be:

ROCE = 197,677 ÷ 3,266,519 × 100 = 6.05%

and

ROE = 195,132 ÷ 3,250,011 × 100 = 6.00%

So, as with direct comparison of profit, accounted returns are almost 25% below the budgeted figures. But how do these returns compare with those obtained by other forest businesses and by industry in general? Unfortunately, in Caledonia there are no published, reliable figures of returns to forestry, although Douglas is aware that his peers across the country are looking for a minimum return of roughly 3-5%. So, at least the return obtained is near the top of this range.

On the other hand, there are published figures, both by government and the private sector. Having recently installed an Internet connection for his office computer, Douglas gingerly 'surfs the net' and comes across two useful sites: calstat.gov, the Caledonian Government Statistical Service, and dud-and-deadbeat.com, the website of Dud and Deadbeat, the main private sector accounts appraisal company. The data for the private sector indicates that real returns would range from 10-16%, depending on the industrial sector while real returns on money invested in lower risk, longer term government stocks would average 6-8%. This information suggests that, given the level of risk and the long-term investment involved in forestry, a return of about 8% might be expected. The ROCE and ROE figures actually obtained for the Menzies Estate are worryingly low in comparison with this figure.

If Menzies is not alone in facing low returns, and this does seem to be a more general experience in Caledonia, then there are probably external reasons for this performance. For instance, if there are special tax breaks for forestry, if investors see the sector as providing a hedge against inflation, or if the owners of the business have other reasons for wanting to own the land, such as for sporting or ostentation reasons, then there might tend to be greater investment in the sector than the rates of return would warrant.

Nevertheless, this does not detract from the fact that the rates of return are rather disappointing and Douglas should look to see if returns can be improved and, in particular, why the rates of return fell well short of the budget expectations.

## Liquidity

Turning next to liquidity, Douglas can obtain a good picture from the Cash Flow Statement and Flow of Funds Statement which were presented in the previous chapter. These indicate that, although there was a sizeable overdraft at the start of the year, thanks to the positive net cash flows in the first and fourth quarters of the year, the account moved into credit by the year end, although the business did move back into overdraft in the middle part of the year. At present there does not now appear to be a liquidity problem. However, Douglas should budget ahead[8] again for the coming year, and also on an annual basis for several years beyond that in order to see if there is likely to be any move back into overdraft. If there is that likelihood then he is best to approach the bank to ensure an overdraft facility is available when the time comes, and if not, to take steps to make cash available in some other way or to avoid the need for an overdraft.

Although Douglas has obtained a detailed picture from the two statements above, he also calculates the snapshot liquidity measures - the Current Ratio and the Liquidity Ratio. The current assets of the business are the cash in hand and in the bank, debtors and stocks of chemicals, etc. Douglas did not include the plants or that timber which would shortly be sold. Of the current assets Douglas only considers cash and debtors as liquid assets. On the liabilities side, the current liabilities are the overdraft and the creditors. Again, Douglas omits some items which might, more wisely, have been included, namely that part of the loan payable in the coming year. Table 11.4 shows the figures.

**Table 11.4** Menzies Estate - current and liquidity ratios.

|  | opening | closing |
|---|---|---|
| current assets | £95,288 | £8,798 |
| current liabilities | £35,114 | £104 |
| **current ratio** | **2.71** | **84.80** |
| liquid assets | £95,108 | £8,698 |
| **liquidity ratio** | **2.71** | **83.84** |

These ratios give a useful summary and indicate that, despite the overdraft at the start, there were sufficient funds likely to come in within a short period to pay it off. Thus, the figure of 2.71 for both LR and CR suggests a reasonably safe state of affairs. The closing figures, in excess of 80, on the other hand, indicate too much liquidity. Is that possible: why not have very high liquidity; surely, the more the better? High liquidity does suggest that problems in paying bills are unlikely to arise. But remember that liquid assets are idle assets - they are not generating a return. Consequently, if there is a lot of idle cash around it is worth considering whether it might be better to tie it up in some form which would generate a return, remembering of course, to retain enough liquidity to avoid problems. For Douglas, it is not so much a case of having vast cash resources, rather it is one of having low current liabilities - just a small accrual of telephone charges. Still, Douglas might consider putting some of the money in an interest paying account or investing in shares or a local enterprise. Whatever it is, it should be some use of funds which will generate an adequate return and, if necessary, can be turned back into cash at reasonably short notice.

---

[8] And he will need a frank estimate of the amounts that the Orffly-Porsh family expect to extract from the business in dividends.

## Stability

Finally, stability. A careful study of the balance sheet tells us quite a lot: Table 11.5 has a summary of some of the key figures.

**Table 11.5** Menzies Estate - key balance sheet figures.

| balance sheet item | opening (£) | closing (£) |
|---|---|---|
| total assets | 3,301,633 | 3,368,301 |
| total liabilities | 51,622 | 13,055 |
| **shareholders' funds** | **3,250,011** | **3,355,246** |

Total assets have risen over the year by 2%, the result of a nearly 5% rise in fixed assets which was partly counteracted by a drop in current assets to less than 10% of their opening level. Total liabilities, on the other hand, have fallen by nearly 75%. These movements have meant that shareholders' funds (the owners' share) have risen by more than 3% - a pleasing development, although if inflation were affecting the Caledonian economy, the rise in wealth might be more apparent than real[9].

The two key stability indicators for Douglas to consider are the percent equity and the gearing ratio. The former can be calculated from Table 11.5 since it is equity divided by total assets. The opening percentage is 98.4 and the closing figure is 99.6, both extremely high, and if one year is anything to go by, showing a rising trend.

The gearing ratio, comparing loans (Douglas decides not to include overdraft) to equity, falls from 0.005 to 0.004, both indicators of extremely low gearing.

As far as the balance sheet figures indicate, the business is in a very stable position with growing assets and equity and a very small amount of liabilities. The liquidity position also appears to be good and profits are reasonable for the forestry sector, but poor when compared to the levels that might be obtained in other sectors. If the shareholders are content then Douglas might steer the business 'steady as she goes'. However, if there is a desire for maximisation of returns, then Douglas might opt for increasing the borrowing, as long as he can find an investment that offers the opportunity of high returns. This might involve investing in more land and forestry, but only if prices are sufficiently low as to represent a reasonable return.[10] Otherwise, apart from diversification and adding value to the product, the alternative might be investment in shares further afield.

---

[9] See Appendix 11.1 for discussion of the effects of inflation.

[10] For instance, a forest expected to yield £5,000 every 50 years would, at a price of £1,000, give a return of 3.6%, but would generate 8.2% if priced at £100:

i.e. $\left(\dfrac{5,000}{100}+1\right)^{\frac{1}{50}} -1 = 0.082$

## Micro-level analysis

Douglas next decides to dig down to see if he can pinpoint the strong and weak parts of the business. The first thing for Douglas to look at is the cost centre profit account, which was presented in Table 10.13. In the budget all of the cost centres were predicted to make a profit and a return on capital of at least 6%, with the nursery managing a return of nearly 15% and compartment 3 nearly 25%. As things turned out, all of the forest cost centres did make a profit, but the nursery lost around £500. The rate of return can be calculated for each cost centre by dividing the cost centre operating profit by the opening valuation.[11]

Most of the cost centres did produce a return of just under 6%, but the figure for the nursery was -1%, for compartments 1, 2 and 3 the returns were about 4, 3 and 5%, respectively, and for compartment 10 it was only 2%. Table 11.7 shows some of the figures for these poorer performing cost centres preceded by Table 11.6 which gives the budgeted figures so that the causes of the performance might be pinpointed.

**Table 11.6** Menzies Estate - poor performance cost centres - budgeted figures.

|  | Nursery | compartment | | | |
|  | | 1 | 2 | 3 | 10 |
| Output | £ | £ | £ | £ | £ |
| valuation change | 0 | 10,135 | 8,655 | 42,029 | -53,786 |
| Total output | 21,000 | 10,135 | 8,655 | 42,029 | 34,473 |
| Costs | | | | | |
| Total direct costs | 9,630 | 0 | 0 | 35,200 | 0 |
| Total overhead costs | 4,165 | 3,575 | 4,085 | 4,085 | 4,085 |
| Total costs | 13,795 | 3,575 | 4,085 | 39,285 | 4,085 |
| Profit | 7,205 | 6,560 | 4,570 | 2,744 | 30,388 |
| Operating profit | 7,227 | 6,813 | 4,858 | 3,032 | 30,676 |
| Opening valuation | 49,021 | 110,816 | 77,856 | 12,214 | 508,149 |
| ROCE % | 14.7 | 6.1 | 6.2 | 24.8 | 6.0 |

One factor that brought down returns across the board, but which had a disproportionate effect on cost centres with lower valuations, was the downward adjustment in the closing valuation, simply due to an upward revision in the expected future overhead costs. This, along with the slightly higher than expected actual overhead costs during the year, was the only reason for the shortfall in profit below what had been expected for compartments 1, 2 and 3.

For compartment 10 the same factors were at work, but the main reason for the low return was that the thinnings revenue was only £70,607, compared to a budgeted figure of £88,258, a reduction of 20%. This, in turn, was due to Douglas obtaining only £31.50 per cubic metre, whereas he had expected nearly

---

[11] Strictly speaking we should divide by the sum of the valuation of the compartment trees and land as well as a share of the other assets, but since the former constitutes the bulk of the assets, using only their value does not cause too much error.

£40. Douglas realises that he needs to look more closely into his marketing approach to see if he can ensure that he obtains better prices next time.

**Table 11.7** Menzies Estate - poor performance cost centres - actual figures.

| | Nursery | compartment 1 | compartment 2 | compartment 3 | compartment 10 |
|---|---|---|---|---|---|
| Output | £ | £ | £ | £ | £ |
| valuation change | -2,486 | 8,334 | 6,597 | 39,970 | -55,844 |
| Total output | 14,315 | 8,334 | 6,597 | 39,970 | 14,763 |
| Costs | | | | | |
| Total direct costs | 10,482 | 0 | 0 | 35,500 | 0 |
| Total overhead costs | 4,353 | 3,695 | 4,223 | 4,223 | 4,223 |
| Total costs | 14,835 | 3,695 | 4,223 | 39,723 | 4,223 |
| Profit | -520 | 4,638 | 2,374 | 247 | 10,539 |
| Operating profit | -497 | 4,904 | 2,626 | 550 | 10,842 |
| Opening valuation | 49,021 | 110,816 | 77,856 | 12,214 | 508,149 |
| ROCE % | -1.0 | 4.4 | 3.4 | 4.5 | 2.1 |

The most disappointing cost centre performance was that of the nursery. Overhead costs were slightly higher than expected, some of the direct costs were lower, but casual labour costs were much higher (£7,020 instead of the expected £5,400): Douglas had underestimated the amount of labour needed for the year's operations. Nevertheless, total costs were only about £1,000 more than expected, whereas the difference between the expected profit of over £7,000 and the actual loss of about £500 was some £7,700. What is the cause of the remainder of the difference? Again, the closing valuation fell, but the biggest shortfall occurred in the revenue from plant sales and transfers. Douglas had been optimistic about the prices, thinking that he might be able to get £100 per 1,000 plants, whereas, in practice he only managed £80. It appears that Douglas is misjudging the markets for both timber and plants: he needs to improve his price forecasting and check that his price assumptions for the valuations are also realistic.

Apart from a disaggregation of the profit performance, Douglas also takes a closer look at the cash flow statement (see Table 10.10) and compares it with the budgeted figures (Table 6.8). On the receipts side, as he identified earlier, the revenue for thinnings and for plants from the nursery was well below what was expected; by around £20,000 overall. Some of the costs were lower than expected, but fencing, planting, casual labour and road maintenance were higher, the net effect of which was to raise trading payments by more than £4,000 compared to the budget. But the greatest effect was caused by the unexpected £45,000 dividend payment. The aggregate effect of the differences was to make the actual net cash flow nearly £70,000 less than the budgeted figure. Douglas will have to meet with the owners to clarify their expectations about future dividend payments and chart the implications for the future cash and capital performance.

All in all the business has performed reasonably well as regards profitability from a forest sector point of view, but not from a wider perspective, has more than enough liquidity and has experienced a modest rise in shareholder's capital. Douglas is aware that he needs to improve his marketing and price forecasting, and aims to carefully monitor the contract and casual labour costs. Finally, management and owners will need to hammer out a clear policy on dividend payments and will need to assess whether investment in forestry is the wisest use of funds in the long term.

## Appendix 11.1 Account Analysis and Inflation

Inflation can severely distort financial performance measures, yet because of the difficulties in understanding its effects and the complexity involved in dealing with it many practitioners prefer to avoid it, taking the view that the effects will cancel themselves out. Unfortunately, that is not the case, and only when inflation rates are relatively modest (no more than, say, 4%) can it be ignored without too much inaccuracy, although even at these rates historically based valuations can quickly fall behind market values and so distort the accounts. Having said all that, despite a debate which has gone on for more than 20 years, accountants are still not agreed upon a single method for dealing with inflation.

**Current Cost Accounting** (as opposed to the normal Historic Cost Accounting) is probably the method most widely accepted as most appropriate. Under this method, adjustments to the profit figure are necessary to make it, and the resulting return on capital measures, meaningful. There are four adjustments necessary: the depreciation, cost of sales, monetary working capital and gearing (or interest) adjustments. Even then, a further adjustment needs to be made when calculating the return on capital to make it a 'real' rate. i.e. a rate of return with inflation effects taken out (see Hill, 1984; Edwards *et al.*, 1987; Bright, 1997).

All of this can be extremely complicated. However, there is a rather easier way of doing things to arrive at a profitability measure known as the **Total Real Return on Capital** (TRROC) and to be able to correctly assess the balance sheet situation. The first step is to value all assets at a particular time in *current* terms, that is, valuing in terms of the price levels at that particular point in time. Imagine, for instance, that you have a stock of harvested timber at the start of the year valued at £1,000. Imagine then, that at the end of the year you have exactly the same amount of timber in store - should we value it at £1,000? To answer this, we have to ask ourselves what are the prices at the moment, i.e. at the end of the year? If the prices had risen by 10%, then the timber should be valued at £1,100, and if prices had fallen by 20%, the figure should be £800.

All assets (including trees, land, machinery and buildings) should be looked at in this 'current value' way. If we are using the expectation approach for tree valuation then we need to re-value each year according to our expectations of the future based on the price level at that moment. For machinery and buildings we did consider the approach back in Appendix 5.2 - this would involve inflating the depreciation charge as well as the closing value.

Once we have done this, the profit figure would include these new valuation changes and an adjusted depreciation charge. The TRROC is then calculated in three steps:

1. Calculate inflation-adjusted profit before interest and tax (IAP) by adding interest, tax and holding gain on machinery and buildings (see Appendix 5.2) to the profit
2. Calculate Total Return on Capital (TROC) as TROC = IAP ÷ Total Assets.
3. Calculate TRROC as:

$$TRROC = \frac{(TROC - f)}{1 + f}$$

where f = the general rate of inflation, expressed as a decimal.

This is a real return measure, that is, with inflation effects removed, so it must be compared with other real rates.

A simple example might make the picture clearer. The opening balance sheet (a horizontal version for convenience) is shown in Table 11.8.

**Table 11.8** Opening Balance Sheet.

| Liabilities | £ | Assets | £ |
|---|---|---|---|
| bank overdraft | 50 | machinery | 10 |
| | | buildings | 30 |
| **net worth** | **290** | trees & land | 300 |
| total | 340 | total | 340 |

The trading receipts for the year are £80, trading payments are £62.50 to which are added interest payments, charged at 13% on the opening overdraft, giving £6.50. Before inflation, the tree and land valuation is calculated to grow by 5% to £315. Finally, depreciation is 10% on buildings with an original value of £50 and 20% on machinery - so the two depreciation charges are £5 and £2 respectively. From this information a profit and loss account can be derived - as shown in Table 11.9.

Following on from this, the closing balance sheet can be derived too: check Table 11.10 to see if this makes sense.

The ROCE in this situation would be (£19 + £6.50) ÷ £340 × 100 = 7.5% and net worth has risen by (£309 - £290) ÷ £290 × 100 = 6.55%.

**Table 11.9** Profit and Loss Account.

| Payments | £ | Receipts | £ |
|---|---|---|---|
| opening valuation | 300 | closing valuation | 315 |
| trading payments | 69 | trading receipts | 80 |
| depreciation | 7 | | |
| **profit** | **19** | | |
| total | 395 | total | 395 |

**Table 11.10**  Closing Balance Sheet.

| Liabilities | £ | Assets | £ |
|---|---|---|---|
| bank overdraft | 39 | machinery | 8 |
| | | buildings | 25 |
| **net worth** | **309** | trees & land | 315 |
| total | 348 | total | 348 |

Now, if there is inflation in the economy, such that the value of trees, buildings and machinery have all gone up during the year in line with the retail price index (RPI) at a rate of 10%, what happens to the accounts?

Of course, the cash payments and receipts need no adjustment since they are expressed in terms of what was actually paid and received during the year. However, the non-cash assets do need re-valuing. The trees and land should be 10% higher at the end of the year[12], i.e. £346.50 instead of £315. Similarly, machinery and buildings need to be inflated to £8.80 and £27.50. Depreciation should also be adjusted - to £2.20 and £5.50 respectively. Table 11.11 shows the effects on the profit and loss account, followed by Table 11.12 which shows the subsequent balance sheet. It is worth working through these for yourself.

**Table 11.11**  Inflation-adjusted Profit and Loss Account.

| Payments | £ | Receipts | £ |
|---|---|---|---|
| opening valuation | 300.0 | closing valuation | 346.5 |
| trading payments | 69.0 | trading receipts | 80.0 |
| depreciation | 7.7 | | |
| **profit** | **49.8** | | |
| total payments | 426.5 | total receipts | 426.5 |

**Table 11.12**  Inflation-adjusted Closing Balance Sheet.

| Liabilities | £ | Assets | £ |
|---|---|---|---|
| bank overdraft | 39.0 | machinery | 8.8 |
| | | buildings | 27.5 |
| **net worth** | **343.8[13]** | trees & land | 346.5 |
| total | 382.8 | total assets | 382.8 |

If you compare these last two tables with the previous two, in other words, comparing the inflation-adjusted figures with the unadjusted ones, the following features stand out:

1. profit is more than two and a half times higher
2. net worth is 11% higher
3. TRROC, calculated from

---

[12] i.e. 10% on top of the 5% real growth, giving a multiplier of $(1 + 0.05) \times (1 + 0.10) = 1.155$

[13] Note that the change in net worth (£343.8 - £290 = £53.8) is made up of the profit of £49.8 plus the holding gain of £4 (machinery £1 and buildings £3).

TROC, which is $=(£49.8 + £6.5 + £4.0) ÷ £340 × 100 = 17.74\%$

and then:

$$\text{TRROC} = \frac{(17.74 - 10)}{1.1} = 7.03\%$$

which is similar to the unadjusted ROCE figure of 7.5%

4. The 'real' percentage change in the net worth[14] figure is calculated using the percentage change in inflation-adjusted net worth, which is

$(343.8 - 290) ÷ £290 × 100 = 18.55\%$,

then:

$$\text{Real net worth change} = \frac{(1 + \% \text{ change in NW})}{1 + f} - 1 = \frac{1.1855}{1.1} - 1 = 7.77\%$$

This figure is roughly 20% higher than the 'nominal' (not adjusted for inflation) net worth change figure of 6.55%.

What do we conclude from this? You might say that, "although the actual profit and net worth figures are very different, when it comes to looking at the percentage figures, there is not much difference at all, so we might as well not bother adjusting in the first place." In this instance, you would not be far wrong. However, if the values of machinery, buildings and the most valuable assets, the trees and land, did not change at the same rate as the RPI, the picture would be very different.

For instance, if only trees and land rose at 5% instead of 10%, then profit and net worth would not rise by so much in absolute terms, and the TRROC and real net worth change percentages would both drop to 2.8%, well below the unadjusted figures of 7.5% and 6.55% respectively[15]. So using the unadjusted figures in this case would give an extremely inaccurate impression.

Furthermore, our inflation-adjusted percentage figures can be compared with external measures if these external measures are also expressed in real terms, whereas the unadjusted figures cannot be compared with external figures with any degree of confidence.

---

[14] Note that this method can be used to calculate the 'real' change in other figures (such as profit, total assets, etc), too.

[15] We should also bear in mind that we are assuming that the unadjusted figures are correct in terms of the price level at the start of the year. But if no adjustment has taken place over a number of years, the figures will be even wider of the mark.

## Appendix 11.2  Further Balance Sheet Ratios

Table 11.13 overleaf lists some of the many ratios which may be used for analysis of business performance. Although their calculation and applications are outlined, readers who wish to make more use of them are advised to consult a good general accounts book; some of these are listed in the References at the end of the book.

   Notice that many of these ratios combine balance sheet elements, which are 'stock' or 'point in time' figures, with profit and loss account elements, which are 'flow' figures. Consequently, the question arises, if we are using a 'flow' figure for a period, should we combine it with an opening, closing or average balance sheet figure? Many analysts would probably use the average of the opening and closing values, although some would use one or the other. Again, if comparing, it is important that we use the same method as that used for the comparative figures.

**Table 11.13** Further Balance Sheet ratios .

| name of ratio | alternative names | formula |
|---|---|---|
| | comments | |
| **Asset turnover ratio** | Utilisation ratio | sales ÷ net assets (or long-term capital) |
| | This and the next ratio are termed 'secondary' ratios since when multiplied together they give the ROCE, which can be termed the 'primary' ratio. | |
| **Net profit ratio** | Net profit margin; net profit percentage; profitability ratio | net profit (before tax and interest) ÷ sales |
| | Note that this and the previous 'secondary' ratio can be broken down to look at the constant elements, e.g. gross profit ÷ sales; expenses ÷ sales; sales ÷ fixed assets; sales ÷ net current assets. | |
| **Stock turnover period** | Stock turnover cycle, stock holding period | stock ÷ cost of sales x 365 days (or x 12 months) |
| | Indicates the average length of time that stocks are on the premises before being sold as produce. It can indicate if stocks are being kept at too high a level, although for forestry the length of the production cycle may dictate a lengthy period. If the reciprocal is used this is termed stock or inventory turnover and is expressed as so many 'times', rather than 'days' or 'months'. | |
| **Debtor payment period** | Debtor collection period; average credit given | debtors ÷ sales x 365 days (or x 12 months) |
| | Indicates the average length of time between sales and receipt from customers. Obviously, the longer this period is, then the higher the interest charges which the business is likely to incur. | |
| **Creditor payment period** | Creditor-days ratio; average credit taken | creditors ÷ purchases (trading payments) x 365 days (or x 12 months) |
| | Indicates the average length of time between purchases and payment of bills by the business. It may be business policy to delay payment of bills in order to save interest, but if the period becomes too long, the supplier may charge interest and even refuse to supply further goods or services and relationships may be soured. Furthermore, if this figure rises it may be an indication of the business finding it difficult to meet payments when due. | |
| **Times interest covered** | Income gearing; interest cover ratio | profit (before tax and interest) ÷ interest (may include leasing and loan repayments) |
| | Similar to gearing, in that it shows how comfortably the profits of the business cover the interest charges. Banks sometimes use related measures such as finance charges (rent and interest) ÷ gross output (sales). | |
| **Fixed asset ratio** | | fixed assets ÷ total assets |
| | Shows the proportion of the assets tied up over the long term. In forestry businesses this might be extremely high. However, if this ratio is high and the liquidity and current ratios are low it may signal danger - bills may not be able to be met in the future. This can arise from the business expanding too fast, acquiring fixed assets, but not leaving sufficient liquid assets to spare - this is termed 'overtrading'. There are many other possible measures like this one, each measuring the share in the total of individual categories of assets or liabilities. They serve to give a clearer picture of the balance sheet structure. | |

# Chapter 12

# Appraising Investments

Although we will need to budget and construct accounts on a regular basis, there are other calculations which we will only make periodically as the need arises. This particularly occurs when we are considering doing something new or considering doing the normal things in a different way. For instance, we may wish to see whether it would be better to fertilise a new crop, to use a forwarder in place of a skidder, to build or upgrade a forest road so that lorries could go closer to the crop with forwarding distances reduced, or to construct a campsite or car park. All of these changes involve weighing up or appraising the alternative courses of action or options, they involve the investment of funds, and they usually affect only part, rather than the whole of the business. Consequently, we can call this management activity *investment* or *project appraisal* or *partial budgeting*; we will use the term **investment appraisal** from now on[4].

What do we want to find out in our investment appraisal calculations? In the examples in the previous paragraph the phrase 'to see whether it would be better' was used. But what do we mean by better? In the context of financial management the primary concern is likely to be profitability; so the first calculation is usually to discover whether the proposed activity is more profitable than the current or alternative activity. But that is not all. Questions also need to be asked about liquidity: will the investment lead to liquidity problems or worsen our liquidity position in general or at specific times? And, apart from liquidity problems, there are other aspects that can make a potentially profitable project fail - such factors as the management skill and expertise needed for the new activity, unfavourable weather conditions, pest and disease, input or product

---

[4] Note that in the USA, the term 'investment appraisal' has very specific connotations (see Appendix A towards the end of the book). In this chapter it has a more general meaning.

markets slumping or not being available, or a changed legal environment. All of these elements affect the **feasibility** of the investment, that is, the likelihood of the investment succeeding in the face of potential constraints.

Thus, when we appraise an investment we normally will wish to consider the *profitability* and *feasibility* aspects.

**Fig. 12.1** An investment with regular receipts: forest car park, Grizedale Forest, England (photo: Colin Price).

## Profitability

Any investment is likely to involve the commitment of resources, both physical and financial, followed by a stream of benefits (and associated costs) in the future. This means that any calculation of profitability involves taking account of the effects of time and, as we saw in Chapter 4, this means the use of *discounting* in some form or other. You will have noticed that if you are involved in forestry you cannot get away from that 'd' word! However, if we carry out the procedures in a methodical way, just as with valuations, discounting does not have to be a minefield. Furthermore, for some investments we can use a shorthand method, which does not have to involve the more long-winded discounting procedure.

We will, therefore, look at two methods of appraising the profitability of investments - discounted cash flow (DCF) and shorthand. After that we will consider how we measure the sensitivity of the profitability to changes in the assumptions - not surprisingly, this is known as *sensitivity analysis*. Finally, we will see how Douglas might use some of these tools for appraising different investments on the Menzies Estate.

**Discounted Cash Flow Method**

The first step in the appraisal of the profitability of an investment is to set out the costs and benefits which we expect will arise from the investment over its lifetime: questions of what and when. More precisely, if we are comparing two options, carrying on as normal (the 'no change' option) or doing things differently,[5] we should set out the extra costs and benefits arising from changing to the new activity. That is, if we wish to appraise whether a new activity is more profitable than the existing or continuing activity then we need to estimate what the *extra*, incremental or marginal benefits and costs of doing so are. If we are to do this, we need to ask ourselves the questions, 'What costs and benefits will be different and by how much?' However, we must be very careful in doing this because it is easy to make errors - either we look too narrowly and miss the wider effects of the change (overheads might rise as well as direct costs, for instance) or because we compare 'before' and 'after' rather than the differences between the two activities over the coming years.

To help to overcome the possible confusion when trying to estimate directly the extra costs and benefits, we can instead simply set out separately the costs and benefits of each activity, work out the profitability of each and then compare them. An advantage of this approach is that we can then compare any number of possible alternatives. If we do wish to estimate the extra costs and benefits directly, all we need do is subtract, for each year, the costs and benefits of the continuing activity from those of the new activity: we might express this as WITH minus WITHOUT.

The picture should become clearer if we consider a straightforward example. However, before we do, there is one question which we need to sort out - this is the subject of the next paragraph.

One key issue that arises concerns the *lifetime* of the investment. How do we decide what this is? If we put it another way: how long will the investment, or project, last? Or for how long will the effects of the investment be felt? Then we can normally arrive at an answer fairly readily. Take, for example, the appraisal of the use of a forwarder in place of a skidder. The lifetime of the forwarder investment will be the period over which it remains in the business, i.e. until we sell it at, perhaps, an age of seven years. A road improvement might pose more of a problem - the road might last for a very long time. The lifetime we assign to this investment could be the period until it requires substantial rehabilitation, or until benefits no longer arise (if, for instance, lorries were unable to use it), but if it was maintained and continued to give benefits for a

---

[5] We are not limited to comparing only two activities - we can compare as many as we like, but if there are a number we are best to list each one separately.

long period, then the lifetime would have to match that. Some lifetimes might be even longer than this: the case of applying fertiliser is one example. If fertiliser application meant that the optimum rotation was reduced, then the fact that this brought the value of subsequent rotations closer to the present would also have to be brought into the calculations, and consequently the lifetime might be considered as infinity, or certainly several rotations[6].

To illustrate what we have covered so far and to help with what follows, let us take, as an example, the consideration of an investment that is expected to yield a constant stream of benefits over its lifetime: the upgrading of a bridge to allow heavier lorries across would fit into this category. Now imagine that this would involve an initial investment of £1,000, followed by transport costs of £100 at the end of every year for 10 years, matched by timber receipts of £350 per year. This would be the WITH situation. If the bridge were not upgraded, then there would be no initial investment, annual transport costs would be £300 and receipts would be £350. Subtracting WITHOUT from WITH, the extra benefits would be zero (£350 - £350), whereas the extra costs would be -£200 (£100 - £300), that is, costs would be lower in the WITH situation. Thus, the extra or incremental investment would be £1,000 and the incremental net benefit would be £200. The lifetime of the investment is taken to be 10 years, the period until major renovation works would be required (don't start criticising this assumption if you think that the bridge would last much longer than this - this is only an example!).

We could set out the incremental cash flow as shown in Table 12.1. Note that, although we considered the WITH and the WITHOUT situations, we did not take into account all of the costs, such as associated overheads. This could have been done, but, since these costs were deemed to be the same in both cases, they would not have influenced the 'extra costs'.

Step two is the discounting step. To carry this out, however, we first have to decide upon the discount rate. This was explained in some detail in Chapter 4 so we will not go over it again here; suffice it to say that the discount rate should reflect the opportunity cost of capital to the business and should be the 'real' rate if we are going to express the cash flows in 'real' terms (that is, with inflation taken out). In the example we will use a rate of 6%.

The fifth column in Table 12.1 shows the discount factors for each year of the lifetime of the investment[7]. Each discount factor is calculated using the formula:

---

[6] Because of the large time delay before the effects of the second, third, and subsequent rotations are felt, discounting means that their present values tend to be quite small, so there is not much loss in accuracy if the investment is deemed to terminate at the end of the fourth, third or even second rotation. For instance, for a 45-year rotation, at a discount rate of 6%, if the first rotation is given a weight of 100, the weight of the next three rotations are respectively 7.27, 0.53 and 0.04, and the value of an infinite series of rotations is 107.83, only a little more than the sum of the first and second rotation weights.

[7] Have you noticed - we implicitly assume that all cash flows occur at the end of the year, rather than at some time within the year. What happens if this is not the case, and what we do about it, is the subject of Appendix 12.1.

discount factor $= \dfrac{1}{(1+r)^n}$

where r is the (decimal) discount rate; and n is the year.
For example, the discount factor for year 3 is:

$$\frac{1}{(1+0.06)^3} = \frac{1}{1.191} = 0.840$$

In the final column of the table, the discount factors are multiplied by the net benefits to give the present values, and then these are summed to give the first measure of profit (or, rather, incremental or *extra* profit), the incremental net present value (NPV), £472.02 in this case.

**Table 12.1** Investment appraisal: bridge example.

| time | extra benefit | extra cost | extra net benefit | discount factor | present value |
|---|---|---|---|---|---|
| years | (£) | (£) | (£) | @6% | (£) |
| 0 | 0 | 1,000 | -1,000 | 1.000 | -1,000.00 |
| 1 | 0 | -200 | 200 | 0.943 | 188.68 |
| 2 | 0 | -200 | 200 | 0.890 | 178.00 |
| 3 | 0 | -200 | 200 | 0.840 | 167.92 |
| 4 | 0 | -200 | 200 | 0.792 | 158.42 |
| 5 | 0 | -200 | 200 | 0.747 | 149.45 |
| 6 | 0 | -200 | 200 | 0.705 | 140.99 |
| 7 | 0 | -200 | 200 | 0.665 | 133.01 |
| 8 | 0 | -200 | 200 | 0.627 | 125.48 |
| 9 | 0 | -200 | 200 | 0.592 | 118.38 |
| 10 | 0 | -200 | 200 | 0.558 | 111.68 |
| | | | | NPV @6% | 472.02 |

What does the NPV tell us? A figure greater than zero signifies that, at the *discount rate employed*, the *incremental* profitability arising from the investment is positive: in other words, the project adds to overall profitability, and *vice versa* for a figure less than zero. Obviously, if we were to use a different discount rate the result might no longer hold.

A third and fourth step can be carried out to calculate other profit measures. Step three concerns the calculation of the (incremental) internal rate of return (IRR), which is the break-even discount rate, or the highest rate of interest that could be charged before the NPV of the investment moved from positive to negative. A more formal definition is:

> "that rate of interest which, when used to discount the cash flows associated with an investment project, reduces its net present value to zero." (Bannock *et al.*, 1978, p. 243)

This is also known as the yield of the investment. We must remember that, as with the NPV, this is the *incremental* IRR, so it is another indicator of incremental profitability, not necessarily *overall* profitability.

To calculate the incremental IRR there are a number of sub-steps[8], but, unlike with the calculation of the NPV, we cannot simply use a formula to arrive at the answer. Instead we need to make an estimate of the discount rate which would move the NPV to zero, then carry out the calculations to see if using this rate does do so, and if not, try again until we get sufficiently close to zero. So, we go round in a loop, or series of iterations until the NPV = 0.

Our first sub-step is to go back to the NPV which we have just calculated. Look at the answer we obtained in the example. The NPV is £472.02 when the discount rate is 6%. So the IRR cannot be 6% because the NPV is well above zero. What do you think would be the discount rate which would give an NPV of zero? Would it be greater or less than 6%?

If you cannot decide, think about what happens to the discount factors when the discount rate is raised. In the formula above, when the discount *rate* goes up, the discount *factor* goes down, so any cash flows in the future will get smaller. So if the benefits occur in the future, then raising the discount rate will lower the present value of these benefits and so lower the NPV. Thus, in this case, we would expect the IRR to be greater than 6%. But how much greater? As Fig. 12.2 shows, we cannot really, having calculated just one point on the graph of discount rate against NPV, have much idea as to what the IRR is likely to be.

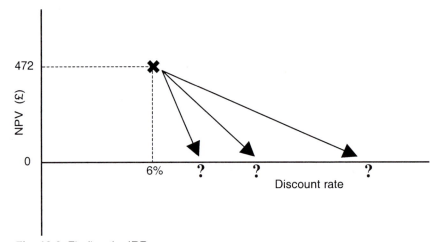

**Fig. 12.2** Finding the IRR.

However, if we can estimate another point on that graph, we will then be able to extrapolate from or interpolate between them. This assumes that, as we change the discount rate the NPV would change in a straight line. But it does not,

---

[8] These steps can be avoided if we have access to a spreadsheet. We can then either use the in-built formula '=IRR' or keep changing the discount rate until we obtain an NPV very close to zero.

as Fig. 12.3 shows. Nevertheless, if we can arrive at two points close enough to the x-axis, the assumption of a straight line gives sufficient accuracy.

The first sub-step, then, is to estimate a second point on the graph. The simplest way[9] of doing this is to take the average annual net benefit and divide it by the initial investment. In this case, since the net benefit each year is the same, £200, then the average would also be £200 and the IRR estimate would be (200 ÷ 1,000) which gives 0.2 or 20%.

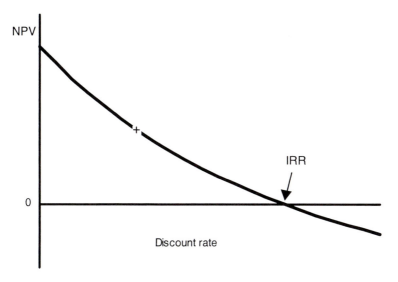

**Fig. 12.3** The relationship between discount rate and NPV.

The next sub-step is to carry out the discounting procedure again, as in Table 12.1, but this time using the estimated IRR. For the example, we will use

---

[9] A more accurate, but also more complicated method, derived from Bright (1997), is to use the formula:

$$\text{IRR} \approx \frac{3 \times \left[ NB - \dfrac{(\text{Investment} - \text{Salvage})}{t} \right]}{(2 \times \text{Investment} + \text{Salvage})}$$

where NB is the average annual net benefit; Investment is the initial investment outlay; and Salvage means the extra benefit (or cost) at the end of the investment lifetime arising from the sale of the assets involved in the project.

In the example, the calculation would be:

$$\text{IRR} \approx \frac{3 \times \left[ 200 - \dfrac{(1,000 - 0)}{10} \right]}{(2 \times 1,000 + 0)} = \frac{3 \times \left[ 200 - 100 \right]}{2,000} = 0.15 \text{ or } 15\%$$

the 20% estimate. If you try recalculating Table 12.1 with this rate, you will arrive at an NPV of -£161.51.

We now have two points on the graph, either side of the x-axis. If we draw a line between them we obtain an estimate of the IRR - where the line crosses the x-axis. Looking at Fig. 12.4, what would you estimate the rate to be?

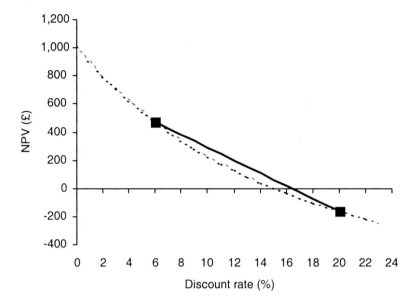

**Fig. 12.4** Estimating the IRR.

Instead of estimating the IRR visually, we can get close to the correct answer either by trial and error or by employing a formula to interpolate between or extrapolate beyond the two points, thus:

$$\text{IRR} = r_1 + \left(r_2 - r_1\right) \times \frac{\text{NPV}_1}{\left(\text{NPV}_1 - \text{NPV}_2\right)}$$

where r is the discount rate; and NPV is the incremental net present value, with subscripts 1 and 2 referring to the first or second round of calculations.

So, for instance, in the example, we take the discount rate of 6% as $r_1$ with the resulting NPV of £472.02 as $\text{NPV}_1$. The second set of figures would therefore be 20% and -£161.51. Substituting these in the formula we get:

$$\text{IRR} = 6\% + (20\% - 6\%) \times \frac{472.02}{472.02 - (-161.51)}$$

$$= 6\% + 14\% \times \frac{472.02}{637.53} = 6\% + 10.4\% = 16.4\%$$

We might accept this estimate of 16.4%, but because the two points on the graph ($r_1$, $NPV_1$ and $r_2$, $NPV_2$) are so far apart it is probably better to carry out at least one more iteration to get closer to the accurate answer - as you can see from the dotted line on the graph, which shows NPV plotted against discount rate, the correct answer would appear to be around 1% less than our estimate.

If we take 16% as our next discount rate we obtain an NPV of -£33.35. If we then use these figures as $r_1$ and $NPV_1$, leaving the other figures the same, we get:

$$IRR = 16\% + (20\% - 16\%) \times \frac{-33.35}{-33.35 - (-161.51)}$$

$$= 16\% + 4\% \times \frac{-33.35}{128.16} = 16\% + -1.0\% = 15.0\%$$

This is probably as far as we would wish to go. The accurate figure is 15.1%, so our figure of 15.0% is reasonably precise.

Now we have the (incremental) IRR, what do we do with it? It is an alternative measure of profitability and signifies a profitable investment as long as it exceeds the discount rate. Although IRR does have its shortcomings *vis-à-vis* NPV in certain circumstances (see Appendix 12.2) it is widely used by international agencies like the World Bank, it can be used to compare with stock market yields, and there is nothing to stop us deriving and using both NPV and IRR.

Finally in this section on the more formal profitability measures, there are two more that might be useful. Little used, but perhaps easier to understand than NPV, is the **EAV**, the **equivalent annual value**. This is simply the NPV, which is a lump sum at the start of the investment, converted into an annuity or equal amount for every year of the lifetime of the investment. This is similar to the way a mortgage involves the repayment over a number of years for the lump sum borrowed at the start - in fact, we use the same formula to derive the EAV. Note, however, that it is not simply the NPV divided by the number of years. This would be wrong since we need to take account of the interest, which means that money effectively received over future years is not the same as the total amount received today. The formula is:

$$EAV = NPV \times \frac{(1+r)^t \times r}{(1+r)^t - 1}$$

where t is the lifetime of the investment.

In the example, the NPV of £472.02 converts to:

$$\text{EAV} = £472.02 \times \frac{(1+0.06)^{10} \times 0.06}{(1+0.06)^{10} - 1} = £472.02 \times 0.136 = £64.13$$

This measure gives a similar picture to the NPV, with a positive figure indicating that the project is worthwhile.

The second of these alternative, or additional, measures of profitability is the **benefit:cost ratio**. Again it is little used and does not really add much to one's understanding of the profitability of an investment, but it has got its advantages (Price, 1989) and is given here in case you come across it. This measure is the ratio of the discounted benefits (DB) of the investment to the discounted costs (DC) and can be derived by dividing DB by DC.

In the example, if we take the cost savings of £200 per year as the benefits, then the DB would be £1,472 and the DC, in the absence of any annual costs, is simply the initial investment of £1,000. The ratio is thus 1.47, signifying profitability since it exceeds 1. If it was less than 1, this would be the same as an NPV below zero - an unprofitable investment.

To summarise, Table 12.2 below sets out the steps for calculating the various discounted measures of project or investment worth.

**Table 12.2** Discounted measures calculation process.

| Step | Description | Sub-steps | Detail |
|------|-------------|-----------|--------|
| 1 | Set out costs and benefits | i | Determine lifetime |
| | | ii | Calculate extra costs |
| | | iii | Calculate extra benefits |
| | | iv | Calculate extra net benefits |
| 2 | Calculate NPV | i | Decide discount rate |
| | | ii | Calculate discount factors |
| | | iii | Calculate present values |
| | | iv | Sum present values = incremental NPV |
| 3 | Calculate IRR | i | Derive approximate IRR |
| | | ii | Use estimate as discount rate to derive a second NPV |
| | | iii | Interpolate/extrapolate to estimate IRR |
| | | iv | Repeat steps ii and iii if necessary |
| 4 | Calculate EAV and B:C | i | Alternative measures: EAV |
| | | ii | Alternative measures: B:C ratio |

*Sensitivity*

When we are carrying out investment appraisal we have to remember that, although our techniques might be highly accurate, the cash flow figures used for the calculations are only estimates, since we are looking into the future with varying degrees of uncertainty. Consequently, we must treat the results with caution. To assist in decision making it is often helpful to check how sensitive the results are to changes in some of the variables. For instance, how sensitive is the profitability of an investment in a stand of Corsican pine to yield class, or timber price or weeding cost variation? To assess sensitivity we simply need to vary different elements, financial and technical, *one at a time*, and measure the degree of change in the NPV, IRR or whatever profitability measure we are using. This is known as **sensitivity analysis**.

There are two ways of carrying out sensitivity analysis of profitability. The first is simply to change elements by a certain amount or percentage and tabulate the consequent change in the profitability measure. The second is to work out the break-even level of that element - that is, how low or high would it have to go before the NPV fell to zero or the IRR fell to the level of the discount rate. These analyses are made much easier if you have a spreadsheet available.

To illustrate the way in which these two forms of sensitivity can be carried out, let us return to our bridge investment example. Imagine that the saved cost of £200 a year was based upon a saving of £0.25 per cubic metre on an expected 800 cubic metres of timber. We might then wish to calculate how sensitive our result is to a 10% reduction in the quantity transported. A 10% drop would mean 720 cubic metres of logs and a saving of only £180 instead of £200. Inserting this annual figure in the discounted cash flow table would reduce the NPV from £472 to £325 and the IRR from 15.1% to 12.4%. So a 10% drop in throughput leads to a sizeable drop (of about one third) in the NPV although the investment remains strongly profitable.

Taking the second break-even approach, we can reduce the throughput until the NPV is zero. Taking the figure down to about 544 cubic metres, with a consequent annual cost saving of £136, gives an NPV of zero and an IRR of 6%, the same as the discount rate. In other words, timber throughput would have to drop by about one third before the bridge investment would fail to generate an improvement in profits. It is up to the decision-maker to decide how likely such an outcome would be.

## 'Shorthand' profitability measures

If you want a quick answer as to the profitability of an investment, as long as the problem is not too complex, you can employ a shorthand method. The key difference between the discounting procedure and the shorthand method is that the former lists the costs and benefits for the whole lifetime of the investment, whereas the shorthand method looks at a single year, representative view. In other words, the latter method distils the problem into a one-year snapshot. How does it do this?

Well, typically, an investment involves a cost outlay at the beginning, a series of annual costs and benefits, and perhaps some extra benefit (such as a salvage value) or cost (such as rehabilitation) at the end of its lifetime. If we can convert these elements into their annual equivalents, we can then simply set out the annual costs and benefits, subtract one from the other, and we are left with the annual extra profit figure, the more accurate version of which we earlier called the EAV.

Taking the annual extra benefits first: if these are the same each year (in our bridge example, for instance, the annual extra benefit was £200 every year) then that is the figure we use for our one-year snapshot. However, if, apart from changing with inflation, the figures vary from year to year by more than about 10%, then our shorthand method will not give sufficient accuracy.

Extra annual costs are determined in the same way as benefits.

Next, we need to convert any lump sum costs and benefits at the beginning and end into their *annual* equivalent. There are two ways of doing this. The first might not be considered a shorthand method because it involves using the formula that we met earlier in converting the NPV into its EAV. In this context it looks like this:

$$EAVI = \left( Investment - \frac{Salvage}{(1+r)^t} \right) \times \left( \frac{(1+r)^t \times r}{(1+r)^t - 1} \right)$$

where EAVI is the equivalent annual value of the investment; Investment refers to the initial outlay; and Salvage means the extra benefit (or cost) arising from the sale of assets at the end of the investment lifetime.

In our example, the investment is £1,000, there is no salvage value, interest is 6% and the lifetime is 10 years, so the calculation becomes:

$$EAVI = \left( 1,000 - \frac{0}{(1.06)^{10}} \right) \times \left( \frac{(1.06)^{10} \times 0.06}{(1.06)^{10} - 1} \right) = 1,000 \times 0.136 = £136$$

The figures, for extra annual costs and EAVIs, can then be subtracted from extra annual benefits to give extra annual profit (or loss), as shown in Table 12.3.

Notice that our answer of £64 extra profit is the same as the EAV we obtained earlier using the discounting procedure.

The are a number of simpler, but less accurate, formulae for calculating the EAVI (see Price, 1989; Bright, 1997); probably the most accurate is the following:

$$EAVI = \left( \frac{Investment - Salvage}{t} \right) + \left( \frac{Investment + Salvage}{2} \right) \times r$$

The squiggly equal sign means 'approximately equal to'. Using this formula in our example, the EAVI becomes:

$$EAVI = \left( \frac{1,000 - 0}{10} \right) + \left( \frac{1,000 + 0}{2} \right) \times 6\% = 100 + (500 \times 6\%) = £130$$

If this is inserted in the calculation in Table 12.3 in place of the figure of £136 calculated earlier, the extra profit is estimated as £70. This is not as accurate as the first answer obtained in Table 12.3, but, to be fair, this formula is based on the assumption that cash flows occur at mid-year, as opposed to the year-end assumption which has implicitly been used for all of the other calculations. This divergence is dealt with in Appendix 12.1.

**Table 12.3** Shorthand profitability calculation – bridge example.

|  | £ |
|---|---|
| Extra benefits | |
| Annual benefits[10] | 200 |
| Total extra benefits | 200 |
| Extra costs | |
| Annual costs | 0 |
| EAVI - bridge | 136 |
| Total extra costs | 136 |
| Extra profit | 64 |

There is also a shorthand means of estimating the IRR - we came across it earlier when deriving the IRR by a series of steps, it is:

$$IRR \approx \frac{3\times\left[NB - \dfrac{(\text{Investment} - \text{Salvage})}{t}\right]}{2\times\text{Investment} + \text{Salvage}}$$

Remember earlier, using this formula we obtained an answer of 15.0%, in this instance, exactly the same as the accurate (DCF) figure; it will not always give such a close approximation, but it is, nevertheless, a useful initial guide.

Sensitivity analysis can be done quite quickly when we are using shorthand methods. If we want to see the effect of a 10% change in timber yield or throughput or log price, for instance, we simply change the item concerned in our profitability table (Table 12.3 for example) and then calculate the changed result. If, on the other hand, we want to calculate the break-even yield, or price, or number of years, for instance, we need to treat the table as an equation, set the profitability to zero (the break-even level) and isolate the unknown term (yield, price, etc.). Thus, the profitability *equation*, in general terms, would be:

Annual extra profit ≈ Annual extra benefit – Annual extra cost –

$$\left(\frac{\text{Investment} - \text{Salvage}}{t}\right) - \left(\frac{\text{Investment} + \text{Salvage}}{2}\times r\right)$$

[10] To avoid confusion, the reduction in annual costs as a result of the investment of £200 is entered as an extra benefit of £200 rather than a negative extra cost!

So, for instance, we could estimate the effect of a 10% reduction in throughput by setting out the profit calculation thus:

$$\text{Annual extra profit} \approx 720 \times £0.25 - \left(\frac{£1,000}{10}\right) - \left(\frac{£1,000}{2} \times 6\%\right)$$

$$= £180 - £100 - £30 = £50$$

a reduction of £20 from the original figure of £70 (using the shorthand EAV equation).

A further manipulation, assigning extra annual profit to zero, gives us the break-even value:

$$0 = \text{throughput} \times £0.25 - \left(\frac{£1,000}{10}\right) - \left(\left[\frac{£1,000}{2}\right] \times 6\%\right)$$

So

$$£130 = \text{throughput} \times £0.25$$

Then:

$$\text{throughput} = \frac{£130}{£0.25} = 520 \text{ cubic metres}$$

which is not far from the more accurate (DCF) figure of 544 which we obtained earlier (bearing in mind that this method is assuming mid-year cash flows).

## Feasibility

Although we may be primarily concerned with the profitability of an investment, we must also take account of other aspects that could lead to failure of the project and also negative knock-on effects on the rest of the business.

To help in covering the possible factors which might lead to the failure of a potentially profitable investment, the checklist in Table 12.4 lists the main areas which should be given consideration. This list is based on the notion that the forest business may face risks or constraints with regard to the resources, which it uses in the production process, and with regard to the environments in which it operates.

The resources (or capitals, as they may be termed) are natural (land), human, physical and financial, and we can assess the various risks attached to each, that might threaten the success of the project. Added to these risks are those posed by the environments surrounding the business. The natural environment may pose problems in terms of climate and pests. But there are other environments: the market, legal, socio-cultural and political environments, aspects of which could affect the feasibility of the project.

**Table 12.4** Checklist for investment feasibility.

| Aspect | Examples |
|---|---|
| Resources | availability - amounts, quality and timing |
|   Natural capital | |
|     Land | location, accessibility, soils, steepness |
|   Human capital | |
|     Labour | expertise and training, workload peaks and availability |
|     Management | expertise, added work load, commitment |
|   Physical capital | |
|     Material inputs | restrictions on use |
|     Machinery | contractors, reliability/breakdowns |
|     Buildings | space availability |
|     Infrastructure | adequacy of roads |
|     Financial capital | cash and overdraft constraints, sources of finance, dividend obligations |
| Natural environment | |
|   Pests and diseases | effects on yield; risks - probabilities |
|   Climate | rainfall, temperature; hazards - drought, windthrow, flooding - effects on yield; risks - probabilities |
| Markets and marketing | availability and accessibility, price variation, transport and storage costs and difficulties |
| Legal restrictions and obligations | access, felling restrictions, pollution and conservation legislation, labour laws, taxes |
| Social restrictions and obligations | fairness, public image objectors, *mores*, indigenous people's rights |
| Political | specific and general government policies, security situation |

It is not the intention here to cover items on the checklist in more detail: the forest manager needs to weigh up the possible constraints specific to the particular situation. However, in a book dealing with financial management we do need to give financial aspects more consideration.

In this chapter we will look at the liquidity aspects (will there be enough extra cash available?), while the sources of finance are covered in the next chapter. As with profitability, there are discounted cash flow and shorthand methods of appraising the likely liquidity of an investment so these will be considered in turn.

**Discounted Cash Flow and Liquidity**

Although not strictly part of the DCF analysis, we can assess liquidity by adding a couple of extra columns to the right-hand side of our DCF table. These are labelled interest and closing balance, and will show what the bank balance would look like over the lifetime of the investment if a new account was used to cover all of the extra cash flows associated with the investment. The final column (labelled 'closing balance') can be termed the **debt profile** since it shows the pattern of outstanding debt associated with a project over its lifetime. Table 12.5 shows the DCF table with the extra columns.

**Table 12.5** DCF table and debt profile.

| time | extra benefit | extra cost | extra net benefit | discount factor | present value | interest @6% | closing balance |
|---|---|---|---|---|---|---|---|
| years | £ | £ | £ | @6% | £ | £ | £ |
| 0 | 0 | 1,000 | -1,000 | 1.000 | -1,000.00 | 0.00 | -1,000.00 |
| 1 | 0 | -200 | 200 | 0.943 | 188.68 | -60.00 | -860.00 |
| 2 | 0 | -200 | 200 | 0.890 | 178.00 | -51.60 | -711.60 |
| 3 | 0 | -200 | 200 | 0.840 | 167.92 | -42.70 | -554.30 |
| 4 | 0 | -200 | 200 | 0.792 | 158.42 | -33.26 | -387.55 |
| 5 | 0 | -200 | 200 | 0.747 | 149.45 | -23.25 | -210.81 |
| 6 | 0 | -200 | 200 | 0.705 | 140.99 | -12.65 | -23.46 |
| 7 | 0 | -200 | 200 | 0.665 | 133.01 | -1.41 | 175.14 |
| 8 | 0 | -200 | 200 | 0.627 | 125.48 | 10.51 | 385.65 |
| 9 | 0 | -200 | 200 | 0.592 | 118.38 | 23.14 | 608.78 |
| 10 | 0 | -200 | 200 | 0.558 | 111.68 | 36.53 | 845.31 |

To construct the debt profile the first figure to be entered is the cash flow at the beginning of the investment, £1,000 in this case. This £1,000 is the amount you would have to borrow on overdraft at the outset. Next, we assume that interest will be accrued on this amount over the first year, so the first interest calculation is:

interest = opening balance × interest rate = -£1,000 × 6% = -£60

where opening balance refers to the bank balance at the start of the year; in this case at the start of year one (which is the closing balance at the end of year zero).[11]

The closing bank balance for the end of year one is then:

closing balance = opening balance + interest + extra net benefit

= -£1,000 + -£60 + £200 = -£860.

These two steps for interest and closing balance are then repeated for each year of the lifetime of the investment.

---

[11] Note that interest could be negative (paid) or positive (received). Using the same rate of interest for both conditions is unrealistic, although this could be the case if the extra money from this investment was simply used to reduce an existing overdraft on the whole business. However, it is quite straightforward to apply a lower (or zero) interest rate on positive balances if we wish.

Note that we can carry out this procedure in either 'real' or 'nominal' terms.

Most of our analyses so far have adopted a 'real' terms approach, assuming that all of the cash flows go up (or down) in line with the general rate of inflation and so stay the same in real terms. To be consistent we must also use the *real* discount (or interest) rate - the rate with inflation excluded.

However, we may instead adopt a nominal terms approach, and this can be especially helpful if we are going to the bank manager to request an overdraft or loan. Why?

Well, can you imagine having arranged an overdraft facility for £50,000 and being called in by the bank manager to explain yourself when it rose to £70,000. The bank manager might not sympathise with your response, "I know five years ago we arranged that I should not exceed an overdraft limit of £50,000, but I was expressing the figures in real terms, and, in fact, although it may seem like £70,000 to you, in real terms it is within the limit."

To get over this potential problem, you could carry out the liquidity analysis in nominal terms, but that would involve inflating each of the cash flows in line with the rates of inflation which you expect to affect them, and using a nominal interest rate (one which includes the expected general rate of inflation).

Once we have completed these calculations, we can view the movement of the figures in the final column (the closing balance) to see the profile of the debt associated with the investment. A better impression is gained if we graph these data, as Fig. 12.5 illustrates.

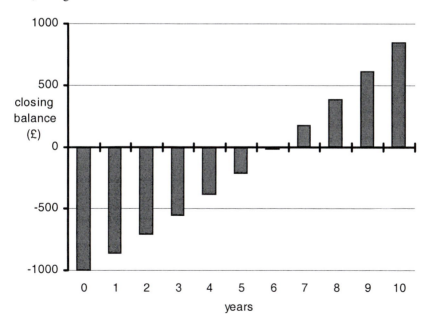

**Fig. 12.5** Debt profile.

What does this profile show us? Several things. It shows the maximum amount of borrowing, the length of time to pay back the money borrowed (the **payback period**) and how much money would be built up in the bank by the end of the investment lifetime (the **terminal value**). In this case, the maximum borrowing is £1,000, the bank balance becomes positive after six years (which is therefore the *payback period*), and goes on to reach a level of £845 at the end of the period (i.e. its *terminal value*). All of this provides the forest manager with information with which to judge the likely feasibility of the investment from a liquidity angle[12].

Finally, if even more detail is required, especially for the early years of the investment, then the profile can be constructed based on monthly or quarterly cash flows and interest charges. This is exactly the same as the cash flow budget, except we may here wish to look at the *extra* costs and benefits, unless we wish to see the liquidity picture in the context of the whole business, in which case we can incorporate the information into the full budget.

**Shorthand Liquidity Measures**

There is no substitute for the detail provided by the debt profile procedure discussed above. However, we can obtain a quick estimate of the payback period. The payback period is, in fact, the break-even life of the investment, so we can arrive at a formula in the same way as we worked out the break-even level of any element. The formula is:

$$\text{payback period} \approx \text{investment} \div$$

$$\left(\text{annual net benefit} - \text{annual net cost} - \left[\frac{\text{investment}}{2}\right] \times r\right)$$

which gives us here:

$$\text{payback period} \approx £1,000 \div \left(£200 - \left[\frac{£1,000}{2}\right] \times 6\%\right) = £1,000 \div £170 = 5.9 \text{ years}$$

So the payback period is about six years, which concurs with the more accurate debt profile calculations above.

Having covered profitability and the cash aspect of feasibility using both DCF and shorthand methods, we return now to Caledonia to see some of the investment ideas which Douglas has in mind.

---

[12] You may be interested to know (well, some of us are) that the terminal value also measures the profitability since it is directly related to the NPV. If the NPV is greater than zero, so will be the terminal value. Hence, if the debt profile becomes positive before the end, this indicates a profitable investment.

To convert the terminal value to the NPV we divide it by $(1+r)^t$. In the example, this is:

$$\text{NPV} = £845.31 \div (1.06)^{10} = £472.02$$

# Menzies Example

Douglas has three different investment problems which he wants to appraise.

Firstly, he wishes to assess whether or not it would be worth fertilising crops of Knots pine - he does not currently do so, but would be willing to adopt the practice if there were a clear profit advantage.

The second investment is not for himself, but a friend of the Orffly-Porsch family, Colonel D. B. H. Blight. 'Blighty' wishes to calculate how much he should charge if he purchases a forwarder and uses it for contracting.

And the third investment is a car park which Douglas is considering constructing on a piece of unused Estate land near the road.

## Fertilising Knots pine

If Douglas were to fertilise at the planting stage, at a cost of £200/ha, he estimates that this would improve productivity to such an extent that thinnings would be brought forward by two years and the optimal rotation length would be 44 years as opposed to 47 years[13]. If we were to try to calculate the extra cash flows by subtracting the 'without' cash flows (no fertilising) from the 'with' cash flows (using fertiliser) the problem would be that the lifetimes of the two scenarios would be different, so it is better to calculate the NPV of each separately and then compare them.

Should we, therefore, carry out the DCF calculations for 47 years in one case and 44 years in the other?

No.

Why not?

Because this would not take account of the fact that, for the 44-year rotation, a new investment (the next rotation) could be started at the end of year 44, three years before it would be possible in the 47 year case. That is, profits from the next rotation could be generated sooner in one case than in the other. And this applies to the rotation after that, and the one after that, and so on.

So what should be the lifetime of the investment to make a fair comparison?

A very long period, is the answer (unless we used IRR or EAV as the profit indicator, in which case different lifetimes do not nullify the comparison).

But, do not despair - we do not need to have a DCF table covering pages and pages. As we saw in Chapter 4, as long as the subsequent rotations are the

---

[13] By optimum rotation age is meant the age of maximum LEV. To find this we set out the costs and benefits for each of the rotation lengths over a likely range (say 40 to 50 in this case), calculate the NPV then LEV and compare them. They will rise with increasing age, but will reach a peak at some point. A quick way of estimating the optimum age is to calculate the percentage change in net felling revenue from one year to the next - this is called the **indicating percent** (Price, 1989). The optimum is reached when the percentage increase is no longer greater than the discount rate, although the point of maximum LEV may be slightly earlier than this.

same as the first, we can calculate the NPV for an infinite series of rotations (called, you may remember, the LEV) from the NPV of the first rotation.

Table 12.6 lists the costs and benefits for the 'without' and the 'with' case[14]. The left-hand half of the table covers the DCF figures for the 'no fertiliser' case, while the right-hand side covers the 'with fertiliser' case.

**Table 12.6** DCF - effect of fertilising.

| | 'Without' - no fertiliser | | | | | 'With' - fertiliser | | | | |
| time | cost | benefit | net benefit | discount factor | present value | cost | benefit | net benefit | discount factor | present value |
| year | £ | £ | £ | @6% | £ | £ | £ | £ | @6% | £ |
| 0 | 880 | 0 | -880 | 1.000 | -880.00 | 1080 | 0 | -1080 | 1.000 | -1080.00 |
| 1 | 200 | 0 | -200 | 0.943 | -188.60 | 200 | 0 | -200 | 0.943 | -188.60 |
| 2 | 200 | 375 | 175 | 0.890 | 155.75 | 200 | 375 | 175 | 0.890 | 155.75 |
| 3 | 100 | 0 | -100 | 0.840 | -84.00 | 100 | 0 | -100 | 0.840 | -84.00 |
| 4 | 100 | 0 | -100 | 0.792 | -79.20 | 100 | 0 | -100 | 0.792 | -79.20 |
| .. | .. | .. | .. | .. | .. | .. | .. | .. | .. | .. |
| .. | .. | .. | .. | .. | .. | .. | .. | .. | .. | .. |
| 21 | 100 | 0 | -100 | 0.294 | -29.40 | 100 | 0 | -100 | 0.294 | -29.40 |
| 22 | 100 | 186 | 86 | 0.278 | 23.91 | 100 | 0 | -100 | 0.278 | -27.80 |
| 23 | 100 | 0 | -100 | 0.262 | -26.20 | 100 | 0 | -100 | 0.262 | -26.20 |
| 24 | 100 | 0 | -100 | 0.247 | -24.70 | 100 | 0 | -100 | 0.247 | -24.70 |
| 25 | 100 | 0 | -100 | 0.233 | -23.30 | 100 | 1370 | 1270 | 0.233 | 295.91 |
| 26 | 100 | 0 | -100 | 0.220 | -22.00 | 100 | 0 | -100 | 0.220 | -22.00 |
| 27 | 100 | 1370 | 1270 | 0.207 | 262.89 | 100 | 0 | -100 | 0.207 | -20.70 |
| 28 | 100 | 0 | -100 | 0.196 | -19.60 | 100 | 0 | -100 | 0.196 | -19.60 |
| 29 | 100 | 0 | -100 | 0.185 | -18.50 | 100 | 0 | -100 | 0.185 | -18.50 |
| 30 | 100 | 0 | -100 | 0.174 | -17.40 | 100 | 2206 | 2106 | 0.174 | 366.44 |
| 31 | 100 | 0 | -100 | 0.164 | -16.40 | 100 | 0 | -100 | 0.164 | -16.40 |
| 32 | 100 | 2206 | 2106 | 0.155 | 326.43 | 100 | 0 | -100 | 0.155 | -15.50 |
| 33 | 100 | 0 | -100 | 0.146 | -14.60 | 100 | 0 | -100 | 0.146 | -14.60 |
| 34 | 100 | 0 | -100 | 0.138 | -13.80 | 100 | 0 | -100 | 0.138 | -13.80 |
| 35 | 100 | 0 | -100 | 0.130 | -13.00 | 100 | 3055 | 2955 | 0.130 | 384.15 |
| 36 | 100 | 0 | -100 | 0.123 | -12.30 | 100 | 0 | -100 | 0.123 | -12.30 |
| 37 | 100 | 3055 | 2955 | 0.116 | 342.78 | 100 | 0 | -100 | 0.116 | -11.60 |
| 38 | 100 | 0 | -100 | 0.109 | -10.90 | 100 | 0 | -100 | 0.109 | -10.90 |
| 39 | 100 | 0 | -100 | 0.103 | -10.30 | 100 | 0 | -100 | 0.013 | -10.30 |
| 40 | 100 | 0 | -100 | 0.097 | -9.70 | 100 | 0 | -100 | 0.097 | -9.70 |
| 41 | 100 | 0 | -100 | 0.092 | -9.20 | 100 | 0 | -100 | 0.092 | -9.20 |
| 42 | 100 | 0 | -100 | 0.087 | -8.70 | 100 | 0 | -100 | 0.087 | -8.70 |
| 43 | 100 | 0 | -100 | 0.082 | -8.20 | 100 | 0 | -100 | 0.082 | -8.20 |
| 44 | 100 | 0 | -100 | 0.077 | -7.70 | 280 | 23845 | 23665 | 0.077 | 1822.21 |
| 45 | 100 | 0 | -100 | 0.073 | -7.30 | | | | | |
| 46 | 100 | 0 | -100 | 0.069 | -6.90 | | | | | |
| 47 | 280 | 23845 | 23665 | 0.065 | 1530.23 | | | | | |

[14] Many of the figures are almost identical to those used in the example in Chapter 4. However, here they have been rounded to avoid cluttering up the table.

You will notice that many of the figures are common to both: the preparation, planting and weeding costs in years 0, 1 and 2, the planting grant in year 2, the annual share of overheads at £100 and the marketing cost of £180 at the end of the rotation.

Even the values for the thinnings and harvest have been assumed to be the same, although when fertiliser is applied these benefits occur earlier. Otherwise, the only difference is the cost of fertilising of £200 which occurs at the beginning.

As in the bridge example, the net benefit is calculated as benefit minus cost, discount factors for each year are based on a 6% discount rate, and present values are derived by multiplying the net benefit by the discount factor. The NPV in both cases is the sum of the final present value column, and the LEV is worked out, as before, from the equation:

$$LEV = NPV \times \frac{(1+r)^t}{(1+r)^t - 1}$$

with t, the length of the rotation, being 47 years in the 'without' case and 44 years in the 'with' case. Table 12.7 shows the results.

**Table 12.7** Profitability of fertilising.

|  | 'without' £ | 'with' £ | difference £ |
|---|---|---|---|
| NPV | 287.68 | 520.19 | 232.51 |
| LEV | 307.57 | 563.59 | 256.02 |

The NPV and the LEV for the 'with' (fertilising) situation are substantially greater than those for the 'without' situation, giving an extra £256 for a perpetual series of rotations.

This can be converted to an annual amount (the EAV) from an LEV simply by multiplying by the discount rate. Thus the extra EAV obtained by using fertiliser would be £15.36 (i.e. £256.02 × 0.06), not bad for an extra payment of £200 for fertilising at planting[15].

Douglas thinks that, on the basis of this information, he might go ahead with fertilising. However, he does appreciate that he needs to take account of other factors, including the impact of risk and availability of cash and management time, so he will do a little more thinking before making a decision.

---

[15] This is assuming that one would fertilise in succeeding rotations too. If not, the 'with' LEV would be:

$$LEV_{with} = NPV_{with} + \frac{LEV_{without}}{(1+r)^t}$$

where t is the length of the 'with' rotation.

**Blighty's forwarder cost**

Colonel Blight is considering the purchase of a forwarder for £150,000, He would expect to use it for 1,200 hours each year for seven years and then sell it for about £40,000. Repairs would cost about £3,000 a year, tax and insurance another £1,500, and fuel £3 per hour.

Blighty does not believe in fancy appraisal methods: "If it can't be done on the back of my cigar packet, then it's too complicated."

So Douglas sets the calculations out as shown in Table 12.7, reminding him that this just shows the extra costs to the business of operating the machine and he may also wish to take account of the operator costs and a share of overheads.

As the Colonel wants a return on capital of at least 10%, that is the discount rate that Douglas uses.

**Table 12.7** Forwarder costs - shorthand method.

| Annual (recurring) costs | £ |
|---|---|
| repairs | 3,000 |
| tax and insurance | 1,500 |
| fuel (1,200 hours @ £3/hr.) | 3,600 |
| EAVI | |
| $capital = \dfrac{150,000 - 40,000}{7}$ | 15,714 |
| $interest = \dfrac{150,000 + 40,000}{2} \times 0.10$ | 9,500 |
| Annual costs | 33,314 |
| Total hours | 1,200 |
| Hourly cost | 27.76 |

Douglas explains that this figure of £27.76 is a 'real' charge, one which should be raised each year with the general level of inflation. The Colonel is happy with this, but Douglas wishes to satisfy himself that the figures of £33,314 for the annual cost, and £27.76 per hour are correct, so he goes home and uses DCF as a cross-check. Table 12.8 shows the figures.

Adding together the present values on the right-hand side gives the NPV of -£168,903. This is the net cost of the machine over its life in the business in today's money. To make this comparable with the shorthand calculation, Douglas then coverts the NPV into the EAV, giving an annual cost of £34,695. Dividing this by 1,200 gives the hourly cost: £28.91. This seems to be reasonably close to the shorthand figure of £27.76, so he is satisfied.

However, because the DCF method has implicitly assumed year-end cash flows, whereas the shorthand method works on a mid-year basis, the comparison is not strictly correct. If the DCF is adjusted to the latter basis (see Appendix 12.1) the answers move much closer - the hourly cost becomes £27.86 - only £0.10 different.

**Table 12.8** Forwarder costs – DCF.

| time | invest-ment | repairs | tax & insur. | fuel | total costs | salvage | net cash flow | disc. factor | present value |
|------|------|------|------|------|------|------|------|------|------|
| yrs | £ | £ | £ | £ | £ | £ | £ | @10% | £ |
| 0 | 150000 | 0 | 0 | 0 | 150000 | 0 | -150000 | 1.000 | -150000 |
| 1 | 0 | 3000 | 1500 | 3600 | 8100 | 0 | -8100 | 0.909 | -7363 |
| 2 | 0 | 3000 | 1500 | 3600 | 8100 | 0 | -8100 | 0.826 | -6691 |
| 3 | 0 | 3000 | 1500 | 3600 | 8100 | 0 | -8100 | 0.751 | -6083 |
| 4 | 0 | 3000 | 1500 | 3600 | 8100 | 0 | -8100 | 0.683 | -5532 |
| 5 | 0 | 3000 | 1500 | 3600 | 8100 | 0 | -8100 | 0.621 | -5030 |
| 6 | 0 | 3000 | 1500 | 3600 | 8100 | 0 | -8100 | 0.564 | -4568 |
| 7 | 0 | 3000 | 1500 | 3600 | 8100 | 40000 | 31900 | 0.513 | 16365 |
| | | | | | | | | NPV @10% | -168903 |

**Car park**

Above the Menzies Estate is a popular local landmark and viewpoint, 'Top Height'. Many visitors take the path leading from the road, crossing the Estate bridge and following along the edge of the boundary and then climbing the 500 m hill. However, many of these walkers park along the road near the estate, a practice which the local council is trying to discourage, but so far to no avail.

Douglas wonders whether this problem could be turned to his employer's advantage. The Estate has a small patch of land near to the road, currently unused, which could be turned into a car park for up to 50 cars with a small picnic area[16]. This would cost £300 per car space with additional outlay of £4,000 needed for barrier, ticket machine, picnic benches, waste bins and installation.[17] Annual maintenance costs would be about £500 and he would aim to levy a daily parking charge of £1 per car. The trade would be seasonal, but overall he would expect 4,500 paid car visits per year, an 'occupancy' rate of about 25% (based on 50 spaces for 365 days = 18,250 spaces). The equipment is expected to last for at least 6 years and he assumes a life of 12 years for the car park itself. No salvage values are taken into account and the discount rate is 6%.

Just as he did for the Colonel, Douglas first obtains a quick picture by using shorthand methods, and since the figures for the rest of the business are not expected to change, he does not need to present 'with' and 'without'. Table 12.9 shows the results.

On the cost side he carries out two separate sets of calculations - one for the car park for a 12-year life and one for the equipment (ticket machine, benches, etc.) for six years.

---

[16] In the calculations no charge has been made for the land itself. Even if it might otherwise be idle, the land should be valued in terms of its opportunity cost. However, since Douglas considers this to be negligible, he has assumed a cost of zero.

[17] Douglas may also find that he is legally obliged to make certain other investments, such as a toilet block, for instance.

**Table 12.9** Car park investment - shorthand calculations.

| | £ | | £ |
|---|---|---|---|
| Costs | | Benefits | |
| EAVI – car park | | Car park revenue | |
| | | 4,500 visits @£1 | 4,500 |
| capital $\dfrac{50 \times 300}{12}$ | 1,250 | | |
| interest $\dfrac{50 \times 300}{2} \times 6\%$ | 450 | | |
| EAVI – additional outlay | | | |
| capital $\dfrac{4,000}{6}$ | 667 | | |
| interest $\dfrac{4,000}{2} \times 6\%$ | 120 | | |
| maintenance | 500 | | |
| Total extra costs | 2,987 | Total extra benefits | 4,500 |
| Extra profit | 1,513 | | |

The extra annual profit is estimated as £1,513, which appears to be a good return on an initial investment of £19,000 (£15,000 for the car park and £4,000 additional outlay).

Douglas also estimates the IRR using the shorthand formula introduced earlier:

$$\text{IRR} \approx \frac{3 \times \left[4,500 - 500 - \dfrac{15,000}{12} - \dfrac{4000}{6}\right]}{2 \times 15,000 + 4,000} = \frac{3 \times [4,000 - 1,250 - 667]}{38,000} = \frac{6,249}{38,000} = 16.4\%$$

Again, this profitability measure, since it is well above the discount rate, indicates a favourable outcome.

The next step is to study the sensitivity of the results to changes in the key variables. He chooses to consider the 'occupancy' rate and the number of years (which also gives a liquidity indicator).

Douglas has used an 'occupancy' rate of about 25%, or 4,500 cars parking per year. He decides to check the effect of a 20% reduction in this to 3,600 and also to calculate the break-even figure. The first of these calculations is straightforward. In Table 12.9 he simply replaces the £4,500 on the benefit side, by £3,600 (i.e. 3,600 × £1). This gives a new profit figure of £613, about 60% below the original figure: so a 20% lower 'occupancy' rate gives a 60% reduction in profits.

To derive the break-even level of 'occupancy', the calculation for annual profit in Table 12.9 can be converted to an equation which looks like this:

Annual extra profit ≈ 'occupancy' × £1 - £500 -

$$\left( \frac{£15,000}{12} \right) - \left( \left[ \frac{£15,000}{2} \right] \times 6\% \right) - \left( \frac{£4,000}{6} \right) - \left( \left[ \frac{£4,000}{2} \right] \times 6\% \right)$$

$$= \text{'occupancy'} \times £1 - £2,987$$

The break-even position implies a profit of zero, and inserting this into the equation gives:

$$0 = \text{'occupancy'} \times £1 - £2.987$$

and rearranging the terms gives:

$$\text{'occupancy'} = \frac{£2,987}{£1} = 2,987$$

In other words, occupancy would have to be below about 3,000, or one-third lower than predicted, before the investment would make a loss, *ceteris paribus*.

Taken together these figures suggest that the profitability of the investment is vulnerable to variation in occupancy and, consequently, Douglas does need to ensure that his prediction is likely to be reasonably accurate. In particular, how popular will this currently 'free' attraction be if people have to pay?

The second element to be considered is the lifetime of the investment - here he goes straight to the break-even value - the *payback period*. Remember, earlier in the chapter we presented the formula as:

$$\text{payback} \approx \text{investment} \div \left( \text{annual benefit} - \text{annual cost} - \frac{\text{investment}}{2} \times r \right)$$

This is straightforward except for the presence of two investment amounts - the car park and the associated equipment, one which had half the expected life of the other in the earlier calculations. Let us see what happens to these in the formula:

$$\text{payback} \approx \left( £15,000 + £4,000 \right) \div \left( £4,500 - £500 - \left[ \frac{£15,000}{2} \right] \times 6\% - \left[ \frac{£4,000}{2} \right] \times 6\% \right)$$

$$= £19,000 \div £3,430 = 5.5 \text{ years}$$

This result suggests that borrowing to finance the investments could be repaid within six years. However, if the project were to continue beyond that period there would need to be a further investment of £4,000 in equipment. To take account of this we could make the total investment in the first set of brackets (£15,000 + 2 × £4,000) in order to cover all the money invested over the life of the car park. This would then increase the payback period to 6.7 or nearly seven years.

Having discovered that the investment appears to be a profitable undertaking, Douglas decides to carry out more formal calculations to confirm these results.

The DCF table, using a discount rate of 6%, is presented in Table 12.10. Notice that the last two columns showing interest and closing balance have been included so as to give debt profile information.

**Table 12.10**   DCF for car park investment.

| time | Total Costs | revenue | net cash flow | disc. factor | present value | Interest @6% | closing balance |
|------|-------------|---------|---------------|--------------|---------------|--------------|-----------------|
| yrs | £ | £ | £ | @6% | £ | £ | £ |
| 0 | 19000 | 0 | -19000 | 1.000 | -19000 | | -19000 |
| 1 | 500 | 4500 | 4000 | 0.943 | 3772 | -1140.00 | -16140 |
| 2 | 500 | 4500 | 4000 | 0.890 | 3560 | -968.40 | -13108 |
| 3 | 500 | 4500 | 4000 | 0.840 | 3360 | -786.50 | -9895 |
| 4 | 500 | 4500 | 4000 | 0.792 | 3168 | -593.69 | -6489 |
| 5 | 500 | 4500 | 4000 | 0.747 | 2988 | -389.32 | -2878 |
| 6 | 4500 | 4500 | 0 | 0.705 | 0 | -172.67 | -3051 |
| 7 | 500 | 4500 | 4000 | 0.665 | 2660 | -183.03 | 766 |
| 8 | 500 | 4500 | 4000 | 0.627 | 2508 | 45.98 | 4812 |
| 9 | 500 | 4500 | 4000 | 0.592 | 2368 | 288.74 | 9101 |
| 10 | 500 | 4500 | 4000 | 0.558 | 2232 | 546.07 | 13647 |
| 11 | 500 | 4500 | 4000 | 0.527 | 2108 | 818.83 | 18466 |
| 12 | 500 | 4500 | 4000 | 0.497 | 1988 | 1107.96 | 23574 |
| | | | | NPV @ 6% | 11712 | | |

Summing the present values gives an NPV of £11,712, which can then be converted to an EAV of £1,397. This latter figure shows that the shorthand answer of £1,513 (see Table 12.9) is not as accurate as we would like. Again, however, if the DCF was carried out on a mid-year basis, the correct figure would be £1,472 - much closer to our shorthand result.

To derive the IRR, Douglas has to find an approximate IRR (see step 3 i in Table 12.2). This he has already done when employing the shorthand method, where he calculated an IRR of 16.4%. He can now use this rate to derive a second NPV, but rather than 16.4 he decides to use 16%. The DCF calculations, for a discount rate of 16%, are shown in Table 12.11; the only figures that differ from Table 12.10 are those in the discount factor and present value columns.

Summing the present values this time gives an NPV of £147. Douglas can now use the two NPVs (at 6% and 16%) to extrapolate and estimate the IRR. The formula, as before, is:

$$\text{IRR} = 6\% + \left(16\% - 6\%\right) \times \frac{11{,}712}{11{,}712 - 147} = 6\% + 10\% \times \frac{11{,}712}{11{,}565} = 6\% + 10.1\% = 16.1\%$$

Douglas could repeat the process to obtain an even more accurate estimate of the IRR, but decides that 16% is sufficiently accurate. If he had continued he would have discovered that this figure was very close anyway; the accurate answer would be 16.19%.

**Table 12.11** IRR calculation - discount rate 16%.

| time | total costs | revenue | net cash flow | disc. factor | present value |
|---|---|---|---|---|---|
| yrs | £ | £ | £ | @16% | £ |
| 0 | 19,000 | 0 | -19,000 | 1.000 | -19,000 |
| 1 | 500 | 4,500 | 4,000 | 0.862 | 3,448 |
| 2 | 500 | 4,500 | 4,000 | 0.743 | 2,972 |
| 3 | 500 | 4,500 | 4,000 | 0.641 | 2,564 |
| 4 | 500 | 4,500 | 4,000 | 0.552 | 2,208 |
| 5 | 500 | 4,500 | 4,000 | 0.476 | 1,904 |
| 6 | 4,500 | 4,500 | 0 | 0.410 | 0 |
| 7 | 500 | 4,500 | 4,000 | 0.354 | 1,416 |
| 8 | 500 | 4,500 | 4,000 | 0.305 | 1,220 |
| 9 | 500 | 4,500 | 4,000 | 0.263 | 1052 |
| 10 | 500 | 4,500 | 4,000 | 0.227 | 908 |
| 11 | 500 | 4,500 | 4,000 | 0.195 | 780 |
| 12 | 500 | 4,500 | 4,000 | 0.168 | 672 |
| | | | | NPV@16% | 147 |

And what about financial feasibility? Back in Table 12.10 the far right-hand side column shows the debt profile. This confirms the earlier estimate of the payback period as being between six and seven years, despite a slight setback in year 6 when the equipment is replaced. The terminal value reaches nearly £24,000.

Thus, the project appears to be both profitable and feasible from a financial point of view, although, of course, Douglas has to ensure that he can obtain suitable funding for the investment and that other feasibility constraints are overcome.

This latter point should not be taken lightly; questions such as: "What could go wrong and how likely would this be?" "How much management time will be involved?" "Does a move into recreation fit into the business ethos?" "Would employment of more people cause extra problems (or bring opportunities)?" need to be asked.

Furthermore, Douglas might want to give further consideration to extra ventures linked to the project, ventures which might be introduced immediately or phased in more gradually. Would it, for instance, be possible to sell ice cream or wood products?

**Fig. 12.6** Douglas feels uneasy about allowing public access.

# Appendix 12.1 Deviations from the Year-end Cash Flow Assumption

There is a discrepancy between the DCF assumptions applied here and those of the shorthand method, namely, that the former is based on year-end and the latter on mid-year cash flows. How do we reconcile them, and what happens if our assumptions are violated?

For many investment scenarios, following the initial investment outlay cash flows will be spread out over the year and so will be centred on the middle of the year. If so, the normal DCF procedure is flawed because cash flows are deemed to occur at time zero, one (end of year 1), two, and so on. However, it is not difficult to deal with this - three methods are:

1. We could split each year's cash flows into two and apply one half at the start of the year (i.e. the end of the preceding year) and half at the end of the year in question. In the forwarder example, instead of the cash flows inserted as in Table 12.8 the annual £8,100 would be split, as shown as Method 1, in Table 12.12. We then apply year-end DCF as before. Using this method for the forwarder example would give an NPV of £170,880, whereas the year-end assumption gave £168,903.

2. Break the lifetime of the investment into half-year periods, apply the annual cash flows at times 1, 3, 5, etc. (i.e. mid-year), and discount using the rate:

$$\text{period discount rate} = (1 + r)^{(1+p)} - 1$$

where r is the annual discount rate expressed as a decimal, and p is the number of periods per year, in this case 2.

This method gives the following half-yearly discount rate for the forwarder example :

$$\text{half - yearly discount rate} = (1 + 0.10)^{0.5} - 1 = 0.049 \text{ or } 4.9\%$$

and an NPV of £170,833. Again, the cash flows and discount factors are shown as Method 2 in Table 12.12.

3. Break the year into even smaller divisions of months or even days, allocate the cash flows evenly over the year, and use the corresponding *period* discount rate. The forwarder investment cash flows are shown in Table 12.12 under Method 3 and the NPV (at a monthly 0.8%) based on monthly cash flows, would be £170,690.

**Table 12.12** Forwarder costs - DCF treatment of mid-year cash flows.

| Method 1 | | | Method 2 | | | Method 3 | | |
|---|---|---|---|---|---|---|---|---|
| time | net cash flow | disc. factor | time half- | net cash flow | disc. factor | time | net cash flow | disc. factor |
| yrs | £ | @ 10% | yrs | £ | @ 4.9% | mths | £ | @ 0.8% |
| 0 | -154,050 | 1.000 | 0 | -150,000 | 1.000 | 0 | -150,000 | 1.000 |
| 1 | -8,100 | 0.909 | 1 | -8,100 | 0.953 | 1 | -675 | 0.992 |
| 2 | -8,100 | 0.826 | 2 | 0 | 0.909 | 2 | -675 | 0.984 |
| 3 | -8,100 | 0.751 | 3 | -8,100 | 0.866 | 3 | -675 | 0.976 |
| 4 | -8,100 | 0.683 | 4 | 0 | 0.826 | 4 | -675 | 0.969 |
| 5 | -8,100 | 0.621 | 5 | -8,100 | 0.787 | 5 | -675 | 0.961 |
| 6 | -8,100 | 0.564 | 6 | 0 | 0.750 | 6 | -675 | 0.953 |
| 7 | 35,950 | 0.513 | 7 | -8,100 | 0.715 | 7 | -675 | 0.946 |
| | | | 8 | 0 | 0.682 | 8 | -675 | 0.938 |
| | | | 9 | -8,100 | 0.650 | 9 | -675 | 0.931 |
| | | | 10 | 0 | 0.620 | 10 | -675 | 0.923 |
| | | | 11 | -8,100 | 0.591 | 11 | -675 | 0.916 |
| | | | 12 | 0 | 0.563 | 12 | -675 | 0.909 |
| | | | 13 | -8,100 | 0.537 | 13 | -675 | 0.902 |
| | | | 14 | 40,000 | 0.512 | 14 | -675 | 0.894 |
| | | | | | | ... | ... | ... |
| | | | | | | ... | ... | ... |
| | | | | | | 84 | 39,325 | 0.512 |
| | NPV 170,880 | | | NPV 170,833 | | | NPV 170,684 | |

As the example shows, none of the methods gives a markedly different result, but they do diverge by just over 1% from the year-end DCF result of £168,903.

If we now wish to convert these NPVs to an EAV, based on *mid-year*, then the original EAV formula needs only slight adjustment:

$$\text{mid - year EAV} = \text{NPV} \times \frac{(1+r)^{(t-0.5)} \times r}{(1+r)^t - 1}$$

So using the NPV of £170,684 from the third DCF method above and for a seven-year life, the mid-year EAV becomes:

$$\text{mid - year EAV} = £170,684 \times \frac{1.1^{6.5} \times 0.1}{1.1^7 - 1} = £170,684 \times \frac{1.858 \times 0.1}{1.949 - 1}$$

$$= £170,684 \times 0.196 = £33,550$$

So we now know how to deal with mid-year cash flows with DCF, but what about the opposite problem, namely if cash flows do occur at the year end? In that case the year-end DCF procedure normally adopted is correct, whereas the shorthand mid-year assumption is wrong. You can do one of two things here: either carry on with the existing formula, in the knowledge that there will be some error, but that this is only a rough and ready measure anyway. Alternatively, you can adjust the shorthand EAV as follows:

$$\text{year - end EAV} \approx \text{mid - year EAV} \times \left(1 + \frac{r}{2}\right)$$

In the forwarder example, using the shorthand method, we obtained an EAV of £33,314. If, however, the cash flows were expected to be centred on the year-end, this figure could be adjusted to:

$$\text{year-end EAV} \approx £33.314 \times (1.05) = £34,980$$

Is this accurate? With what do we compare it to gauge its accuracy? If we return to the DCF calculations in Table 12.3, these were based on assumptions of year-end cash flows, so the EAV calculated there, of £34,694, is correct in this instance. Therefore, our adjusted shorthand figure is not far out. If this has left you somewhat confused, it may help to remember these rules:

If cash flows are centred on the *year-end*, then *normal DCF* is correct, but the *shorthand method needs adjustment*;
if cash flows are centred on *mid-year* then the *shorthand method* does *not need adjustment*, but the *DCF method does*.

# Appendix 12.2  NPV versus IRR

Which of the two main DCF measures of profitability is better?

There are at least four key areas in which the two measures are compared in trying to answer this question, namely:

- ease of understanding,
- multiple roots,
- ranking non-mutually exclusive alternatives, and
- ranking mutually exclusive alternatives[18].

## Ease of understanding

As far as ease of understanding is concerned some would suggest that the NPV, a lump sum equivalent at the start of the investment lifetime, is difficult to understand or gauge when considering the whole lifetime of the investment. If an annual figure is preferred then the EAV can readily be calculated from the NPV. However, the NPV can still be criticised in that it does not give a picture of how good the profitability is, but only that the investment is profitable if the figure exceeds zero. To overcome this problem the B:C ratio might be used instead. The IRR, on the other hand, does give an indication of the rate of profitability in relation to the size of the investment and should be readily understood and compared both with other projects and with returns in the financial markets.

## Multiple roots

One, less trivial, criticism which can be levelled against IRR, but not NPV, is that, under certain circumstances, there may be more than one discount rate which gives an NPV of zero. This is known as the problem of **multiple roots**, and confronts the user with the problem of deciding which rate to use. This occurs if there is more than one change of sign in the net cash flows. What does this mean?

Typically an investment appraisal problem might involve negative net benefits early on, followed by a stream of positive net benefits subsequently - that is, the sign of the cash flows changes once over the lifetime, from negative to positive. However, if, for instance, the cash flow is negative at the start, followed by a series of positive cash flows, but with a change to negative cash flows later, then there would be two changes of sign - from negative to positive and then back to negative again. As a result, the mathematics of discounting means that there will be two discount rates which would give a zero NPV.

For instance, in the 10-year investment considered in Table 12.1, if the extra cost at the start were £500, followed by annual extra net benefits of £200 from years 1 to 9, but then in year 10 a net outflow of £1,400 occurred, using a

---

[18] Brealey and Myers (1991) and Price (1993) provide interesting discussions of these and other points.

discount rate of 6% would give an NPV of £78.59. You would normally, therefore, expect the IRR to be somewhere above 6%. And you would be right: if you raise the discount rate until you obtain a zero NPV, you will obtain an IRR of about 30%. But if you instead try discount rates below 6% you will find that you eventually obtain a zero NPV again, this time between 2 and 3%. You will see more clearly what is happening if you take a look at Fig. 12.7.

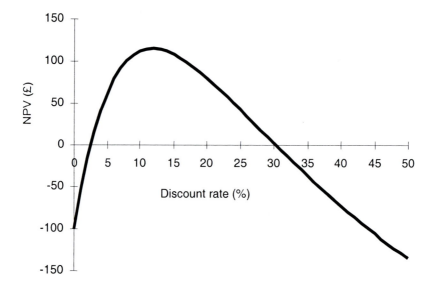

**Fig. 12.7** Investment problem with multiple roots.

This problem of multiple roots is confusing and leaves the decision-maker in a quandary as to which IRR to use. Some solutions to this problem have been suggested (extended yield method, modified internal rate of return, and realisable or composite rate of return) and criticised[19]. In such circumstances it is probably best to use the NPV instead or, as Brealey and Myers put it rather more strongly:

> "A number of adaptations of the IRR rule have been devised for such cases. Not only are they inadequate, they are unnecessary, for the simple solution is to use net present value."    (Brealey and Myers, 1991, p. 84)

Fortunately, this problem is not likely to be that common for foresters - most of the time you will be dealing with net benefit streams which have only one change of sign. The only likely situations in which you might get multiple sign changes are when there are environmental costs of the project which occur

---

[19] For discussion of these methods see Barnard and Nix (1979); Schallau and Wirth (1980); Foster and Brooks (1983); and Klemperer (1996).

towards (or beyond) the end of its lifetime: costs arising from reduced productivity or costs of necessary reinstatement or rehabilitation of the site.

### Ranking non-mutually exclusive alternatives

As far as the ranking problem is concerned, there are two possibilities: either undertaking one project does not stop another project also being undertaken, or the undertaking of one project means that another cannot be undertaken (if they involve doing different things with the same site, for instance). That is, they are either not mutually exclusive or are mutually exclusive.

If projects are non-mutually exclusive and if we wish to rank according to profitability we are effectively wanting to know which project gives the most profit per pound spent. Now NPV alone does not necessarily tell us this: it tells us only the overall profitability. However, a correct picture can be obtained simply by calculating the NPV per £ initial outlay or by calculating the benefit:cost ratio. But it might further be objected that, even for two projects with the same initial outlay, if one had a shorter lifetime than the other and could be repeated, then comparison on the basis of NPV would still be unfair. In that case the NPV per £ outlay could be annualised to the EAV per £ outlay.

The IRR, on the other hand, could be used without adjustment since it is measuring the return on the money invested.

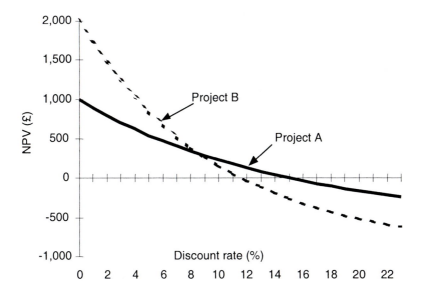

**Fig. 12.8** Ranking non-mutually exclusive investments: crossover discount rate.

Nevertheless, IRR can give an erroneous ranking if the stream of benefits for two projects being compared follow a different pattern. Consider, for instance, our example in Table 12.1 in which the NPV was £472.02 and the IRR 15.1%; we will call this project A. If an alternative investment (project B) involved the same initial outlay of £1,000, but no benefits arose until year 10, when a net benefit of £3,000 occurred, then the NPV would be higher at £675.18 (i.e. £3,000 $\div (1.06)^{10}$ - £1,000), but the IRR would be lower at 11.6% (i.e. £3,000 $\div (1.116)^{10}$ - £1,000 = £0). Thus, because of the different cash flow pattern, the NPVs of the two investments cross over at a certain discount rate, as Fig. 12.8 illustrates. Hence, the term **crossover discount rates** is used.

Because of this problem, the first project would be ranked higher than the second if IRR was used, whereas the positions would be reversed if NPV (at a discount rate of 6%) were to be used. Which is correct? If there were no limit on funds (no *capital rationing*) these would not be a problem, since as both have positive NPVs, and IRRs greater than the discount rate, both projects would be chosen. If, however, there were capital rationing, so that only one project could be undertaken, the NPV would lead us to the correct choice.

**Ranking mutually exclusive alternatives**

If, instead, mutually exclusive projects were being compared (for instance, two types of harvesting system or two tree species for a specific compartment), then NPV would again give the correct ranking as it shows which investment gives the largest amount of profit. IRR would not necessarily show this, since there might be two mutually exclusive investments, one showing a high return on a small investment while the other showed a low return on a large investment, yet the latter might give a higher NPV.

Take our first example again: an initial investment of £1,000 giving an NPV and IRR of £472.02 and 15.1% respectively. Consider an alternative which involves an initial investment of £2,500 followed by 10 years of annual net benefits of £450. At a discount rate of 6% the NPV would be £811.02, whereas the IRR would be 12.4%. Ranking by NPV would give the larger investment precedence, whereas ranking by IRR would favour the smaller investment.

The IRR can be made to give the correct ranking if the smaller project cash flows are subtracted from the larger and the incremental IRR calculated using the resulting incremental cash flows. If the incremental IRR exceeds the discount rate (i.e. the opportunity cost of capital) then the larger project should be preferred. Table 12.13 shows the figures.

The incremental cash flows would be -£1,500 (i.e. -£2,500 - [-£1,000]) for time zero and -£250 for the following years, which would give an incremental IRR of 10.6%. Being greater than the discount rate of 6%, this shows, as did the NPV comparison, that the larger project is preferable.

**Table 12.13** Comparing project IRR s - incremental IRR.

| time | large project net benefits | small project net benefits | incremental net benefits |
|---|---|---|---|
| years | £ | £ | £ |
| 0 | 2,500 | -1,000 | -1,500 |
| 1 | 450 | 200 | 250 |
| 2 | 450 | 200 | 250 |
| 3 | 450 | 200 | 250 |
| 4 | 450 | 200 | 250 |
| 5 | 450 | 200 | 250 |
| 6 | 450 | 200 | 250 |
| 7 | 450 | 200 | 250 |
| 8 | 450 | 200 | 250 |
| 9 | 450 | 200 | 250 |
| 10 | 450 | 200 | 250 |
| NPV@6% | 812 | 472 | 340 |
| IRR | 12.4% | 15.1% | 10.6% |

## Conclusion

Weighing up the pros and cons of the two measures, NPV and IRR, on balance one has to conclude that the NPV, albeit sometimes needing adjustment, is the better measure, although this does not mean that IRR should be automatically thrown out. It should be particularly borne in mind that, despite the divergent results highlighted here, one can expect NPV and IRR to concur in most cases.

Perhaps the advice should be: NPV is better, but either can be used, albeit with care and with appreciation of their shortcomings.

# Chapter 13

# Finance

So far we have spent a lot of time considering some of the key elements of the management cycle - planning, recording, accounting and analysing, but one question which we have not yet dealt with is, "Where does the money to set up, run and expand the business come from?"

This question provides us with a useful definition of **finance**, namely:

> "the money to set up, run and expand the business."

To help forest managers reach a decision on 'Where the money should come from', this chapter covers three further questions: "What do we want the finance for?" "What are the characteristics which the desired finance should have?" and finally, "What are the sources and types of finance available to meet our needs?"

## What for?

Financing decisions should be made at the planning stage: Step 1 of our budgeting procedure. But we can only really see how much money we need by looking at the cash flow budget, which is only constructed in the third budgeting step. Does that mean we have to complete Step 3 before we can finish Step 1? Unless money is readily available and we are sure of what we want to do, then this is true: we initially make plans, then follow them through to Step 3 to see how the financial picture looks, and then we may go back to revise our plan in the light of that information or to see the effect of different financing options. So, budgeting can be an iterative process, which proceeds until we are happy that the plan's financial effects are acceptable. In fact, if we are using a computerised budget we may run through all of the steps several times to see, not only the cash flow, but also the profitability and balance sheet effects of the alternatives.

For instance, we may plan to buy a new machine over the coming year. At first, we may assume that it is going to be financed purely from within the bank current account. But after seeing the cash flow effects of this we may then go back to the original plan and check the effects of using some other form of finance.

What this means is that although we may have in mind the assets or expenditures that we are going to have to finance: what we specifically choose to finance depends on how these things fit within the overall context of the business.

Nevertheless, within this process we can identify more generally the sorts of expenditures that we need to finance: perhaps we are acquiring a whole business, or it may be some more land and growing stock, or putting up a building, investing in roading, machines, equipment, staff training, material inputs, paying off existing debts or a combination of these things. And this identification of types of expenditure is important because what we use the money for is a major determinant of what form of finance is appropriate.

## Characteristics

Having in mind what we need to finance, we then proceed to look at what forms of finance are available. But before doing so, we need some guidelines as to what we should be looking for - what characteristics should the finance have in order to most aptly satisfy the needs of the forest business? This section lists a number of these characteristics, or rather, some tips on what to look for.

1.   'There are many ways of felling a tree'.
Remember that there may be a number of ways of financing a particular need; which is the best depends upon the particular circumstances.

2.   'Horses for courses'
The finance should fit in with the asset, particularly in terms of its lifetime and the cash flows arising from its use. For instance, unless there is a very good reason, do not take out a five-year loan to finance purchase of land and a stand of trees which will take much longer to pay back, nor agree to repay on a monthly basis when revenues only arrive annually.

3.   Cost
Obviously, one of the chief characteristics to look for is that of low cost. However, the cost is not always apparent or easy to gauge. Perhaps the best way of comparing costs of alternatives is to construct a cash flow budget for the lifetime of the finance: this is effectively a detailed DCF table. From this, the terminal value or the NPV will allow comparison of costs.

When considering particular 'products' from financial institutions (loans, lease, mortgage, etc.) the cost of borrowing is usually provided, but may be expressed in a confusing way. For instance, 'flat rate', 'rental', or 'interest rate' do not give a measure of cost which is comparable with other products. Furthermore, there may be other items in the 'small print' which add extra costs. To allow fair comparison, for a particular financial product we can calculate its **annual percentage rate** or APR. This is the true rate of interest calculated using DCF in the same way as one calculates the IRR, but as a rate *paid* instead of a rate *earned*. The calculations are carried out in the same way as for the forwarder example in the last chapter; we will see how it can be done for a finance example later in this chapter.

4.   Flexibility
The finance should be sufficiently flexible in terms of what it is used for and when it is repaid. In some situations and for some assets we may not be so concerned that the funds are rigidly tied to the asset, but in others (having cash available to meet short-term and perhaps unforeseen, debts, for instance) this may be important.

5.   Independence
The manager and owner of the business would probably prefer to be free to decide how they use the funds at their disposal, but some forms of finance may involve interference by those who are providing it. An overdraft, for instance, may involve having to satisfy the bank manager, before the funds are granted, that certain conditions are met, but after that, there is a certain amount of freedom regarding how the money is used, as long as the overdraft conditions are adhered to. A family loan, on the other hand, may be interest free, but granny or uncle may want to be a 'back seat driver'.

6.   Privacy
Many people value their privacy, particularly as regards their financial affairs. But if funds are sought from outside the immediate family, some degree of privacy is lost. This leads to some individuals foregoing extra funds or only using sources where their financial affairs do not enter the public domain. This may seem strange, but in Britain, for instance, where one does not ask adults their age, salary, wealth or waist size, privacy is a very real factor which must be taken into account!

7.   Control
Although the forest manager may enjoy the flexibility of some forms of finance, that very flexibility can become a trap if provisions are not carefully made for repayment. Students know how easy it is to use an overdraft as a bottomless pit which can then spiral out of control. If, instead, one knows that regular repayments or dividends have to be met, then it is more likely that the funds will be carefully used and monitored.

8.   Security

Very often, to obtain finance it will be necessary to provide security: some title to assets or guarantee which the supplier of funds can claim if repayments are not met or if the business gets into difficulties. Other forms of finance may not require security. Generally speaking, however, finance without security will be more costly than that with security, *ceteris paribus*[1].

9.   Bureaucracy

Top of the list of headaches for most managers would be the massive load of paperwork and bureaucracy faced in their day to day activities. When obtaining finance from formal sources there is likely to be an application process involving meetings, form filling and legal agreements, This can be off-putting and have real costs in time spent, delays and paying for help and advice. Nevertheless, this bureaucracy should not be avoided at any cost - a poor vetting procedure or the absence of a legally binding agreement can lead to much higher costs later.

10.   Timeliness

How quickly can finance be obtained? If the procedure for obtaining the finance from one particular source takes too long, there may be a danger of opportunities being lost, and it might be worth going for a more expensive, but speedier option.

11.   Vulnerability

When considering a finance option, the question needs to be asked, "What if I don't pay?" Failure to meet the terms or expectations of those supplying the finance can have severe consequences - the asset financed may be repossessed, the business may be taken over, or even the proprietor's own home and possessions might be seized. The risks of default need to be carefully weighed up before any agreement is signed.

Depending on the situation of the business and the personal preferences of the owner and manager, some of these characteristics might be assigned greater weight than others. Moreover, these characteristics do vary between the different types of finance, so the forest manager needs to understand these characteristics and gauge their importance before making a decision.

## Sources and Types

The sources of finance can be divided into two main areas - internal and external, but within these there are many categories of finance possible. Table 13.1 illustrates the sources and main types of finance available.

---

[1] Economists' favourite phrase meaning: 'with other things being equal'.

**Table 13.1** Finance sources and types.

| source | general type | category | name |
|---|---|---|---|
| internal | personal | own | sole trader |
| | | | partnership |
| | | | company |
| | | family gifts & loans | |
| | business | profit retention | |
| | | sell assets | |
| external | grants | capital and production grants | |
| | equity | company/ corporation | private |
| | | | public |
| | debt | trade credit | |
| | | overdraft | |
| | | bank term loan | short/medium/long |
| | | quasi-loans | lease |
| | | | hire purchase |
| | | mortgage | repayment |
| | | | endowment |

## Internal sources

It would surprise many people to learn that a considerable amount of the money to run businesses, especially small to medium-sized ones, comes from internal sources. By internal we mean from within the business or within the family of the proprietor. An individual may have acquired land and other resources many years ago through purchase, as a reward for work, or through conquest or ancestry and this might be added to by other gifts or loans from wealthy benefactors.

The advantage of using personal or family funds is that often there is no, or very little, charge made for their use: there are no interest or dividend payments expected, unless, for instance, my brother has lent me some money, but in this case the interest rate is likely to be low. However, although the profits may look healthier because of this, when assessing whether it is wise to tie the money up in the business, one must be mindful of their **opportunity cost**: the return or interest rate which they could generate in their next best alternative use. Other advantages of using personal funds to finance the business lie in the retention of privacy and freedom from interference by bank manager or shareholders. But interference may come in another form: if they have provided money or if they feel that some of the money should be theirs, family or friends may want a say in business decisions. Although such problems might appear from the outside to be petty and unimportant, they can be a severe hindrance for the smooth management of the business.

One other problem, namely the lack of limited liability, occurs if the owner of the business is so concerned about privacy and interference by strangers that he or she shuns turning the business into a company. To understand this we need a little explanation as to the legal form that a business can take.

If the proprietor of the business wishes to own the business alone then they will remain as a **sole trader**. Such a business is unincorporated - it is not a company (Hussey, 1995) so the business is not deemed a separate entity from its owner. This is the traditional 'family business' which allows the owner to retain privacy and independence, but limits access to funds.

Similar to the sole trader is the **partnership**. A partnership may be formed if the proprietor wishes to give decision-making powers to, and enable benefits to be shared by, their spouse or other close friend or relation. It may also be done to gain tax advantages, or a partnership can be formed in order to bring in extra skills or funds from outside. The partnership is a legal entity and the partners will often share benefits in proportion to their financial contribution, but, unless there is a 'sleeping partner', decision-making rights will also be shared. However, because both the sole trader and the partnership are unincorporated, the assets and profits are normally considered, for legal and tax purposes, part of the assets and incomes of the individuals owning them, i.e. business and individual fortunes are inextricably mixed. Consequently, if the business is unable to pay its debts, the partners' personal assets as well as the assets of the business can be seized: they have **unlimited liability**. And for tax purposes the income from the business is considered as part of the personal income of the proprietor(s) along with any income they have from other sources.

If the potential problem of unlimited liability and the need to gain access to a wider supply of finance do outweigh the privacy issue, the proprietor or partners can form a company or corporation. This will be dealt with in the section on external finance later in the chapter.

Apart from family fortunes, another key way in which a business might expand is by making profits which, instead of all being paid as dividends or withdrawn by the owner, are retained within the business, thus enabling the acquisition of additional assets. Another means of obtaining finance for further expenditure is by selling assets, although this does not really mean extra funds, but rather a change of use or conversion of assets from one form (e.g. selling a machine) to another (e.g. to pay for seedlings and fertiliser). Again, the use of funds is apparently costless, but not when the opportunity costs are accounted for. And interference may occur, but in a slightly different form: family members may complain or shareholders may revolt if profits are ploughed back into the business instead of being used to fund acceptable levels of private drawings or dividends!

Internal funds would often be preferable to external sources, particularly because of their low cost. However, in the circumstances in which they are not available, external funding must be sought.

**External sources**

There are three types of external finance: grants, **equity** (funds obtained from the issue of ordinary shares) and **debt** (borrowing from financial institutions).

*Grants*

Grants are usually provided by government in the form of production or capital grants. Production grants include planting grants and crop management grants. Grants may also be provided for capital expenditure such as roading, fencing or the provision of environmental or recreational amenities.

Grants are for specific purposes so the recipient has little flexibility as to how the funding money is spent, and they are often only paid in arrears (after the expenditure has been incurred). Nevertheless, they can provide a sizeable amount of finance for certain items.

*Equity*

Businesses can be organised in a number of ways, although this will vary somewhat from one country to the next. The simplest form of business is the sole trader which was, along with partnerships, discussed earlier. What could be viewed as a natural progression from these unincorporated forms of business is the company or corporation. Normally this will give limited liability, separate tax treatment for the organisation as distinct from the individual, and enables the business to appeal for funds more widely than the narrow group of family, friends and colleagues.

A **company** can be defined as

"an incorporated body recognised by law as having an existence entirely independent from that of its members and directors"

(Hussey, 1995, p. 81)

When a company or corporation (although that can have a rather wider definition) is set up **shares** are issued to those who have contributed the finance necessary for its establishment. It is therefore owned by its shareholders, while it is run by its directors and managers under them.

If further finance is required the company can issue additional shares either to existing shareholders or to a wider public. However, a **private company** is limited in the number of shareholders it may have (in the UK the maximum is 50) and only a **public company** (public limited company or plc) can appeal for funds in the wider market known as the stock exchange. **Ordinary shares** confer the right of their holder to receive dividends, a pay-out from profits, if and when they are paid. Such shares also give voting rights, so that if the financial performance of the company is not satisfactory and insufficient dividends are paid, directors are likely to be voted out of office.

The company may also issue **preference shares**, which, as their name suggests, confer a right to receipt of dividends before ordinary shareholders, but do not give voting rights. However, strictly speaking, equity is only the value of the ordinary shares issued.

A third category of share is known as a **debenture**, although this is really a form of debt as it is a type of long-term loan which, unlike shares, has to be repaid and usually obliges the company to pay a fixed rate of interest (Hussey, 1995).

Turning the business into a company has two major advantages. Firstly, as we have already seen, there is limited liability. Secondly, there is access to much greater funds, constrained by the maximum number of shareholders for the private company, but for the public company there is no limit. Companies may also be formed because of tax advantages; the differences between tax on companies and individuals will be discussed in the next chapter.

On the other hand, with the formation of the company, particularly if it goes public, the treasured privacy is lost and the original owner of the business may lose control if so many shares are issued that more than 50% of the shares are owned by others.

Before we move on to consider debt, there is one other form of business organisation that deserves mention: the **co-operative**. Although not a company, the co-operative is similar in certain respects: it is formed with a legally binding agreement, is a separate entity and conveys limited liability. The co-operative members contribute funds (in money or in kind), make decisions about its management and have voting powers, although each member has one vote rather than a number in proportion to their financial contribution.

In a forestry context however, a co-operative would probably not be formed with the major objective being to obtain greater funds[2]. Nor would forestry businesses or estates amalgamate all of their assets with others as a single entity to carry out all of their business within the co-operative. Rather forestry businesses might contribute some funds towards the formation of a co-operative in order to gain economies of scale in some aspect of the business. For instance, they may join a buying co-operative to gain bulk buying clout in the purchase of fuel or other inputs, a training co-operative so as to afford the training of groups of forest workers, a machinery ring to share specialist and expensive machinery, an advisory co-operative so as to employ a forest science graduate to advise on various aspects of silviculture, or a marketing co-operative to employ a marketing manager and again gain advantages from selling larger amounts of timber.

Strictly speaking, therefore, the formation of a co-operative is not usually a means of gaining extra funds, but other benefits. And the co-operative is not something that has really taken hold of the imagination of foresters throughout the world, perhaps because of the feared loss of independence and privacy.

*Debt*

Forming a company and issuing shares takes time. If funds are needed more quickly and/or if the business owner wishes to avoid interference, then debt

---

[2] Japan being one exception.

might be viewed as a preferable source.

The market for borrowed money is, in many countries, extremely sophisticated with the banks, the main suppliers, 'selling' a wide range of 'products' tailored to meet the needs of the 'customers'. Some of the main 'products' are shown under the debt section of Table 13.1 where they are listed, more or less, in order of length of life.

The form of debt with the shortest life is probably **trade credit** which arises when the forest manager purchases material inputs, but does not pay for them immediately. Normally, the bill should be paid within a month, after which quite a hefty interest charge is added. Therefore, it might be worth delaying payment for up to a month, as during that period we are getting interest free credit, but delaying beyond that period is not wise. Earlier we came across the term trade creditors which refers to the amount of trade credit outstanding at a point in time.

Another form of borrowing which is intended to be short term, but which may be allowed to stretch out over several years is **bank overdraft**. We first came across this term, meaning a negative bank current account balance, when dealing with cash flow. Overdraft is an extremely flexible form of finance since, once it has been arranged with the bank, it can be used to pay for anything within the limit of the maximum amount and period agreed. Furthermore, the interest rate is often relatively attractive, depending upon the bank's view of the size, security and riskiness of the borrower. You might think that discovering the interest rate would be quite straightforward - just ask the bank manager. The rate might be quoted as so many percent (probably from 1 to 3% in the UK) over the bank base rate.

So, if the base rate is 6% and we pay 2% over base, then surely the overdraft interest rate is 8%?

Not exactly.

You see, the banks normally calculate interest on overdraft on a daily basis, but only charge it to your account each month or quarter. Now, the way they calculate the monthly or quarterly rate is by dividing the quoted rate, say 8%, by 12 or 4. Because of the compounding effect of charging interest in one period, on accumulated interest from the previous period, the APR is higher than the quoted rate. It won't differ by that much, but if you want to calculate the APR the formula is:

$$APR = \left(1 + \frac{\text{decimal interest rate}}{\text{periods}}\right)^{\text{periods}} - 1$$

For example 8% charged monthly gives an APR of:

$$APR = \left(1 + \frac{0.08}{12}\right)^{12} - 1 = 8.3\%$$

. . . not much different.

Incidentally, with overdraft, trade credit or any other debt, you can simply ask the company providing the finance to quote the APR and they are legally obliged to do so, although it might take them a little time to find out what it is!

Overdraft can be one of the cheapest forms of debt, but it does have its drawbacks. Although many businesses use overdraft as a medium- or even long-term source of finance, and banks may allow land-owning businesses to do so because of the security inherent in the land, it is not intended nor wise to use it in this way. In theory, but rarely in practice, an overdraft can be called in within a few days, i.e. the borrower would have to clear the overdraft within that period, which could leave the business in an extremely dangerous liquidity position. Even if this does not occur, if overdraft is used to finance longer term asset purchase (not applying the 'horses for courses' idea) then there is less money available to meet the varying short term needs, and again, liquidity difficulties may arise (see Fig. 13.1).

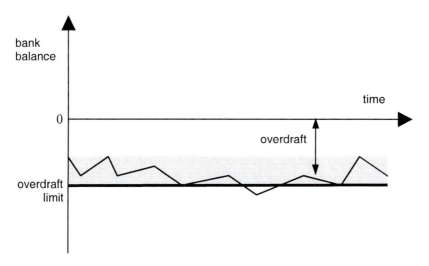

**Fig. 13.1**  Overdraft - constant and variable elements

What we see in Fig. 13.1 is a time profile of the bank current account. The gap between zero and the line labelled overdraft limit shows how much can be borrowed on overdraft and the jagged line shows the actual amount overdrawn. Note, however, that in this situation the overdraft is never completely cleared; in fact, it is never reduced above the shaded area. In effect, therefore, the non-shaded part of the overdraft is a constant, or long-term element, and the amount available for short-term needs consists only of the amount within the shaded area.

One other problem with overdraft is due to its flexibility; flexibility, that is, in terms of what it is used for and when it is paid back. Because the borrowing is not linked to a specific asset, which has a predictable lifetime and, possibly, benefit stream arising from its use, there is no repayment schedule tied to it. Consequently, it is easy to let slip any proposed repayment and to lose control. And with that loss of control can come the "spending a little more won't make much difference" attitude which leads to the treatment of overdraft as a bottomless pit, particularly if the bank manager is fairly lax on overdraft limits and repayments because of the perceived security of the land assets.

Less flexible, but more structured, are **bank term loans**, which can have terms of anything from three months to 20 years or more. These loans are contractual arrangements with a set term and repayment schedule and may have a fixed rate of interest or a rate that varies with the bank's base rate. They also tend to be linked to the purchase of a specific asset. For instance, a short-term loan (with a specific product title like 'Growloan') may be used for fertiliser purchase, a medium-term loan for the purchase of a forwarder, and a long-term loan for erection of a building. The contract between the borrower and lender has the advantage that, as long as repayments are met as scheduled, the money cannot be called in, and with the added certainty of term and repayment timings, as well as the option of a fixed interest rate, details of the loan can be known from the outset. The interest rate may be somewhat higher than that for overdraft and there is a lack of flexibility, but their use instead of overdraft is advisable in all but those situations where a short-term cash reserve is needed.

Alternatives to bank term loans for acquisition of assets with medium-term (say two to eight years) lifetimes have usually arisen to take advantage of tax loopholes. Used mainly for machinery financing, **lease** and **hire purchase** are the main alternatives to bank term loans.

There are two main types of lease. The **operating lease**, which can be the same as **contract hire**, is really just the rental of machinery, and usually the costs of depreciation, repairs, maintenance, insurance and vehicle tax, are covered by the rental charge. Only fuel has to be paid for by the forester, known as the **lessee**. The operating lease is therefore not a means of taking possession of the asset, but of borrowing it for a period.

On the other hand, the **finance lease**, although never giving legal ownership of the machine to the lessee, does so for all practical purposes. Again, there is a contractual arrangement between the financial institution (the *lessor*) and the forester or forest company (the *lessee*). The machine is effectively paid for over the primary period, which may last from two to about five years. Payments occur on a regular (monthly, quarterly, etc.) basis in the form of 'rentals' which are paid in advance, with a number (one twelfth or more) being paid in the form of a deposit at the outset. The rental covers the capital cost of the machine along with interest, and rates may be slightly lower than those for a term loan or if offered at subsidised rates by a machinery dealer, can apparently be as low as 0%. However, the APR may not be quoted unless pursued by the customer, and calculation of the true APR can be clouded by the fact that the apparent low interest is counterbalanced by the absence of a discount (which may reach 30% of the manufacturer's recommended retail price if the machine were to be purchased instead of leased).

The APR may also be calculated without account being taken of what happens at the end of the primary period. For legal and tax purposes the machine cannot be owned by the lessee. Therefore, at the end of the primary period, the machine may be sold (but this should not be to the lessee) and most or all of the proceeds passed on to the forester. Alternatively the forest manager may choose to retain the machine for an indefinite period known as the **secondary period**. To signify that ownership remains with the financial institution a small, 'peppercorn' (or 'peanuts') rental is payable, at something like £1 per £1,000 of the machine's original cost: it is worth finding out, however, whether the rental really is 'peppercorn'.

**Fig. 13.2** Loan, lease and hire purchase may be appropriate for financing machinery. Forwarder in Kielder Forest, England (photo: Colin Price).

If the lessee does own the machine to all intents and purposes, what difference does it make that it is not legally his? One advantage, which was at one time claimed for the lease, was that it did not have to appear on the balance sheet. In other words, you could hide the liability. For reported accounts this practice has now been proscribed (Chopping and Skerratt, 1998). Anyway, trying to fool others about the financial health of the business would not be advocated here, and, for management purposes, one can include the outstanding rentals on the lease as a liability and you may also choose to include the depreciated value of the leased machine as an asset.

Another effect of this ownership position concerns how this is dealt with by the tax authorities. The financial institutions may claim that because they retain ownership they can offset the costs of the machine against company tax and pass on these benefits in the form of lower rentals. Whether this is the case needs to be calculated in each particular case. There will also be an effect on the tax position of the lessee - ownership would have allowed the lessee to offset the cost of the machine and any interest on borrowings to finance its purchase against income or company tax. The lessee could not do this, but would still be able to claim the rentals against tax, which amounts to the same thing. The crucial difference is often in timing - when the different amounts can be used to offset tax influences the net discounted cost. More of this when we deal with tax in the next chapter.

The lessor can be asked to convert the rentals quotation into its APR, but to calculate the true APR, taking account of deposit, primary and secondary period rentals, the refund from sale of the machine and even the effect of tax, requires the use of DCF. There is, however, a shorthand method of calculating the APR (Bright, 1986), albeit ignoring some of the complications just listed:

$$APR = (rental - \frac{1000}{years \times periods}) \times periods \times 0.23$$

For example, for a four-year lease, with monthly 'rentals' of £23.75 per £1,000 machine cost, the APR would be approximately:

$$APR = (23.75 - \frac{1000}{4 \times 12}) \times 12 \times 0.23 = (23.75 - 20.83) \times 2.76 = 8.1\%$$

Not a bad approximation to the correct answer of 8.2% derived using DCF[3] (see Appendix 13.1).

Note that with this form of finance, unlike the trade credit, overdraft and term loan, the forestry business has to provide some of the money for the item itself in the form of payment of one or more rentals in advance. This also to applies to the next 'product', which is hire purchase.

**Hire Purchase (HP)**[4] is similar to leasing in many respects, but the details may be expressed in different terms. Instead of having to pay a number of 'rentals' in advance at the start, with HP a deposit is required and this may be substantial (up to 25% of the price of the machine). Also, instead of 'rentals' being paid in advance, payments are made in arrears. The period and the number of payments will be about the same as for leasing. However, these payments are not usually expressed as 'rentals per £1,000', but as a **flat rate of interest**. Not to be confused with the APR, the flat rate is the amount of interest charged per year per £100 of the machine cost, on top of the capital cost recovery. For instance, taking the lease rental of £23.75 per £1,000 in the example above. This implies that over a year a total payment of £23.75 × 12 = £285 per £1,000 machine cost, would be payable. Out of this the repayment of the capital element would be

---

[3] Do not look for a theoretical justification: there is none. The figure of 0.23 in this formula and the 1.9 in the hire purchase formula in the next section have been arrived at by trial and error.

[4] People who purchased consumer goods using HP used to call it 'the never-never', probably because they seemed to be paying off the debt for a considerable time!

£1,000 ÷ 4 = £250 (since the total amount for the machine would be repaid over four years). The difference, £35, is the interest element, which constitutes a flat rate of £35 per £1,000 or 3.5%. However, whereas in the lease calculation the 'rental' is applied to the whole cost of the machine (e.g. if the machine cost £6,000, the rental would be 6 times the £23.75 charge per month), the HP flat rate applies only to the net amount borrowed (i.e. cost less deposit). Consequently, a different shorthand formula needs to be applied:

$$APR = \text{flat rate} \times 1.9$$

For example, for a three-year hire purchase agreement, with quarterly payments and a flat rate of interest of 4% the APR would be approximately:

$$APR = 4\% \times 1.9 = 7.6\%$$

Again, quite an accurate result: the correct figure is 7.4%, the calculation for which is shown in Appendix 13.1.

Whereas the APR for a lease could be below the rate on a term loan, for HP it may be higher. However, unlike for the lessee, with HP, for tax purposes, the machine is owned by the borrower[5], which may then bestow tax advantages.

In the foregoing discussion we have demarcated lease and HP. However, in practice it is hard to be so clear - there are a lot of 'products' with names like 'Lease Purchase', 'Lease Hire', 'Credit Sale' and so on. Some are forms of lease, and some HP. It is, therefore, important to read the small print to determine just what sort of finance they are and what the specific costs involved are.

Finally, besides long-term loans for the purchase of such assets as land and related property, the forest business may wish to take out a **mortgage**. Actually, this is a form of loan and it is likely that a long-term loan would be in the form of a mortgage, because the latter is simply a loan which is secured on title to land or property. If you have played 'Monopoly', particularly if you have lost, you will know all about mortgaging property! Mortgages can be taken out to purchase the assets on which they are secured, i.e. land and property, or they can be used to purchase other assets, often land and property again, with security provided by the land or property already held. Because of the security, interest rates are likely to be lower than they would be on unsecured loans. Interest rates can be variable (varying with the base rate) or fixed for part or the whole lifetime of the loan - which of these is chosen depends on whether you want the certainty of the fixed rate, you prefer a lower rate in the early stages or if you believe that the lender has misjudged interest rate trends by pitching the fixed rate too high.

Mortgages work just like normal bank term loans, although they will usually involve monthly repayments and not exceed 25 years, although in special

---

[5] There are some legal complexities here since the purchaser may not be allowed to sell the machine until the end of the HP agreement, and there may be some problems in claiming tax allowances immediately.

cases they may do so. This type of mortgage is termed a **repayment mortgage**. Alternatively, although not so common as in the past, a borrower may choose to take out an **endowment mortgage**, particularly if there are tax benefits from doing so. The endowment mortgage, also known as an 'interest only' mortgage, involves only paying interest over its lifetime, but not paying back the capital or principal element until the end. In order to make this final payment, the borrower would normally take out an endowment assurance policy which would guarantee to pay off the principal should the borrower die before the end of the period, and otherwise to provide a lump sum at the end, which, hopefully will be sufficient to meet the amount owing. In Britain endowment polices have gone out of fashion, largely because of a reduction in the inflation rate and thence the nominal rates of return on investments as well as previous unfounded optimism and misjudgement on the part of companies offering endowment policies.

Mortgages are usually tied to particular assets, but are unlikely to be available for the whole of the cost of the assets concerned - the borrower will probably have to provide a substantial proportion of the cost him or herself.


## Menzies Example

Douglas wishes to review the finance position of the business before proceeding to consider future financing options. The first step, then, is to look at the most recent balance sheet: if you refer back to Table 10.14 you will be able to see the detail on which Douglas bases his review.

From the latest figures Douglas first calculates the value of all assets: this is the sum of Total Fixed Assets (£3,359,503) and Total Current Assets (£8,798), £3,368,301 altogether. Where does the money come from to finance all of this? Going down the list, Douglas notes that the overdraft which was outstanding at the start of the year, has now been cleared, so the only liabilities are a mere £104 for trade creditors and an outstanding loan of £12,951. So the remainder, (£3,355,246), shown under Shareholders' Funds, belongs to, and is therefore supplied by, the owners of the business. In fact, if you look more closely, you will see that the shareholders (the Orffly-Porshes) have provided less than two-thirds of that (£2.1 million) the remainder being profits ploughed back into the business over a number of years.

The finance position of the business is therefore, as the net worth or shareholders' funds figure suggests, highly favourable, being virtually independent of debt and with the family not reliant on the financial input of a wider group of shareholders. It does mean, however, that there is probably a lot of leeway for Douglas to use borrowed funds should he spot potentially lucrative investment opportunities (as long as the O-Ps agree, of course).

One such investment which Douglas planned to make, although he avoided checking on whether it would be likely to be a worthwhile one, was the replacement of his four-wheel-drive vehicle, costing an estimated £16,000 (see Table 6.7). Although he had decided to make the purchase from the cash reserves available, leasing was available as an alternative. This involved 12 quarterly rentals of £87 per 1,000 payable in advance, with 98% of the salvage value returned to the lessee.

To calculate the APR of the lease, Douglas constructs a DCF table (Table 13.2). The costs are the quarterly leasing rentals as well as the salvage value (which he estimates at £6,000) foregone at the end of the third year (quarter 12). The benefits are the initial costs saved (£16,000) and the net salvage value (98%) at the end. Although he could buy the vehicle from cash reserves, he uses a discount rate of 8% since this is his estimate of the opportunity cost of that money[6].

**Table 13.2** Calculating the cost of leasing.

| time | cost | benefit | net cost | disc.factor @ 8%/yr = 1.94%/qtr | present value | disc.factor @ 3%/yr = 0.74%/qtr | present value |
|---|---|---|---|---|---|---|---|
| qtrs | £ | £ | £ | £ | £ | £ | £ |
| 0 | 1392 | 16000 | -14608 | 1.000 | -14608 | 1.000 | -14608 |
| 1 | 1392 | 0 | 1392 | 0.981 | 1366 | 0.993 | 1382 |
| 2 | 1392 | 0 | 1392 | 0.962 | 1339 | 0.985 | 1371 |
| 3 | 1392 | 0 | 1392 | 0.944 | 1314 | 0.978 | 1361 |
| 4 | 1392 | 0 | 1392 | 0.926 | 1289 | 0.971 | 1352 |
| 5 | 1392 | 0 | 1392 | 0.908 | 1264 | 0.964 | 1342 |
| 6 | 1392 | 0 | 1392 | 0.891 | 1240 | 0.957 | 1332 |
| 7 | 1392 | 0 | 1392 | 0.874 | 1217 | 0.950 | 1322 |
| 8 | 1392 | 0 | 1392 | 0.857 | 1193 | 0.943 | 1313 |
| 9 | 1392 | 0 | 1392 | 0.841 | 1171 | 0.936 | 1303 |
| 10 | 1392 | 0 | 1392 | 0.825 | 1148 | 0.929 | 1293 |
| 11 | 1392 | 0 | 1392 | 0.809 | 1126 | 0.922 | 1283 |
| 12 | 6000 | 5880 | 120 | 0.794 | 95 | 0.915 | 110 |
| | | | | **NDC** | **-846** | **NDC** | **157** |

Calculating the Net Discounted Cost (NDC) in the same way as the NPV[7], the answer is -£846, that is, it costs less to lease than to purchase. But what is the APR? Since the APR is effectively the IRR in this context, we should calculate it in the normal way. So far, we have one discount rate and one NDC. We now need a second discount rate and a second NDC. To obtain an estimate of the APR, which can be used as the second discount rate, we simply use the shorthand formula for leasing, thus:

$$\text{APR} = (87 - \frac{1000}{3 \times 4}) \times 4 \times 0.23 = (87 - 83.33) \times 0.92 = 3.3\%$$

---

[6] Note that this is a nominal rate, since the lease charges are in nominal terms - those are the amounts which are actually paid. Note also that the estimate of the salvage value should also be in nominal terms, i.e. what the machine is actually expected to be sold for in 3 year's time.

[7] Except that, because we are calculating the *cost* of leasing relative to purchasing, the net cost (cost minus benefit) is used instead of net benefit. A negative NDC therefore implies a negative cost, which is, in fact, a benefit.

A second NDC can now be obtained by using 3% (as the nearest integer value) as the discount rate - Table 13.2 shows the result, £157.

The final step is to apply the interpolation formula from Chapter 12, replacing NPV with NDC:

$$\text{IRR} \equiv \text{APR} = r_1 + (r_2 - r_1) \times \frac{\text{NDC}}{(\text{NDC}_1 - \text{NDC}_2)}$$

which gives:

$$\text{APR} = 8\% + (3\% - 8\%) \times \frac{-846}{-846 - 157} = 8\% + (-5\%) \times 0.843 = 3.7\%$$

"Subsidised leasing really is cheap", says Douglas to himself when he sees this result. "But wait a minute. Would I have been able to obtain a discount if I had driven a hard bargain for cash payment?" And when he thinks further, he is sure that he could obtain a discount of at least 10%. But how should he deal with this in the DCF calculations?

The only thing that changes as far as extra costs and benefits are concerned is the benefit at the start in terms of the initial amount which he avoids paying out when going for the leasing option. Instead of £16,000, this figure now drops by 10% to £14,400. Altering this one figure in Table 13.2 changes the two NDC figures to £754 and £1,757 for the discount rates of 8% and 3% respectively. This suggests, therefore, that the break-even discount rate (the APR) is higher than 8%. Let's see from the formula:

$$\text{APR} = 8\% + (3\% - 8\%) \times \frac{754}{(754 - 1757)} = 8\% + (-5\%) \times -0.752 = 11.8\%$$

Douglas should really carry out another iteration in order to get a more accurate answer (you might like to try it yourself by using 11.8 or 12% as a discount rate and then using the results in the interpolation formula). Had he done so, he would have obtained a figure of 12.3%, although his rounded up figure of 12% was near enough to tell him that with the assumption of a discount for cash, leasing becomes relatively expensive.

The conclusion that Douglas comes to here is that if he can obtain a reasonable discount for cash, then he should not go for the leasing option. However, he also realises that he should take each case on its merits and, furthermore, he has not considered the effects of tax on the relative costs. We must leave this issue aside until we have considered taxation in the next chapter.

## Appendix 13.1   APR Formulae for Lease and HP

We have seen that shorthand formulae exist to give approximate APRs for lease and HP. However, to obtain *accurate* APRs we must use DCF. Nevertheless, in the absence of complications (refund, secondary periods, etc.) it is possible to obtain accurate answers by the use of formulae instead of constructing a DCF table. The correct answer would be obtained by iteration: a good starting point would be the approximation derived from the shorthand formula.

The APR for leasing is that interest rate derived from that value of r which satisfies the formula:

$$1,000 - (\text{advance rentals} \times \text{rental}) - \text{rental} \times \left[ \frac{(1+r)^{\text{rentalsleft}} - 1}{(1+r)^{\text{rentalsleft}} \times r} \right] = 0$$

where: advance rentals = number of rentals paid in advance; rental = the rental payment per £1.000 borrowed; rentals left = total rentals minus advance rentals; and r = decimal interest rate on a *period* basis corrected to an annual decimal rate using the formula:

$$\text{APR} = (1+r)^{\text{periods/yr.}} - 1$$

where periods/yr is the number of periods used per year to cover the frequency of rentals. Note also, that if by paying cash we could obtain a discount, we would subtract this percentage from the 1,000 in the formula[8].

In the leasing example in the text, with rentals of £23.75 per month over four years, and assuming four advance payments (i.e. a 1/12 deposit), the formula would be satisfied by an interest rate of 0.66% per month, thus:

$$1000 - 4 \times 23.75 - 23.75 \times \frac{(1.0066)^{44} - 1}{(1.0066)^{44} \times 0.0066} = 1000 - 95 - 23.75 \times 38.08 \approx 0$$

The APR is then $(1.0066)^{12} - 1 = 8.2\%$

Similarly, the formula for hire purchase is:

$$1 - \left( \frac{1}{\text{total periods}} + \frac{\text{flat rate}}{\text{periods / yr}} \right) \times \frac{(1+r)^{\text{total periods}} - 1}{(1+r)^{\text{total periods}} \times r} = 0$$

where total periods = periods/year × years; and flat rate = flat rate of interest expressed as a decimal.

---

[8] For instance, if a 20% discount could be obtained if the machine were purchased, then instead of 1000 in the formula, 800 would be used.

Again, if a discount could be obtained for outright payment, then the first figure 1 in the formula should be reduced by the percentage discount.

In the hire purchase example in the text, with a flat rate of 4%, a three-year agreement and quarterly payment, the rate, r, which satisfies the formula is 1.79%, thus:

$$1 - \left( \frac{1}{3 \times 4} + \frac{0.4}{4} \right) \times \frac{(1.0179)^{12} - 1}{(1.0179)^{12} \times 0.0179} = 1 - 0.0933 \times 10.713 \approx 0$$

The APR is then $(1.0179)^4 - 1 = 7.4\%$.

# Chapter 14

# Taxation

It would not be right to complete a book on forestry budgets and accounts without dealing with taxation. Tax can affect profitability, liquidity and stability, and much time and effort is spent on trying to reduce the tax burden on a business and its owners. In fact, decisions may even be taken with regard to the forestry business to minimise the tax burden in another, unrelated business or within the personal affairs of the proprietor.

However, it would be foolish to write too much concerning the detail of taxation and tax planning, since the author is not qualified to do so and the details of taxation can vary so much over time and between countries that much of what was said would not be likely to be relevant to many readers. What should be useful, however, are some general hints and principles, so this will be the focus of attention here.

The first part of this short chapter will, therefore, be concerned with some general points about taxation as it affects the forestry business. We next look at the main types of taxes affecting forestry, and then finish with consideration of its effects and how they might be estimated. But, before we begin, it must be emphasised that a lot of money can be lost if tax affairs are not carefully dealt with, and therefore the forest manager and owner should seek expert advice about their own particular situation.

## General Points

1.   Taxation has negative financial effects...usually!
It may be stating the obvious, but taxation is likely to have a negative effect on cash flow, and via cash flow, on retained profits and the size of the shareholders' stake in the business. Consequently, tax is likely to make the financial situation

worse than would appear if it were not brought into the calculations, and this must be kept in mind when budgeting.

However, when comparing options, because the effects of tax may vary, it may make one option relatively *more* profitable than another. For instance, tax effects may make leasing cheaper than loan in some circumstances, or because of different and more favourable tax treatment, investing money in forestry might bring advantages over investment in industry.

2.   Tax aversion

Some people do not like the idea of paying tax and go to enormous lengths to avoid paying it, but great care should be taken lest rash decisions are made simply to keep financial gains out of the hands of the 'tax man'. Decisions should be made in the light of the objectives of the organisation; tax effects will come into those decisions, but should rarely be allowed to drive the process.

3.   Tax evasion *versus* tax avoidance

Tax evasion is not only wrong, it is also illegal. Tax avoidance, however, is neither, and it is common for businesses to spend a good deal of time and money on finding legal ways of minimising the amount of tax paid. The forest manager can gain an understanding of the rules, such as what allowances can be claimed and how assets might be valued, but the complexities of the rules and loopholes and how they might be used to the best advantage of the business are only likely to be understood by experts who are dealing with such matters on a daily basis.

4.   Tax Returns

For individuals and companies there may be, annually and sporadically, a sizeable amount of time needing to be spent on providing information to tax authorities. And the onus may well be on the individual and the company to volunteer such information rather than waiting to be asked, with penalties for those who do not or who provide incorrect information. It is, therefore, worth not only planning in order to minimise tax, but also planning to provide tax information, rather than waiting until the last minute.

# Types of tax

There are a number different types of taxation; here we will concentrate on those that may be most important from the viewpoint of the forest manager and the forest owner, namely:

1.   Sales and purchase taxes
2.   Production levies
3.   Income and profits taxes
4.   Tax on inheritance
5.   Wealth tax

6.   Tax on inflationary gains on assets

1.   Sales and purchase taxes

Taxes, duties and levies may be charged on items sold or inputs purchased (or both in the case of value added tax) Such indirect taxes may be on all items across the board or only on specific items, such as all fuel, on just certain types of fuel, or on certain imports or exports, with others exempted. Certain individuals or organisations may also be exempted. There may also be varying rates applied to different items or in different locations.

Such taxes will normally make costs higher or revenues lower. However, if taxes are paid but refunds claimable later, there may be no apparent net cost, but there can be a cost because of extra interest charges incurred in the period between payment and refund. The effect may not even be obviously financial: if the business effectively has to act as the government's tax collecting agent or if recording or other administration required entails bureaucracy, then the disruption, delay and additional staff time can be seen as costs even if they do not have a readily measurable financial impact on the business.

2.   Production levies

Royalties payable for logging concessions are similar to sales taxes in that they reduce the revenue arising from the harvest and sale of timber. And like the taxes above, there is little that can be done to avoid such taxes. Their incidence may affect the courses of action which might be chosen by the forest manager, but otherwise they are best treated as a fact of life which must be factored into the calculations.

3.   Income and profits taxes

These are taxes on incomes of individuals and profits of companies. As we saw in Chapter 13, the forest business can be run in an unincorporated form (the sole trader or partnership) or as a company. And the government's tax authorities will deal with the profits from these two forms of business in different ways. The profits of the unincorporated business will be treated as part of the sole trader's or partners' personal incomes and **income tax** will be levied on the whole of this income. Income tax is therefore a tax on the income of the private individual.

On the other hand, if the forest business has been 'incorporated' (turned into a company), the tax authorities will assess only the profits of the business (before distribution) for **company** or **corporation tax**. Individuals who work for the company will pay income tax on the wages or salary they receive from the company and shareholders will also pay income tax on dividends received, but all of this is entirely separate from the tax levied on the company as an entity.

Income and corporation taxes will generally lead to lower profits[1], but there are various allowances which can be used to reduce the amount of taxable

---

[1] They may also effectively lead to lower losses too, since any loss may, in certain circumstances, be set against profits from the previous or following year, or profits from associated businesses.

income or profit. For instance, individuals may have a 'personal allowance' and the business may also be able to claim 'capital (depreciation) allowances' relating to buildings, machinery and equipment.

Conversely, certain costs are not allowable against tax so must be excluded from the profit calculations. The portion of the cost of a company vehicle and fuel which is assessed as being used for private purposes by the employee is excluded, as also are depreciation charges, since the capital allowance amounts to the same thing.

There may be a single tax rate applied to all taxable income or profits, or there may be a series of tax bands, so that as profits rise, additional amounts may be taxed at a higher rate. Thus we can talk about the average rate of tax, which is the total amount of tax payable divided by the profit, and the marginal rate of tax, which is the tax paid on the last, or extra £1, of profit. The general policy of the business, such as whether to trade as a partnership or a company, is likely to be influenced by the average expected tax rate, but decisions about specific investments, such as the purchase of a forwarder, will be influenced by the marginal tax rate.

One final point concerning income and profits taxes relates to the time delay between when the profits are generated and when the resulting tax is paid. For calculation of tax effects it would be very convenient to assume that tax is levied instantly, but this is rarely the case. In fact, the **tax lag**, as it can be called, may be a year or more. This is good for the tax payer, but complicates the calculations (as you will see if you read Appendix 14.1) and possibly the required record keeping. The net effect of tax lags is to dampen the effect of tax. Why? Because, as we discussed in Chapter 4, money in the future is worth less to us than money today.

The foregoing may seem to have been a waste of breath, or rather, ink, from the viewpoint of British forest owners and managers since income and corporation tax are not currently levied on timber sales, neither can tax relief be claimed on forestry costs. However, since the situation in Britain is likely to change, and because tax regimes elsewhere may be very different, the ink has not been wasted.

4.   Tax on inheritance

Governments may levy a tax on individuals who have received gifts from another individual at or within a few years of death. As with income and profits taxes there are allowances and certain transfers are exempt and the tax may be at a single rate or in bands. Exemption, or a considerable amount of relief (reduction in proportion of the value liable to tax), is likely to be given for business assets.

As inheritance tax is levied on individuals it is not of direct relevance to the forest business, but the actions of the owner or major shareholder to reduce liability to this tax may have major effects on the business. In fact, if not adequately planned for, inheritance tax can put a business out of business.

5.   Wealth tax

Taxes on inheritance and transfers are forms of tax on the wealth of an individual passed on to others. However, a wealth tax may be levied, not at death or on transfer, but on an annual basis. Such a tax is levied on the *net worth* of the individual. As with other taxes, there can be exemptions, different tax rates, and even an upper limit above which no further tax is levied. The Netherlands and India currently have wealth taxes in force.

6.   Tax on inflationary gains on assets

An individual may make a 'windfall' gain by selling an asset for much more than the cost of purchase. If the gain is proportionately greater than the general rate of inflation over the same period, then a real gain will have been made. The government may apply a 'capital gains tax' on such gains when the asset is sold or passed on to another individual. Again, allowances and reliefs are available, particularly if the item is a business asset which is retained, rather than sold by the recipient (this is called 'roll-over relief'). The taxable amount is added to income from other sources. Such 'capital gains' taxes are also applied to companies, the amount of gain being added to profits and taxed under company taxation.

# Tax Effects

Although income and corporation tax will generally lower profits, as was pointed out at the start of the chapter, tax can make certain options relatively more profitable than others. One of the key reasons for this, particularly in forestry, is time - different investments, different courses of action for the business, will have different cash flows at different points in time associated with them, and this will then influence the amounts and timings of the tax levied.

The taxes which are of particular significance to the forestry business itself are the taxes on profits; namely income tax and company (or corporation) tax. It is helpful to trace, firstly, the tax effects of the overall activities of the forestry business, and secondly, the effects of a particular investment or activity.

### Tax effects of overall activities

Profits taxes are levied on profits so the first place to look for the effects is the Profit and Loss Account. Firstly, however, we have to estimate, if we do not know already, how much tax will be paid. If, for instance profits are estimated at £10,000 (after having subtracted depreciation of machinery and buildings of £6,000), Table 14.1 shows how company tax might be calculated.

Depreciation is first added back, then capital allowances (and any other allowances) are subtracted to give the taxable profit. Company tax is then applied at the appropriate rate, in this case 20%, giving £1,880 tax and an after-tax profit of £8,120.

Table 14.2 shows how this appears in the bottom half of the vertical Profit and Loss Account for a forestry business operating as a company (refer back to Chapter 7 if you need reminding).

**Table 14.1** Calculation of company tax.

|  |  | £ |
|---|---|---|
| profit before tax |  | 10,000 |
| *add back* depreciation |  | 6,000 |
|  |  | 16,000 |
| *less* capital allowances |  |  |
| machinery | £25,000 @20% | 5,000 |
| buildings | £40,000 @ 4% | 1,600 |
| total capital allowances |  | 6,600 |
| taxable profit |  | 9,400 |
| company tax | £9,400 @ 20% | 1,880 |
| net profit |  | 8,120 |

So company tax is subtracted from profits to give 'net profit'. Even if tax has not yet been paid on the profits for the year an estimate should be made and inserted here - it is effectively a type of creditor. Thus company tax reduces the final figure which is available for distribution to shareholders as dividends or retention within the company enabling it to grow. So obviously, if the management wish to pay a certain amount of dividends and retain a certain amount for growth they will have to plan to generate sufficiently high profits, taking account of the estimated tax payable.

**Table 14.2** Section of Profit and Loss Account showing effect of company tax.

|  |  |
|---|---|
| . . . . |  |
| . . . . |  |
| **Profit before Tax** | £10,000 |
| *less* |  |
| Company/Corporation Tax | £1,880 |
| *equals* |  |
| **Net Profit** | £8,120 |

The effect on cash flow may be delayed, depending upon the tax lag. As with profits, the cash flow will be reduced by the amount of the tax, but there may be a further cash flow effect via the extra overdraft interest paid or the reduction in interest received because of the reduction in the bank balance when tax is paid.

Finally, the balance sheet will look worse than it otherwise would, by the amount of the tax and any consequent interest. The balance for the top part of the balance sheet will be reduced relative to the 'no tax' situation because of the worsened bank balance resulting from the payment of tax (and extra interest). This will be mirrored in the balance at the bottom of the balance sheet, since the tax (and extra interest) will reduce retained profits by exactly the same amount.

For forestry businesses operating as sole traders or partnerships, income tax would be calculated slightly differently. Taking the same profit, for instance, the calculations are shown in Table 14.3. Here, however, the business profits would be added to any income from elsewhere.

**Table 14.3** Calculation of income tax for the sole trader or partnership.

|  | £ | £ |
|---|---|---|
| other income |  | 0 |
| profits |  | 10,000 |
| *add back* depreciation |  | 6,000 |
|  |  | 16,000 |
| *less* personal allowances |  |  |
| personal |  | 4,000 |
| married couples' |  | 2,000 |
| total personal allowances |  | 6,000 |
| *less* capital allowances |  |  |
| machinery | 25,000 @25% | 5,000 |
| buildings | 40,000 @ 4% | 1,600 |
| total capital allowances |  | 6,600 |
| taxable profit |  | 3,400 |
| income tax |  |  |
| lower rate | 1,500 @ 10% | 150 |
| middle rate | 1,900 @ 23% | 437 |
| total income tax |  | 587 |

We do not normally talk about 'after-tax' profits in this case since the tax is not strictly levied upon the profits of the business, but on the income of the individual, and would not apply only to profits if there were some other income as well. The effect of tax is the same, however: the after-tax profit can be calculated (£9,413) and the effect on profits, cash flow and balance sheet traced in the same way.

## Tax effects of particular investments

For the tax effects of particular investments things are rather more complicated. For profits, the amount of extra tax paid as a result of the investment would have to be calculated for each year of the life of the investment and then subtracted from the cash flow. The resulting tax-adjusted cash flow would then be discounted and summed to arrive at the profit measures of NPV and IRR.

The effect on cash flow could then be calculated by appending a debt profile to the DCF table as we did in Chapter 12. And to see the effect on the balance sheet we would need to take account of these cash flows as well as estimating, for each year, the written-down values of any assets involved. We will see in the next section how Douglas copes with the calculations. However, the principles can be understood from a simpler example.

Take the investment of £1,000, which yields £4,000 in 12 year's time[2], with additional annual running and management costs. Because taxation deals with *nominal* rather than real cash flows, the figures have to be inflated by the expected inflation rate, and the discount rate should also be in nominal terms. In this example, inflation is 2% and the discount rate is 8%. Tax is charged on all cash flows at 30% with no lag.

Table 14.4 shows the DCF table, along with the debt profile, for the 'pre-tax' situation.

**Table 14.4** Investment pre-tax DCF.

| time | cost | benefit | net benefit | disc. factor | present value | interest[3] | closing balance |
|---|---|---|---|---|---|---|---|
| years | £ | £ | £ | @8% | £ | £ | £ |
| 0 | 1000 | 0 | -1000.00 | 1.000 | -1000.00 | | -1000.00 |
| 1 | 102 | 0 | -102.00 | 0.926 | -94.45 | -80.00 | -1182.00 |
| 2 | 104 | 0 | -104.04 | 0.857 | -89.16 | -94.56 | -1380.60 |
| 3 | 106 | 0 | -106.12 | 0.794 | -84.26 | -110.45 | -1597.17 |
| 4 | 108 | 0 | -108.24 | 0.735 | -79.56 | -127.77 | -1833.19 |
| 5 | 110 | 0 | -110.41 | 0.681 | -75.19 | -146.65 | -2090.25 |
| 6 | 113 | 0 | -112.62 | 0.630 | -70.95 | -167.22 | -2370.08 |
| 7 | 115 | 0 | -114.87 | 0.583 | -66.97 | -189.61 | -2674.56 |
| 8 | 117 | 0 | -117.17 | 0.540 | -63.27 | -213.96 | -3005.69 |
| 9 | 120 | 0 | -119.51 | 0.500 | -59.75 | -240.46 | -3365.66 |
| 10 | 122 | 0 | -121.90 | 0.463 | -56.44 | -269.25 | -3756.81 |
| 11 | 124 | 0 | -124.34 | 0.429 | -53.34 | -300.54 | -4181.69 |
| 12 | 127 | 5073 | 4946.14 | 0.397 | 1963.62 | -334.54 | 429.92 |
| | | | | NPV@8% | 170.26 | | |

The NPV, at a discount rate of 8%, is £170.26, and the IRR is 9.0%.

If we introduce tax, you will see from Table 14.5, that there is an extra cash flow column (for the other costs and benefits refer to Table 14.4) which is calculated by multiplying the pre-tax net benefit by the tax rate. For example, the pre-tax net benefit in year 3 is £106.12. Multiplying this by 30% gives £31.84, which appear under 'tax' for year 3 in Table 14.5. Negative figures show tax paid and positive, tax reduced. These extra costs or benefits are added to the pre-tax cash flow to give the 'post-tax net benefit' column. Obviously, all cash flows

[2] In the example, this figure is inflated over 12 years at 2% to give £4,000 × $1.02^{12}$ = £5,073.

[3] Interest is negative (paid rather than received) over the whole period since the net benefit is negative until the final year.

are reduced by exactly 30% and if we discount at 8% then we get a figure of
£119.51, which is 70% (i.e. 30% taken off) below the pre-tax NPV of £170.26.

However, in the post-tax situation we should also use a post-tax discount
rate (Audsley and Wheeler, 1978). Why? Because, if we could otherwise invest
funds at 8% (the pre-tax discount rate) elsewhere, then in a tax paying situation
the interest received would be subject to tax[4]. Thus, in the absence of any tax
lag, the post-tax discount rate should be:

post-tax discount rate = pre-tax discount rate × (1 - tax rate)

where the tax rate is expressed as a decimal, in this case it gives:

post-tax discount rate = 8% × (1 - 0.3) = 8% × 0.7 = 5.6%

**Table 14.5** Investment after-tax DCF.

| time | tax | post-tax net benefit | discount factor | present value | interest | closing balance |
|---|---|---|---|---|---|---|
| years | £ | £ | @5.6% | £ | £ | £ |
| 0 | 300.00 | -700.00 | 1.000 | -700.00 | | -700.00 |
| 1 | 30.60 | -71.40 | 0.947 | -67.62 | -39.20 | -810.60 |
| 2 | 31.21 | -72.83 | 0.897 | -65.33 | -45.39 | -928.82 |
| 3 | 31.84 | -74.28 | 0.849 | -63.07 | -52.01 | -1055.12 |
| 4 | 32.47 | -75.77 | 0.804 | -60.92 | -59.09 | -1189.98 |
| 5 | 33.12 | -77.29 | 0.762 | -58.89 | -66.64 | -1333.90 |
| 6 | 33.78 | -78.83 | 0.721 | -56.84 | -74.70 | -1487.43 |
| 7 | 34.46 | -80.41 | 0.683 | -54.92 | -83.30 | -1651.14 |
| 8 | 35.15 | -82.02 | 0.647 | -53.06 | -92.46 | -1825.62 |
| 9 | 35.85 | -83.66 | 0.612 | -51.20 | -102.23 | -2011.51 |
| 10 | 36.57 | -85.33 | 0.580 | -49.49 | -112.64 | -2209.48 |
| 11 | 37.30 | -87.04 | 0.549 | -47.78 | -123.73 | -2420.25 |
| 12 | -1483.84 | 3462.30 | 0.520 | 1800.40 | -135.53 | 906.52 |
| | | | NPV@5.6% | 471.28 | | |

If the post-tax discount rate is used the NPV is, surprisingly, £471.28. The
reason for this is, of course, that although the cash flows are reduced by 30% in
the 'after tax' situation, the lower discount rate means that the later cash flows
have a greater impact, particularly the revenue received in the twelfth year. To
satisfy yourself as to what is happening, compare the present value columns in
the two tables.

The higher NPV shows that, in this case, tax makes the investment **more
profitable**, not less[5]. The post-tax IRR stays the same, at 9.02%: not surprising

---

[4] Does this mean that in a tax-paying situation our interest rate is lower? Yes, in a sense, it does
because we can effectively obtain tax relief on interest paid.

[5] If the pre-tax discount rate were lowered, the gap between the NPVs would close and eventually
reverse. In this case, the crossover occurs at a discount rate of about 4.5% (3.15% after tax).

since all of the cash flows are proportionately the same. But again this signifies greater profitability since the gap between this and the post-tax discount rate is greater than in the pre-tax situation (i.e. 9.02% compared to 5.6% rather than 8%).

How can this be; how can tax make the investment more profitable? Well, it does not make the investment more profitable, *per se*, but it does make it more profitable *relative* to the next best alternative. But how have we compared it to the alternative? Via the discount rate, which is the opportunity cost of capital, the rate of return in the next-best alternative use of the money tied up in the investment.

In other words, if we were to compare the post-tax investment cash flows with an alternative use of the funds which did not involve taxation, then the discount rate would stay the same and the NPV would be, as mentioned above, lower by 30% - so it would be *less* profitable, *relative to the next best alternative*. However, if the next best alternative would be affected by tax, then its rate of return falls, and this investment's post-tax NPV would be better, relative to the alternative.

That deals with profit effects. Next, what about cash flow effects? You will have noticed that in the two tables above (14.4 and 14.5), the two final columns gave the debt profile information, which is, in fact, the cash flow picture on an annual basis. To see the effect of tax on the cash flow over the investment life, the two pre- and post-tax closing bank balances can be compared. Figure 14.1 shows the results.

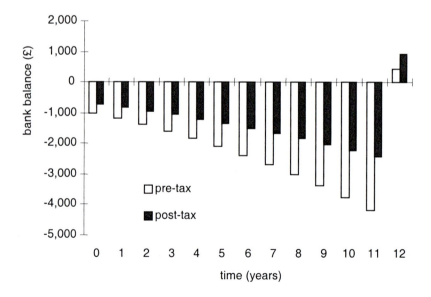

**Fig. 14.1** Pre-tax and post-tax closing balance (tax at 30%).

In the post-tax situation, not only are each of the cash flows smaller, but the interest rate applied is also lower in the post-tax situation. As a result, the closing balance in the latter situation does not reach the same depths of overdraft, and the revenue in year 12 lifts the bank balance to a higher positive terminal value.

Finally, what are the effects on the balance sheet? The investment has two balance sheet items associated with it - the valuation of the assets tied up in it, and the cash balance resulting from it. If the expectation value is used for the valuation then in this example as we move through each year of the lifetime of the investment the valuation gets higher (as we get closer to the final year receipts) while the overdraft gets worse. Nevertheless, because the NPV of the project is profitable, the net effect of these will be positive throughout. Furthermore, because the NPV of the post-tax scenario is greater than the pre-tax scenario, the net effect on the balance sheet will be more favourable in the post-tax case.

Thus we have seen how we might deal with the tax effects on an investment. But what about the tax effects of different finance options?

In principle, the problem can be viewed in the same way as the investment problem. In practice, however, it can be rather difficult to get your head around the problem. Nevertheless, if taken logically, and asking the question, "What if?", the problem need not be insurmountable (see Appendix 14.2).

## Menzies Example

### Tax effects of overall activities

Back in Chapter 10 we saw how Douglas had constructed his accounts. In the Profit and Loss Account the profit before tax was £150,471, yet there was no corporation tax payable on that amount. In Caledonia the government thinks so much of its forestry industry that it exempts forest businesses from corporation tax. As a result Douglas does not have to worry about this. However, it is rumoured that the new government under President Taxum will introduce a 30% rate of tax which will be applicable to forestry, and this will apply to the latest year. Douglas wishes, therefore, to estimate the likely effects of this on the business.

Table 14.6 shows the tax calculation, based on figures from Chapter 10. The figures are then transferred to the P&L Account, the lower part of which is reproduced in Table 14.7.

Although the capital allowances ameliorate the effects somewhat, the imposition of the tax would have a drastic effect on net profit, reducing it by nearly 30%, and after the dividends are subtracted the retained earnings would fall by more than 40%.

As far as the cash flow is concerned, the tax would obviously not work retrospectively on the bank balance since it is normally levied after profits have been made. However, it is likely to affect the coming year's cash flow. Given that the current balance at present is only £8,648, unless there is a substantial inflow of cash during the coming year, payment of tax could lead to a large overdraft.

The tax owed would become a liability in the balance sheet. However, given the size of the Shareholders' Capital (over £3.3 million) this would only serve to reduce it by a little over 1%.

**Table 14.6** Calculation of corporation tax for Menzies Estate.

|  | £ |  | £ |
|---|---|---|---|
| Profit before tax |  |  | 150,236 |
| *add back* depreciation |  |  | 6,960 |
|  |  |  | 157,196 |
| *less* capital allowances |  |  |  |
| machinery | 26,300 | @ 25% | 6,575 |
| equipment | 3,800 | @ 25% | 950 |
| buildings | 56,000 | @ 4% | 2,240 |
| total capital allowances |  |  | 9,765 |
| taxable profit |  |  | 147,431 |
| company tax | 147,666 | @ 30% | 44,229 |
| net profit |  |  | 106,007 |

Douglas is concerned about the reduction in net profit and particularly the possibility of slipping back into overdraft. He needs to monitor the situation carefully and will seek advice from Mr Fiskle, the tax adviser to the business.

**Table 14.7** Effect of proposed Corporation Tax on Menzies Estate profits.

|  | £ |
|---|---|
| PROFIT BEFORE TAX | 150,236 |
| Company/Corporation Tax | 44,229 |
| NET PROFIT | 106,007 |
| dividends | 45,000 |
| Retained Earnings | 61,007 |

## Tax effects of specific investments

In the light of the change of government, Douglas wishes to estimate the potential tax implications of the lease for the four-wheel-drive vehicle. However, Colonel Blight has walked into Douglas' office and has noticed the tax calculations on the table. "If I were to charge the amount you suggested for hiring out the forwarder," he asks, "if that awful man Taxum has his way, what effect will the taxes have on my profits?"

Douglas deals with this one first.

If you go back to Table 12.8 you will see that the forwarder cost £150,000, annual costs totalled £8,100 and the salvage value was forecast to be £40,000. We came up with an hourly charge of £28.91 to give a real return of 10%, for annual usage of 1,200 hours. If we work out the IRR with these costs and benefits, what would it be? 10%. Why? Because we calculated the £28.91 charge to give this return! If we were to calculate the NPV, using a real rate of 6%, however, we would not get a figure of zero (this would only occur for a discount rate of 10%), but £25,049. The question Blighty now wants answered is, "What effect would tax have on the NPV and IRR?"

Table 14.8 shows the original costs and the benefits arising from hiring out the machine (1,200 hours @ £28.91/hour = £34,692). Because we have to carry out the analysis in *nominal* terms for the post-tax scenario, we have done the same in the pre-tax scenario; since Blighty expects inflation under Taxum to average 3%, this rate has been used to inflate costs and benefits. The nominal discount rate of 9.18% has also been used[6]. The figures have been rounded to the nearest whole number to save space (see next page).

Adding the figures in the present value column gives the NPV of £25,070, the same (except for rounding effects) as the NPV calculated using the real rate of 6% in Table 12.8. The IRR is 13.3%. Why not 10%? The DCF in Table 14.8 has been conducted in *nominal* terms, so even the IRR is in nominal terms, i.e. a real rate of 10% combined with inflation at 3%.

**Table 14.8** Pre-tax DCF for forwarder purchase and use.

| time | cost | benefit | net benefit | discount factor | present value |
|------|------|---------|-------------|-----------------|---------------|
| yrs | £* | £* | £ | @9.18% | £ |
| 0 | 150000 | | -150000 | 1.000 | -150000 |
| 1 | 8343 | 35733 | 27390 | 0.916 | 25089 |
| 2 | 8593 | 36805 | 28211 | 0.839 | 23669 |
| 3 | 8851 | 37909 | 29058 | 0.768 | 22316 |
| 4 | 9117 | 39046 | 29930 | 0.704 | 21070 |
| 5 | 9390 | 40218 | 30827 | 0.645 | 19884 |
| 6 | 9672 | 41424 | 31752 | 0.590 | 18734 |
| 7 | 9962 | 91862 | 81900 | 0.541 | 44308 |
| | | | | NPV@ 9.18% | 25070 |

\* inflated at 3% per annum

Table 14.9 shows the post-tax situation. The pre-tax cost and benefit information is transferred from Table 14.8 with an extra column added for the tax calculations. Tax is charged at 30%, with no lag and capital (depreciation), allowances available at the annual rate of 25% of the written down value. So, an

---

[6] i.e. [1.06 × 1.03] - 1 Although we normally do not need to be so accurate, this rate will be used here to show the precise effects. Also, a nominal discount rate of 9.18% instead of the real rate of 6% is used.

immediate capital allowance of £37,500 (£150,000 × 25%) is claimed (time 0), at the end of year 1 the figure is £28,125 ([£150,000 - £37,500] × 25%) and so on. When the machine is sold after seven years, £20,022.58 of allowances remain and these will be used to offset tax on the revenue from the sale of the machine. The after-tax discount rate is 6.43% (i.e. 9.18 × [1 - 0.3]).

**Table 14.9** Tax effects on forwarder purchase and use.

| time | pre-tax net benefit | capital all'nces | taxable income | tax paid | post-tax net benefit | disc. factor @6.43% | present value |
|---|---|---|---|---|---|---|---|
| yrs | £ | £ | £ | £ | £ | | £ |
| 0 | -150000 | 37500 | -37500 | -11250 | -138750 | 1.000 | -138750 |
| 1 | 27390 | 28125 | -735 | -221 | 27610 | 0.940 | 25954 |
| 2 | 28211 | 21094 | 7118 | 2135 | 26076 | 0.883 | 23025 |
| 3 | 29058 | 15820 | 13237 | 3971 | 25087 | 0.830 | 20822 |
| 4 | 29930 | 11865 | 18064 | 5419 | 24510 | 0.779 | 19093 |
| 5 | 30827 | 8899 | 21928 | 6579 | 24249 | 0.732 | 17750 |
| 6 | 31752 | 6674 | 25078 | 7523 | 24229 | 0.688 | 16669 |
| 7 | 81900 | 20023 | 61877 | 18563 | 63337 | 0.647 | 40979 |
| | | | | | | NPV @ 6.43% | 25543 |

The effect of tax is interesting: the post-tax NPV is found to be £25,543, and the IRR can be worked out by iteration as 10.9%. So, as Table 14.10 shows, the NPV is slightly higher than the pre-tax scenario, but the IRR is lower. Do the two measures tell a different story? No, because the post-tax IRR should be compared with the (lower) post-tax discount rate, giving a relatively more favourable comparison than for the pre-tax situation. The conclusion in this instance is that the net effect of tax on profitability is positive, but small.

**Table 14.10** Pre-tax and post-tax DCF results compared.

| | pre-tax | post-tax |
|---|---|---|
| (nominal) discount rate | 9.18% | 6.43% |
| NPV | £25,070 | £25,543 |
| IRR | 13.3% | 10.9% |

Apart from the profitability effects, would tax have an impact upon the feasibility of the investment from a liquidity point of view? The effect on cash flow is shown in Table 14.11 where the pre-tax and post-tax cash flow profiles are displayed together.

Tax tends to reduce the cash flows, both positive and negative and also leads to lower interest charges because even the post-tax interest rate is reduced. Consequently, the negative balance does not reach the same depths early on, but neither does the positive balance reach the same heights at the end. The liquidity effect of the proposed tax is therefore not considerable; it tends to dampen both positive and negative cash flows.

**Table 14.11** Tax effects on forwarder cash flows.

| time | Pre-tax | | Post-tax | |
|------|---------|---------|----------|---------|
| | interest | closing balance | interest | closing balance |
| yrs | £ | £ | £ | £ |
| 0 | | -150000 | | -138750 |
| 1 | -13770 | -136380 | -8916 | -120056 |
| 2 | -12520 | -120688 | -7715 | -101694 |
| 3 | -11079 | -102710 | -6535 | -83143 |
| 4 | -9429 | -82209 | -5343 | -63975 |
| 5 | -7547 | -58929 | -4111 | -43837 |
| 6 | -5410 | -32586 | -2817 | -22426 |
| 7 | -2991 | 46322 | -1441 | 39470 |

Having satisfied Blighty again, Douglas can turn his attention to the other question, namely the effect of tax on the lease of the vehicle. However, because of its complexity this problem has been dealt with in Appendix 14.2.

# Appendix 14.1 Tax Lag Effects

Dealing with tax lags in DCF is fairly straightforward. The only real complication is the discount rate and we will come to that in a minute. Otherwise, we set the DCF table out as normal, listing the cash flows when they occur. The only difference is, of course, that the tax payments or receipts will be inserted with a lag. And if the lag is not a whole unit of a year (one year, two year, etc.), then the DCF will have to be broken into relevant periods of a year. For instance, if the tax lag is 18 months, then the DCF table might be constructed on a half-year basis. And, because of the lag, there will be an extra period or periods beyond the lifetime of the investment.

Taking the investment problem dealt with in Table 14.4 and 14.5 as an example, if we move from a no tax lag to a one-year tax lag position, the DCF table should be adjusted, as Table 14.12 indicates. The pre-tax benefits are the same as in Table 14.4 and the tax figures are the same as in Table 14.5, except that now they occur one year later, and consequently the table ends at time 13 rather than time 12.

But the discount factors are not the same as those used in Table 14.5 since, in the latter, a post-tax (unlagged) discount rate of 5.6% (8% × [1 - 0.3]) was used, but in the latest version a rate of 5.73% replaces it. Why?

For the lagged version the discount rate itself must take account of the tax lag. Audsley and Wheeler (1978) presented the following formula for the lagged, after-tax discount rate:

$$r^* = r \times \left(1 - \frac{t}{(1+r^*)^g}\right)$$

where: r* is the lagged post-tax discount rate; r is the pre-tax discount rate; t is the tax rate; and g is the length of lag.

However, because the answer, r*, is on both the left- and right-hand sides of the equation, a solution requires us to follow a series of iterations.

**Table 14.12** Tax lag effects on investment.

| time | pre-tax net benefits | tax | post-tax net benefits | disc. factor | present value |
|------|------|------|------|------|------|
| years | £ | £ | £ | @5.73% | £ |
| 0 | -1000.00 | | -1000.00 | 1.000 | -1000 |
| 1 | -102.00 | 300.00 | 198.00 | 0.946 | 187.31 |
| 2 | -104.04 | 30.60 | -73.44 | 0.895 | -65.73 |
| 3 | -106.12 | 31.21 | -74.91 | 0.846 | -63.37 |
| 4 | -108.24 | 31.84 | -76.41 | 0.800 | -61.13 |
| 5 | -110.41 | 32.47 | -77.94 | 0.757 | -59.00 |
| 6 | -112.62 | 33.12 | -79.49 | 0.716 | -56.92 |
| 7 | -114.87 | 33.78 | -81.08 | 0.677 | -54.89 |
| 8 | -117.17 | 34.46 | -82.71 | 0.640 | -52.93 |
| 9 | -119.51 | 35.15 | -84.36 | 0.606 | -51.12 |
| 10 | -121.90 | 35.85 | -86.05 | 0.573 | -49.30 |
| 11 | -124.34 | 36.57 | -87.77 | 0.542 | -47.57 |
| 12 | 4946.14 | 37.30 | 4983.44 | 0.512 | 2551.52 |
| 13 | 0.00 | -1483.84 | -1483.84 | 0.485 | -719.66 |
| | | | | NPV@5.73% | 457.20 |

In the example, with a discount rate (r) of 8%, tax at 30% and a one year lag, the iterations, in which the r* on the right-hand side is the estimate of r* obtained from the previous iteration, are:

Iteration 1

$$r^* = 0.08 \times (1 - \frac{0.3}{(1+0.08)^1}) = 0.08 \times (1 - \frac{0.3}{1.08}) = 0.08 \times 0.716 = 5.78\%$$

Iteration 2

$$r^* = 0.08 \times (1 - \frac{0.3}{(1+0.0578)^1}) = 0.08 \times (1 - \frac{0.3}{1.0578}) = 0.08 \times 0.716 = 5.73\%$$

Iteration 3

$$r^* = 0.08 \times (1 - \frac{0.3}{(1+0.0573)^1}) = 0.08 \times (1 - \frac{0.3}{1.0573}) = 0.08 \times 0.716 = 5.73\%$$

Three iterations are sufficient, since the answer has reached a steady state by then. However, we can avoid this iteration process since the following first approximation is often sufficiently accurate:

$$r^* = r \times \left(1 - \frac{t}{(1+(r \times (1-t)))^g}\right)$$

Let us see what answer this approximation formula gives:

$$r^* = 0.08 \times \left(1 - \frac{0.3}{(1+(0.08 \times (1-0.3)))^1}\right)$$

$$= 0.08 \times \left(1 - \frac{0.3}{(1+0.056)^1}\right) = 0.08 \times 0.716 = 5.73\%$$

*Voila!* Of course it will not always be quite this accurate, but generally will be sufficiently so.

Back in Table 14.12, having used the rate of 5.73% to generate the discount factors and thence the present values, the latter can be added to give the NPV of £457.20. This is slightly lower than the £471.28 obtained for the unlagged version, which shows that the lag has the effect of lessening the, relatively beneficial in this case, effects of tax.

## Appendix 14.2  Tax Effects on Finance Options

To show how tax effects can be dealt with when considering different finance alternatives, we will see how Douglas dealt with the question of the lease for the four-wheel-drive vehicle.

Table 13.2 showed the DCF calculations when tax was not an issue. In that case the costs and benefits of leasing compared to purchase were derived immediately without having to resort to 'with' and 'without' calculations first. However, when tax is introduced things become rather complicated. To avoid errors, Douglas sets out the 'with' (lease) and 'without' (purchase) pictures separately and then subtracts the latter from the former.

The 'with' situation involves the 12 payments of £1,392 in advance and the proceeds from the sale of the vehicle after three years, net of the 2% of its value held back by the leasing company. Tax at 30% is paid on the vehicle proceeds, and reclaimable on each of the instalments. However, we are assuming that there is a one year lag from the end of the year in which the relevant cash flows occur. So the tax reclaimed on the instalment at the start (time zero) will be received at the end of one year (end of quarter 4), that on the instalments paid in year 1 (quarters 1-4) will be received at the end of year 2 (end of quarter 8), and so on. Table 14.12 presents the figures; note that, because of the tax lag, 16, rather than 12, quarters are listed.

As an example of how the figures are worked out, take the net benefit in quarter 16, a figure of -£511.20. This arises from the three remaining instalments paid in quarters 9-11, totalling £4,176, subtracted from the money received in quarter 16 from the sale of the vehicle, £5,880. The net cash flow from these transactions is (during the third year) £1,704, which then incurs tax at 30%, which is £511.20 (payable one year later).

**Table 14.12** Vehicle lease ('with') - tax effects.

| time | cost | benefit | taxable income | tax paid | net benefit |
|------|------|---------|----------------|----------|-------------|
| qtrs | £ | £ | £ | £ | £ |
| 0 | 1392 | 0 | 0 | 0.0 | -1392.0 |
| 1 | 1392 | 0 | 0 | 0.0 | -1392.0 |
| 2 | 1392 | 0 | 0 | 0.0 | -1392.0 |
| 3 | 1392 | 0 | 0 | 0.0 | -1392.0 |
| 4 | 1392 | 0 | -1392 | -417.6 | -974.4 |
| 5 | 1392 | 0 | 0 | 0.0 | -1392.0 |
| 6 | 1392 | 0 | 0 | 0.0 | -1392.0 |
| 7 | 1392 | 0 | 0 | 0.0 | -1392.0 |
| 8 | 1392 | 0 | -5568 | -1670.4 | 278.4 |
| 9 | 1392 | 0 | 0 | 0.0 | -1392.0 |
| 10 | 1392 | 0 | 0 | 0.0 | -1392.0 |
| 11 | 1392 | 0 | 0 | 0.0 | -1392.0 |
| 12 | 0 | 5880 | -5568 | -1670.4 | 7550.4 |
| 13 | 0 | 0 | 0 | 0.0 | 0.0 |
| 14 | 0 | 0 | 0 | 0.0 | 0.0 |
| 15 | 0 | 0 | 0 | 0.0 | 0.0 |
| 16 | 0 | 0 | 0 | 511.2 | -511.2 |

The 'without' situation involves an initial outlay of £14,400 (remembering that there was a discount of 10% on the £16,000 vehicle) and a salvage value of £6,000 at the end of year 3. Unlike the leasing option, capital allowances could be claimed against tax at the rate of 25% of the written down value. Table 14.13 shows the results.

To explain, a capital allowance of 25% of £14,400 (i.e. £3,600) is claimed against tax at the end of the first year. Tax at 30% of this (£1,080) is reclaimed. The written down value for tax purposes is £14,400 - £3,600 = £10,800.

This procedure continues until the vehicle is sold. It is assumed that, at the end of the fourth year (quarter 16), with reference being made to the cash flows and allowances for the third year, the remaining capital allowances[7] (£6,075) are used to offset the revenue from the sale of the vehicle (£6,000). This gives -£75 taxable income and results in £22.50 worth of tax being *reclaimed* at that time[8].

---

[7] In practice, the full amount of capital allowances remaining might not be usable at that point. Rather, if allowances were pooled, then only 25% of the WDV would be claimed, and the remainder passed on to future periods.

[8] This negative figure is not an income but a loss. We are, therefore, assuming that tax can effectively be refunded by using the loss to offset tax payable on income from other years or other sources.

**Table 14.13** Vehicle purchase ('without') - tax effects.

| time | cost | benefit | capital all'nces | WDV | taxable income | tax paid | net benefit |
|---|---|---|---|---|---|---|---|
| qtrs | £ | £ | £ | £ | £ | £ | £ |
| 0 | 14400 | 0 | 0 | 0 | 0 | 0.0 | -14400.0 |
| 1 | 0 | 0 | 0 | 0 | 0 | 0.0 | 0.0 |
| 2 | 0 | 0 | 0 | 0 | 0 | 0.0 | 0.0 |
| 3 | 0 | 0 | 0 | 0 | 0 | 0.0 | 0.0 |
| 4 | 0 | 0 | 3600 | 10800 | -3600 | -1080.0 | 1080.0 |
| 5 | 0 | 0 | 0 | 0 | 0 | 0.0 | 0.0 |
| 6 | 0 | 0 | 0 | 0 | 0 | 0.0 | 0.0 |
| 7 | 0 | 0 | 0 | 0 | 0 | 0.0 | 0.0 |
| 8 | 0 | 0 | 2700 | 8100 | -2700 | -810.0 | -810.0 |
| 9 | 0 | 0 | 0 | 0 | 0 | 0.0 | 0.0 |
| 10 | 0 | 0 | 0 | 0 | 0 | 0.0 | 0.0 |
| 11 | 0 | 0 | 0 | 0 | 0 | 0.0 | 0.0 |
| 12 | 0 | 6000 | 2025 | 6075 | -2025 | -607.5 | 6608.0 |
| 13 | 0 | 0 | 0 | 0 | 0 | 0.0 | 0.0 |
| 14 | 0 | 0 | 0 | 0 | 0 | 0.0 | 0.0 |
| 15 | 0 | 0 | 0 | 0 | 0 | 0.0 | 0.0 |
| 16 | 0 | 0 | 6075 | 0 | -75 | -22.5 | 22.5 |

Douglas can now proceed to subtract the 'without' cash flows from the 'with' figures for each period and discount those extra, or incremental, costs and benefits by the post-tax discount rate. Table 14.14 shows the figures.

The post-tax discount rate is the same as that used for the example in Appendix 14.1, but here converted from the annual rate of 5.73% to a quarterly rate of 1.40%.

Adding the figures in the final column gives an NPV (or NDC as we called it in Chapter 13) of -£577.41 and further calculation gives an IRR (or APR) of 9.07%. These figures can be compared to the pre-tax values of -£754 and 12.3% respectively, signifying that, in this particular case, tax would still not make leasing as cheap as purchase, but it would close the gap.

**Table 14.14**  DCF of vehicle purchase showing tax effects.

| time qtrs | 'with' net benefit £ | 'without' net benefit £ | extra net benefit £ | discount factor @1.4% | present value £ |
|---|---|---|---|---|---|
| 0 | -1392.0 | -14400.0 | 13008 | 1.000 | 13008 |
| 1 | -1392.0 | 0.0 | -1392 | 0.986 | -1373 |
| 2 | -1392.0 | 0.0 | -1392 | 0.973 | -1354 |
| 3 | -1392.0 | 0.0 | -1392 | 0.959 | -1335 |
| 4 | -974.4 | 1080.0 | -2054 | 0.946 | -1943 |
| 5 | -1392.0 | 0.0 | -1392 | 0.933 | -1299 |
| 6 | -1392.0 | 0.0 | -1392 | 0.920 | -1281 |
| 7 | -1392.0 | 0.0 | -1392 | 0.907 | -1263 |
| 8 | 278.4 | -810.0 | -532 | 0.895 | -476 |
| 9 | -1392.0 | 0.0 | -1392 | 0.882 | -1228 |
| 10 | -1392.0 | 0.0 | -1392 | 0.870 | -1211 |
| 11 | -1392.0 | 0.0 | -1392 | 0.858 | -1194 |
| 12 | 7550.4 | 6608.0 | 943 | 0.846 | 798 |
| 13 | 0.0 | 0.0 | 0 | 0.834 | 0 |
| 14 | 0.0 | 0.0 | 0 | 0.823 | 0 |
| 15 | 0.0 | 0.0 | 0 | 0.811 | 0 |
| 16 | -511.2 | 22.5 | -534 | 0.800 | -427 |
| | | | | NPV@1.4% | -577.41 |

# Chapter 15

# Computers and Forest Accounts

As with taxation in the previous chapter, there would be no point in an amateur giving specific advice in such a rapidly changing environment as that of computers. Again, therefore, the aim of this chapter is to provide some information and some general guidelines which might help in the choice and use of computer hardware and software for forestry budgeting and accounting.

For the uninitiated, by **hardware** we mean the equipment: the keyboard, the screen or monitor, the mouse, and the box which contain the parts such as the processor, which do the work. Up until 20 years ago computer hardware used to be very bulky and one main-frame computer would be shared by many users. Since then, however, desk-top computers have become available and increasingly powerful, so that most of us now find that these personal computers (PCs) are able to comfortably meet our needs. IBM and other compatible makes of PC are probably the most common, although there are others such as the Apple Mac. Our PC can run without linking to any other computer, although we may have a telephone link which will then enable us to have access to computers all over the world via the World-Wide Web (also called 'the web' and 'www'). Some organisations, however, choose to link up (network) computers with one known as the *server*, controlling communication between them.

**Software**, on the other hand, consists of the programs and packages of programs which run on the computers. The collection of software that runs the computers and what goes on the screen is known as the *operating system*. The types of software for typing letters and reports, for storing, retrieving and analysing data, for producing lectures and presentations, for teaching, and for many other purposes are known as *desktop applications*.

Why should we consider the use of computers in forestry budgeting and accounting? In our specific context, computers are useful because of their:

1. *speed* - they can carry out vast quantities of complex calculations and information sorting operations incredibly quickly

2. *accuracy* - they are almost invariably 100% accurate

3. *information storage* - vast amounts of data and other information can be stored in a very small space.

It should, therefore, be obvious that in the forestry accounting context the computer is potentially a very powerful tool. We now turn to consideration of what hardware and software might be most appropriate for us.

## Hardware

Buying or leasing a computer is a little like buying a car. What make and model is appropriate depends upon what we need it for and what features it has. We therefore need to ask ourselves, "What are we looking for?" and "What does it need to do?" The following checklist might help:

- Capacity.
We need to ensure that it is capable of dealing with the software that we want to run and the information which we wish to store.
- Track record.
If we are computer experts we might wish to go for the latest model with innovative features. Otherwise, we are wiser to choose a computer company and a model which is popular because it has shown that it meets users' needs. The term 'tried and tested' probably best describes this advice.
- Technical assistance.
As with a car, we need to be able to get effective help quickly if things go wrong. So proven after-sales service provision should be sought.
- Economy.
Cheap may correlate with shortcomings in the computer and the related technical support; expensive may mean that we are getting a machine with bells and whistles, many of which we will never need[1]. What we should look for is a product which meets our needs most economically.

The final piece of advice is homespun: 'look before you leap'. Shop around and ask questions - of the retailers, computer experts and, especially, fellow forest managers who have bought computers themselves.

---

[1] Although our children probably will!

# Software

Thinking back over the management cycle which provided the basis for the stepwise layout of the book, the types of software most likely to be useful are the following.

## Word processing package

Perhaps the software of which you will make most use is the word processing package (e.g. Word, Word Perfect, Write). Although you will carry out the calculations on a spreadsheet, your reports, letters and even accounts and budgets will be presented and stored using such a package.

## Spreadsheets

These are packages (e.g. Excel, Quattro-Pro, Lotus) which effectively provide us with a sheet, divided into boxes or pigeon holes, on which we can set out our calculations and process them in a transparent way. Budgets and accounts work very well in this medium, as do all of the other forms of calculation carried out in this book. In fact, all of the calculations which we have worked through have been verified on a series of spreadsheets.

## Databases

Although spreadsheets can be used for data recording and storage, above a certain scale and complexity these are likely to be more efficiently managed by a database, such as Access, Dbase or Paradox. A database is simply a program for storing, retrieving and analysing data and information in an ordered fashion.

## Accounting packages

For large or complex businesses you may find it easier to buy an off-the-shelf, general package designed, for instance, to store data and produce a set of accounts. If one of these is not available, or does not fit your needs appropriately, then, if you have the money or the connections, you may purchase a tailor-made program or package of programs. If you can obtain such a package it may save you a lot of time in trying to 'reinvent the wheel' for your own proposes, and you can still use your own home-made spreadsheet or database file for special activities like budget construction or accounts analysis.

## Self-teach packages

There are many self-teach CAL (computer-aided learning) packages available for general topics such as accounting fundamentals, spreadsheet construction and so on. What are much more rare are programs written specifically for forestry. There are some[2], however; a search of 'the web' can prove fruitful.

### The World-Wide Web

The web consists of millions of computers linked by communications systems, such as telephone lines, which allows users across the globe to browse through the information offered by millions of web site owners. The web has been a major part of the information revolution and since better information can mean better decisions, it can be extremely useful for the forest manager. However, as with the television, what is a most useful piece of technology can also have very negative effects since, like television, the excellent presentations are in danger of being engulfed by the trash. Consequently, when looking for information on the web one has to have a well thought-out strategy.

Here are a few hints. A lot of time can be wasted waiting for information to be transferred, so have something else to do while you are waiting. And searching for information is rather like detective work - plan where you are going and ask others for tips, follow leads, and save information about useful sites to save looking for them again.

**Fig. 15.1** Douglas is quite new to computing.

## General Hints

Finally, some general points about the use of computers to bear in mind. Because of the hi-tech characteristics of computers it is easy to fall into a number of traps

---

[2] Budget Builder (CLUES, 1997) is a CAL package which was designed by staff in several UK universities for teaching budgeting for agriculture. However, much is applicable to forestry too.

in their use. The first four points refer to these traps, and these are followed by two further pieces of advice.

- Only a tool - for management

When employing computers we should be careful not to lose sight of the objective in using them. Their use is not an end in itself, but helps improve the effectiveness of our work. In practice this means that the computer should not determine how we do things and we should use its output to aid our decision making, not to make the decisions for us.

- Rubbish in - rubbish out

Output from a computer can often have an aura of absolute, unquestionable accuracy. Although its high degree of accuracy is one of the strong points of the computer, we should always cast a critical eye over the results, for two reasons.

Firstly, the data fed into the computer may be of questionable accuracy, and consequently, even the most accurate computer calculation cannot magically make the results correct. Furthermore, if the input data is only roughly correct, there is not much point in producing calculated results to many decimal places.

Secondly, the computer may actually be carrying out incorrect calculations, usually because a mistake has been made in entering the calculation, or, rarely, because something is wrong with the computer. In spreadsheets, for example, the computer may seem to give wrong answers if there is a circular reference - the value in one cell depending on the value in a second cell, which itself is dependent on the value in the first cell. I like to blame the computer for this, but I suppose that responsibility really lies with the user!

It is, therefore, most important to check computer-generated results before they are used in further analysis or passed on to someone else.

- Time waster (and time saver)

Once set up for a particular task, computers work incredibly quickly; this is one of the reasons for their adoption. However, as with the claim that they would save paper, it sometimes seems that the opposite is true. Because of getting carried away by the enjoyment of the toy or because of the time taken to set up the program to solve the problem with which we are wrestling, or because of the enforced wait for the system to respond or the time taken to sift through the masses of information produced, we can find ourselves spending a great deal of time staring at the screen. In order to avoid this, we need to be organised (knowing what we want and how to get it) and disciplined (limiting the time we spend and not getting carried away).

- Quickly outdated

Developments in computer hardware and software are taking place at such a speed that within a short space of time the product which we acquired will be superseded by an updated and superior version. A balanced approach is needed to this. We need to keep reasonably up to date so that we can make use of the extra information and facilities and so that we can continue to tie in with other computer users and systems. However, we need to beware of following fashions and the cost of too regular replacement, remembering too that some of the 'improvements' may be little more than window dressing. The best approach might be one of following the crowd at a more leisurely pace, without losing contact.

- Training (or lack of it)

Although we might keep our system up-to-date, it is likely that our own skills will lag behind. If we want to make full use of the improvements in the computer hardware and software we must invest in regular updating of the skills of ourselves and our staff.

- Value for money

When purchasing computers and software we need to decide firstly what we really need and then assess the products in the light of this. It is now possible to obtain some good software free via the web, and there are some tempting package deals for computers with scanners, printers, CD players and software thrown in for good measure. But we do need to ask ourselves, "Do we need all of this, what is the quality of the products, which of these items do I really need, and is there a better way of meeting my requirements?" As with buying a car, it is best to ask an expert to advise us on what the quality aspects of importance to us are likely to be, and these will include the quality of after-sales service.

Computers, then, can be hugely valuable in the field of forestry accounts as in many others, but they also need to be kept firmly in their place and we need to regularly remind ourselves that our computer systems should fit in with our requirements, not the other way round.

# Chapter 16

# Epilogue

If you have reached this chapter after working through the whole book you, like Douglas, are reaching the end of the journey.

We saw, at the start, the dynamic nature of management and that financial management ties in with other aspects. The management process involves looking forward (budgeting) and looking back (accounting), always bearing in mind the profitability, liquidity and stability aspects of financial performance.

Together we worked through the budgeting steps, the plan, the profit budget, the cash flow budget, the budgeted profit and loss statement and the budgeted balance sheet, branching off, on the way, to explore deeply into the crucial subject of valuations and the related topic of depreciation.

Before embarking on the next, looking forward, part of the journey, we covered the recording part of financial management: the humdrum, but necessary, part of the process involved with the present and enabling us to evaluate the performance of our business.

Moving on to the 'looking back' aspects, we saw that the records are used to construct a set of accounts which can then be analysed.

Looking forward, recording and looking back: these are all elements of the dynamic management process of plan-decide-monitor-control-evaluate and then plan again.

But there were other topics which we had to explore before we could claim that the journey was complete.

At the planning stage, we may wish to consider something new - a different way of doing things, a new investment or another way of financing the business, for instance. To understand how these should be evaluated we looked at the appraisal of investments in terms of their profitability (via shorthand and discounted cash flow techniques) as well as their feasibility.

Our next stop involved the question of financing such investments, or the business as a whole, using internal (business or personal) funds or grants, equity or debt from outside the business or the family: also part of the planning stage.

To make the journey complete we could not avoid or evade the tollbooth: taxation. The advice provided here was not specific but general - we need to be aware of tax, we can calculate its effects and above all, we should plan for tax.

And finally, we met PC Kid, a fast-growing, knowledgeable, but rather blinkered youth, who could give us enormous assistance, but should never be allowed to make decisions for himself.

Now that you have an overall picture you may wish to go back and dip into some of the areas that interest you or that relate particularly to issues you are currently facing. You may even wish to explore some of those narrow alleyways in the various appendices to some of the chapters. And if you wish to see how the main text can be more suitably applied in the United States, New Zealand, Australia or countries with similar systems, then your journey is not over: Appendices A and B, following on from this chapter, are there to help.

The journey is over, or perhaps for you it is continuing or only just beginning. Some final words of advice: remember, this book has, hopefully, provided you with some useful tools and understanding, but these must be applied within a specific context and used to guide and assist in decision making. Over to you!

# Appendix A

# United States Overview

Norman E. Elwood

*Department of Forest Resources, College of Forestry, Oregon State University, Corvallis, Oregon 97331-5703, USA.*

This author has been asked to discuss this book's topics from the United States' (US) perspective. These comments are in no way comprehensive, they reflect this author's perspective of the book's topical highlights. To help readers coordinate these comments with the rest of the book, the organisation of this appendix mirrors the book's sequence of chapters. Pertinent references are cited within the book's reference list.

Mention of some introductory points, including conventions used here, is pertinent:

## Author's Background

This author's background and 28 years of work-focused specialisation is forest management, economics, project analysis, and taxation - not cost accounting.

## Terminology Conventions

This author has been asked to, where possible, provide the US equivalent of key terms used in this text. Thus, UK terms are enclosed in single quotes ('xxx') and US terms in double quotes ("xxx"). *Unless specifically noted*, readers should assume that discussion pertains to the US situation. "This author" refers to the writer of this appendix. The 'text author' refers to the writer of the main body of this book.

## US Forest Ownership Classification

US forest ownership can be categorised as follows:

- Government
  Federal
  State
  County
  Local (town, township, parish, city)

- Private

Federal forest land is managed by several agencies and is usually referred to by the agency's name, e.g. "Forest Service" or "Department of Interior" land, etc. Private industrial forest land is typically called "commercial", "corporate", or "industry" land. Non-industrial private forest land is variously called "small private", "small woodlot", "small woodland", "woodlot", "family forest", and an acronym of some popularity, "NIPF".

## Similar Textbooks

While numerous US cost accounting and analysis books exist, this author is unaware of any that approach this book's level of detail and/or pertain to private forest operation[1].

## Chapter 1: Introduction

US readers should be very comfortable with the definition of "management" and the discussion of strategic and tactical objectives. The concept of a dynamic, non-linear, decision-making process is commonly accepted as are the aspects of profitability, liquidity, and stability.

---

[1] Gregory (1972), Forbes (1976), Duerr et al (1982), Gunter and Haney (1984), Wenger (1984), Davis and Johnson (1987), Haney and Siegel (1993) and Klemperer (1996) may, however, prove helpful.

## Chapter 2: Budgeting - Step 1 - The Plan

US readers will easily identify with this chapter, especially the five-step planning process. Plans are plans after all, pretty much the world over. The notion of objectives, resources/assets, and liabilities/constraints are as applicable for US owners as anywhere else. Some US forest owners will refine this particular planning approach to include both a formal forest management plan *and* a formal business plan. The completeness and formality of both will depend on the size, complexity and form of the forest business enterprise.

The only major terminology differences are that US readers will more likely refer to business "sections" or "sectors" rather than 'enterprises'. When disaggregating further, "production units" would be a more familiar term than 'cost-centres'. Equally common, will be reference to the production unit by its actual name, e.g. the "sawmill", "trucking", or "livestock operation". The common descending hierarchy of NIPF land units would be "tracts ➤ blocks ➤ stands". Government and industry configurations might use "tracts ➤ blocks ➤ compartments ➤ stands".

The plan outline and 'organisational plan' discussed in the book will be quite familiar to US readers. Borrowing from common business planning, some forest owners will augment the 'organisational plan' with a "SWOT" analysis. This involves analysing the operation's Strengths, Weaknesses, Opportunities, and Threats. It can be as formal and detailed, or informal and sketchy as needed.

US owners will be very familiar with a five-year planning/budgeting horizon, although 10 years is also quite common.

Finally, regarding the Menzies Estate example begun in this chapter, US readers will, of course, identify with the profit maximisation objective. Industry owners will, almost certainly, share this objective. NIPF owners will, however, embrace a much broader set of ownership objectives with profit seldom leading the list, and in fact, frequently being of considerably lower priority.

## Chapter 3: Budgeting - Step 2 - Profit Budget Based on Cost Centres

US readers will feel very comfortable with the concept of budgeting based on "production units" ('cost centres'). In this chapter, however, they will struggle with the term 'estate' being used synonymously with 'business'. In the US context, "estate" is usually reserved for the aggregate of one's real and personal assets which, upon death, are passed to heirs (see Chapter 14 discussion in this Appendix). As used in this chapter and the remainder of the book, US readers will find "operation", "business", or "tree farm" more common substitutes for 'estate'.

Regarding 'Outputs', while in the US we do, of course, have 'grants', the term is more commonly used in academic and/or philanthropic settings. Again, while in common practice by various levels of government in the US, 'subsidies' usually refer to "cost-share" and/or "incentives payments". Ignoring the technical differences between grants, loans, cost-sharing payments, all of these exist in US forestry at the Federal, state, and local level.

Reference to the forest operation's 'staff' begins in this chapter and continues throughout the book. In the US setting, only government, industry, and "mega-sized" NIPF operations will have staff. The vast majority of NIPFs operate solely through the efforts of the owner, his/her family, other volunteer labour, and the occasional hired contractor.

The term 'On-costs' used here will be totally unrecognised by US readers who will be more comfortable with cost classifications like "fixed", "variable", "direct", and "indirect".

## Chapter 4: Valuations

US readers use the same terms and concepts of 'Replacement cost (RC)' and 'Present value (PV)'. They are, however, more likely to use "Net sale value" rather than 'Net realisable value (NRV)'. The collection of terms used in Table 4.1 sees similar use here, except 'slaughter value' which would refer strictly to a livestock operation. When including '...expected price changes...' in a budget, US readers almost exclusively use "actual" instead of 'nominal' which is generally used only in academics and finance.

The 'Accumulated net costs' method is widely used to value immature US forest stands. While the 'Expectation value' method is also widely used in exactly the same manner, US terminology would simply call it the "Discounted cash flow (DCF)" approach. 'Discount rate' is a very common US term, but equally common alternatives include "guiding" or "interest" rate and "opportunity cost of money/capital".

Regarding the 'market value' approach to land valuation, US foresters face challenges similar to those mentioned in this text. The 'land expectation value (LEV)' described in the text is quite common in US usage and is alternatively called "soil expectation value (SEV)" and less commonly "Faustmann value". While conceptually valid, the text's 'adjusted LEV' value has not seen widespread US use, nor, to this author's knowledge, been given an accepted name. This author has used it in the same context presented in the text, calling it simply a "Net Present Amount (NPA)". Concluding this section, US readers will feel very comfortable with the contents of Table 4.7.

This author agrees with the text author's concluding and qualified preference for the 'expectation method' of valuation with the caveat that the US and UK situations may differ considerably regarding environmental restrictions, regulations, constraints, and the subsequently associated forest management activities.

A discussion of the differences goes beyond the scope of both the text and this appendix. Readers should consult more specialised legal and environmentally-oriented references.

## Chapter 5: Depreciation

This chapter's concepts are handled exactly the same in the US context. The terms 'straight line method', 'diminishing balance method', 'book value', and 'sum of the digits method' are all quite common. As shown in Fig. 5.5, US practitioners will employ various accelerated rates in the diminishing balance method. At twice the straight-line rate, the "double-declining balance method" is a very common alternative.

Readers should know that under the Modified Accelerated Cost Recovery System (MACRS), the US Internal Revenue Service prescribes depreciation rates and asset service lives from which accountants construct and implement "depreciation schedules". Table 5.4, 'Machinery Depreciation Table' illustrates what most US accountants would call a "Depreciation Schedule". The MACRS approach covers the vast majority of depreciation cases, leaving only a few highly specialised cases where an older depreciation system is used. Under the older system, accountants have more flexibility to set depreciation rates and asset service lives.

It must be recognised, however, that the book deals primarily with accounts for management purposes, rather than for the tax authorities.

US practice gives a unique definition to 'basis' (used in Table 5.1 as 'Straight Line Basis'). "Basis" refers exclusively to the total amount of money expended to acquire an asset, i.e. "original basis". Over time, various adjustments are made to create "adjusted basis" including the "stepped-up basis" permitted when valuing inherited assets.

## Chapter 6: Budgeting – Step 3 – Cash Flow Budget

The general process presented in this chapter should be familiar to any US forest owner who has ever compiled a *bona fide* budget, thus, only minor comments on differences are offered here. Regarding what the cash flow budget '…enables us to do…' (item 3: 'Monitor, by proxy, technical and biological performance'), it is worth emphasising that care must be taken to achieve timely follow-up. Many forest operations will see infrequent activity, possibly allowing considerable time before the manager discovers that things have gone "off the tracks" and can begin corrective action.

US readers will likely find the terms "Operational Receipts" and "Operational Payments" more familiar than 'Trading Receipts' and 'Trading Payments' used in the text.

Also, unless the operation is very complex, US owners are much less likely to budget by months and quarters. "Years" is the more common time frame.

Similarly, the 'Annotations' presented will be most applicable to larger US operations. They will be overly detailed for most US NIPF owners and thus receive from some to considerable simplification in practice, if used at all.

## Chapter 7: Budgeting - Step 4 - Budgeted Profit and Loss Statement

US readers and practitioners will be quite familiar with accounts and the Profit and Loss (P&L) Statement. The vertical P&L statement is most commonly used by US businesses and financial institutions. US practitioners will call the 'Income Account' an "Income Statement". The horizontal P&L statement is used by the Internal Revenue Service in audits and is called the "Cash-T" method.

Figure 7.2 will present no problems for US readers. Many NIPF owners will, however, use "personal" rather than "corporate" income tax figures.

## Chapter 8: Budgeting - Step 5 - Budgeted Balance Sheet

US readers will be quite familiar with liabilities and with assets of various service lives. They will, however, identify more easily with the term 'short-term capital' rather than 'circulating capital'.

Figure 8.1 contains an important terminology difference. US readers will associate the "financial stock market" with the term 'stocks' used here - considerably different from this text's meaning.

Finally, since the preponderance of US NIPF businesses operate as sole proprietorships, Table 8.1 will see most owners more interested only in the top half of the vertically oriented Balance Sheet. In the US context, this top half is called the "Net Worth Statement". As noted by the text's author, given some minor refinements, sole proprietors may find the Balance Sheet's horizontal form the more preferable approach.

US practitioners will structure the "Balance sheet" slightly differently than Fig. 8.1. They will identify two halves of the sheet, "Assets" vs. "Liabilities and Capital". Despite being rearranged somewhat, all terms shown in Fig. 8.1 are contained in the US-style balance sheet.

## Chapter 9: Recording

US readers will be very familiar with the 'What' and 'Why' of forestry 'Recording', but will more commonly call it "record keeping". They will refer to the 'Cash Analysis Book (CAB)' as the "Account Book". US owners will, however, quite typically make entries in a "Journal" as a step before transferring data to the CAB or Account Book.

As presented in the text, 'Valuation Records' and the process of maintaining them are much the same in the USA. Many US NIPF owners, and this author suspects other countries' owners, will maintain those records somewhat less often than the recommended frequency. It would not be uncommon for an owner to faithfully track some of these items through each accounting period but, for example, to measure and record growing stock data only when preparing for a product harvest and sale.

Regarding 'Labour records', the situation for US owners having a staff was explained earlier. Nevertheless, for legal and tax purposes, US owners must maintain records on any contract labour working on their property. Further, US owners should track inputs of their own labour. While not legally required, there will be practical management questions, tax requirements, loan applications, etc. where this information is needed.

Regarding 'Who should record?', in the US either the NIPF owner him/herself or another family member usually does the recording - or, they will pay their bookkeeper or accountant to do it.

The text author's statement of objectives guiding '...what records you need to help achieve those objectives and whether the benefit of those records outweighs their cost' is true regardless of what country and/or forestry system is involved. This author would add that the record system should be only as complex as absolutely necessary. Simplicity promotes ease and consistency of use. The overly complex recording system that goes unused is essentially useless!

Finally, this author uses an effective memory device, "the 4-D Method" to help owners remember what *minimum* components each "good" record should have. Simply put, each record should contain **D**ate, **D**ollars, **D**etail, and **D**irection. **D**ate, **D**ollars and **D**etail are self-explanatory. **D**irection refers to cross-referencing (1) *within* the records themselves (e.g. noting in the journal what maps pertain to the timber sale being described and where they are stored) and (2) *between* major pieces of the entire recording system (e.g. the contents of a file box, filing cabinet, or storage shed). Retrieval time and hassle saved even with minimal cross-referencing can be significant.

## Chapter 10: Accounts - Construction

US readers will have little trouble with this chapter. Table 10.1 is an excellent "map" of where to find the data for constructing the accounts.

# Chapter 11: Accounts - Analysis

The text's discussion of 'profitability' and its measures will be easily understood by US readers. They will, however, be more interested in after-tax than before-tax situations and measures. Similarly, there will be no problems with 'Return on Capital', 'Liquidity', and 'Stability' concepts. While there should be no conceptual problem with the 'Solvency Ratio' measure, 'Percent Equity' will likely be more intuitively familiar for US readers. Likewise, rather than 'gearing ratio', they will be more familiar with the terms 'debt ratio', 'debt:equity ratio' and especially, as acknowledged by the text's author, 'leverage'.

Table 11.2 is an excellent summary and guide for all readers. US practitioners might, however, call the 'direct' and 'tracing' type of measures by the term "absolute measures". 'Return measures' and 'ratios' would be called "relative measures". As presented in the table, the 'specific measures' themselves are the same in both countries. The notion behind the US terminology is intuitive: "absolute" measures reflect an absolute amount of money; "relative" measures reflect a relationship, i.e. ratio or percentage, rather than amount of money.

The text's author introduces the much debated question of how to handle inflation in Appendix 11.1, acknowledging that inflation is a complex topic with many pitfalls and traps. Often, determining how an analyst, accountant, or bookkeeper has treated inflation - included or excluded - is the first question to be answered. A rather common set of terms in US usage can signal the answer: "real" indicates that inflation has *not* been included, i.e. excluded/ignored - and, "market" indicates that inflation *has been* included in the calculations. "Adjusted for inflation" and "Not adjusted for inflation" are alternatives also used. The level of detail in Appendix 11.1 clearly illustrates why economists prefer to ignore inflation and conduct "real" analyses!

Table 11.13 provides an excellent summary of additional business ratios. US readers will recognise many familiar terms and applications.

# Chapter 12: Appraising Investments

While this chapter's content will be familiar to US readers and they will easily understand its purpose, the title deserves comment. In US real estate and forestry systems, "Appraising" and "Appraisal" are specifically reserved for the formal process of valuation. An entire group of professionals dedicates their work to this process supported by licensing/certification boards, competency examinations, and standards maintained in several states. While this author and US owners and foresters acknowledge the more general meaning of *evaluating* or *taking stock of* something, "appraisal" generally carries the above-mentioned more specific meaning.

Discounted cash flow methods, marginal analysis, and sensitivity analysis are all common in US practice as are the associated measures 'net present value

(NPV)' and 'internal rate of return (IRR)'. Often, 'net present value' is called "net present worth (NPW)".

Regarding Fig. 12.1, this author instructs practitioners to first find three points on the NPV/interest rate graph and to ensure that at least one NPV is negative (preferably two positive and one negative) and second, to then sketch in a curved, compound-interest style line. As explained in the text, the IRR is indicated where the curve crosses the interest rate x-axis. This author has found that when just *estimating* IRR, 0.5% accuracy is usually acceptable. Since yielding just an estimate, this approach seems to represent a less sophisticated refinement to the text's process illustrated in Fig. 12.3. This author's estimation method, however, is fast, minimises calculation, and has proven serviceable when compared to subsequently calculated precise IRR values.

'Equivalent annual value (EAV)', while known in the US context, tends to be less used. 'Benefit:cost' ratio, however, sees common usage as does 'Payback Period' mentioned later in the chapter.

Table 12.2 raises two important points that are mentioned perhaps only tangentially in the text: (1) the general approach to selecting a financial measure and (2) the two-step decision rule when using financial measures. This author recommends that practitioners review/consider all the financial measures available, decide which best reflects what is actually being sought in the evaluation, and then calculate just that one (or more). Even minimal, up-front planning of the analysis can save subsequent time and work.

This author also recommends a two-step decision rule or decision-making process after calculating the financial measure. While certainly not "rocket science", it introduces an important consideration - politics. Numerous examples exist where projects of poor financial potential were implemented for political rather than financial reasons. After calculating the measure(s), the first step is to examine it/them in gross terms, e.g. array NPV in descending order from highest positive to lowest negative (or similarly best to worst for other measures). Then, since all measures have an implicit minimum threshold of acceptability, the second step is to consider all projects above that minimum threshold as "candidates for acceptance" and those below as "candidates for rejection". Next, one considers the question: "Are any candidates for rejection, sufficiently attractive for *any* reason to merit acceptance, despite appearing as poor financial propositions?" If the answer is "yes", then those are moved onto the list of "acceptance" candidates. From here on, the text's recommended decision process is followed.

The text's sensitivity analysis shorthand approach will be considerably less familiar in US practice than the usual "change-one-item-and-repeat-the-entire-analysis" approach. This traditional, more labour intensive method is, however, almost a "no brainer" for those conducting computerised analyses.

While they should feel entirely comfortable with Table 12.4, US owners will nevertheless consider a somewhat more robust set of factors in the 'Examples' section. Following are some typically considered additional factors in the format of Table 12.4:

| Aspect | Example |
|---|---|
| Resources | Type of resource: timber, minerals, oil, natural gas, non-timber forest products |
| Natural Capital | |
|   Land | History of activities, direction of slope (aspect) |
| Human Capital | |
|   Labour | Cost, commitment |
|   Management | Availability (owner or hired consultant) |
| Physical Capital | |
|   Material Inputs | Needs, inventory on hand, cost, sources (borrow, share, purchase, supplied by cooperative, etc.) |
|   Machinery | Same as for 'material inputs' |
|   Buildings | Space needs (amount, type, location, duration, special features needed) |
|   Infrastructure | Availability, location and condition of firebreaks, water supply for fire fighting, work trails, property boundary markings, fences, etc. |
| Financial Capital | Cost and duration of financing |
| Natural Environment | |
|   Pests/Disease | Types, potential damage and treatments |
|   Climate | Significant micro-climate zones and effects |
| Markets/Marketing | Timing of marketing opportunities, marketing assistance (availability, need, cost) |
| Legal Restrictions & Obligations | Formal requirements and customs for notification about forest operations |
| Social Restrictions & Obligations | Similar to legal restrictions, but less formal |

Concerning reconciliation of DCF assumptions and the shorthand method of Appendix 12.1, the end-of-year cash flow convention gets predominant use by US practitioners and financial operators.

Appendix 12.2 contains several items needing comment. Naturally, US practitioners face the same problem of multiple IRR roots (Fig. 12.5). Rather than using the 'crossover discount rate' discussed in the text, the US approach seems to have settled on an alternative rate of return criterion known by three names: "Modified Internal Rate of Return (MIRR)", "Realisable Rate of Return (RRR)", or "Composite Internal Rate of Return (CIRR)". All three refer to the same criterion; MIRR and RRR seem most common which is unfortunate because CIRR more intuitively reflects how the criterion operates.

CIRR depends on the assumption that intermediate positive net cash flows are reinvested at some specified rate of reinvestment that is different from the inherent IRR (remember, IRR assumes that reinvestment occurs at a rate equal to the IRR). With CIRR, intermediate positive net cash flows are compounded (reinvested) to the end of the analysis horizon at the *specified reinvestment rate*. Negative net cash flows (costs) are discounted to the present by the *discount rate* used in the analysis. The sum of future net returns is divided by the sum of present net costs and the $n^{th}$ root of that number calculated (where "n" is the number of periods in the analysis horizon). Expressing the resulting decimal in per cent, then, the $n^{th}$ root is the CIRR. This is easily depicted as:

$$CIRR = \left[ \frac{\text{Sum FV}_{\text{Net Returns}}}{\text{Sum PV}_{\text{Net Costs}}} \right]^{1/n}$$

**Fig. A.1** Thinning corridor of a cable thinning harvesting operation - Douglas fir – Western Oregon region, USA (photo: Norman Elwood).

Finally, US practitioners face the same problems regarding choices between mutually exclusive (ME) and non mutually exclusive (NME) projects. The issue often arises in a "capital budgeting" context where ME and NME projects are the focus. As identified in the text, NPV is the correct choice in ME project situations. While one may have to deal with "discreteness" (can I do the entire project or just pieces of it?), that does not change NPV's appropriateness.

Also as presented in the text's discussion of NME projects, NPV alone is inadequate. A relative criterion is needed. NPV per initial dollar (pound) outlay, IRR, CIRR, and B/C ratio are all considered appropriate options. US practitioners will often implement one intermediate step in the traditional process of ranking NME projects in descending order of a relative criterion like IRR. The thinking goes like this: "If I rank the projects in descending order of IRR *and* note each project's NPV, I can then *first* form a list of "candidates for acceptance" (i.e., all projects whose IRRs exceed the minimum acceptable rate) and then *second* from that list of acceptable candidates select the particular combination that maximises cumulative NPV. This approach becomes more attractive when typical constraints like budget, discreteness, labour, etc. are factored into the situation.

US practitioners may deal with another topic, "normalising" projects, somewhat differently than as presented in this text. As mentioned in Appendix 12.2, theoretical problems arise when comparing IRRs of two projects that follow different patterns, cash flow timings, for example. Classically-trained US analysts will attempt to achieve *exact* (or as close as practical) comparability through a process called "normalising". Following are the major factors generally considered for normalisation:

—Project length               — Cash flow timing
—Inflation assumption         — Initial investment costs
—Reinvestment assumption      — Risk condition

Project length, inflation and reinvestment are the easiest to handle, so not surprisingly, they are the ones most frequently normalised - if, in fact, it gets done at all. Inflation has been adequately discussed by this text's author - either include it or exclude it - and, don't mix the two when comparing projects. Project length has been dealt with in two ways: (1) repeat all projects until a common, finite length of analysis horizon is found or (2) establish an infinite analysis horizon with 'LEV' ("SEV") straightaway.

To normalise reinvestment rate, discussed indirectly in this text, practitioners are advised to specifically consider the reinvestment situation, choose a rate, and then apply it consistently to all projects being evaluated. The following are the general strategies usually recommended for selecting a reinvestment rate:

1. *Project earning rate* - New projects (i.e., reinvestments) are assumed to exist with the same cash flows, and hence earning rate, as the initial project. Reinvestments are thus made at a rate equal to the project earning rate. This is a very intuitive choice because it says "reinvest in the same project".

2. *Project discount rate* - All reinvestments are assumed made at the rate equal to the discount rate used to analyse the set of projects being evaluated. This is a slightly "theoretical" choice because there is no explicit assumption about the

type of project in which to reinvest - it could be anything. The only implicit assumption is that the reinvestment will earn the project's discount rate.

3. *Reinvestment rate "Z"* - All reinvestments are assumed made at a rate that is different from options 1 and 2 above - and, that is the analyst's choice completely. There are no implicit assumptions about what type of project might be chosen for reinvestment, only that such a project exists somewhere and that it will return the specified rate of reinvestment.

These three options span the spectrum of available choices. None are either "right" or "wrong". The practitioner must choose the one most appropriate for the situation. They are presented here in what is commonly seen as an increasing order of uncertainty ("aggressiveness"), i.e. number one is the most certain (conservative) option; number three is the least certain (most aggressive).

While, overall, this book is about "Forestry Budgeting and Accounts", this is a key chapter because one of the reasons for doing budgeting and accounting is to provide data for evaluating/appraising investments/projects. The process of evaluation/appraisal uses much of this budgeting and accounting data. For most businesses, the overall objective is, after all, to prosper, not just stay afloat. That occurs when the best investments/projects are identified and implemented - the purpose of this chapter.

# Chapter 13: Finance

US owners will be very familiar with the 'Characteristics' discussed early in this chapter. Equally comfortable will be the discussion of 'sole trader' ("sole proprietor") and 'partnership' financing. In the US context, 'production grants' and 'grants...for capital expenditure' are generally rolled into one category of financing called "cost sharing" or "financial incentives". These are programmes of various descriptions that provide funding for specifically identified activities. Most commonly, they are government sponsored. Owners may also receive funding from non-government sources varying from forest industry (quasi-grants often carrying "first right of refusal" conditions on future timber sold) to philanthropic organisations (generally traditional, outright grants with few, if any, "strings" attached).

Forestry cooperatives have seen little success in the US It has been this author's experience elsewhere, however, that cooperatives are extremely popular, highly used, and in some countries embrace the key mission of securing funds for their members' activities.

US owners will be very familiar with the concepts of 'trade credit' and 'bank overdraft'. This text's example of 'trade credit' where the owner buys but then makes payment within a month, would in US terms be known as "thirty days same as cash". And, while "overdraft protection" is a common feature of most US checking/share draft accounts, as used in this text, 'bank overdraft' would be called a "line of credit", "operating credit" or "operational credit". US "overdraft protection" is short-term coverage of an inadvertent overdrawing of one's account - not smiled upon by the bank, not tolerated as routine, and resulting in from token to significant penalty charges.

Finally, there seems to be no more appropriate place than here to discuss the common, basic forms of US business organisation. While UK and US business forms may be similar, some differences merit clarification. US entrepreneurs organise their businesses under one of four principal forms: the sole proprietorship, partnership, corporation, or limited liability company.

As mentioned earlier in this appendix, the UK 'sole trader' and US "sole proprietor" appear to be equivalent. From this chapter's discussion, partnerships in both countries seem nearly identical in almost all respects except terminology. US partnerships are divided into "general" and "limited" partnerships. General partners share all aspects of the operation: work, debts, income, decision-making authority and liability. Limited partners contribute only financing, and have no say in business operation (perhaps the 'sleeping partner' mentioned in this chapter). Partnership taxation appears to be similar in both countries.

Both countries appear to share similar forms of corporate business organisation, but use different terminology. Often referred to as a 'company' in this text (called a 'corporation' less often), the US also has both such 'private' and 'public' companies. In the US context, "Corporation" is the more formal term used and "Company" gets more day-to-day use. US practice recognises (1) the "Standard" or "C" corporation (often called "C Corp.") and (2) the "Sub-chapter S" corporation (often called "S Corp."). They are governed by quite different tax provisions and organisational, operational, and reporting requirements. Limits on the number of shareholders and taxing under the personal rather than corporate structure are key determinants of the S Corp., which is often used by NIPF business owners.

Finally, the "Limited Liability Company (LLC)", available in many states, attempts to blend the partnership's tax advantages with the Standard corporation's limited liability features.

## Chapter 14: Taxation

The 'General points' discussed in the text apply equally to the US context.
The following overviews the principal types of taxes in the US:

| Federal | State | Local |
|---|---|---|
| Income | Income | Income |
| Estate & gift | Sales/use | Sales/use |
| Excise | Estate & gift | Property |
| | Timber | Transit |
| | Excise | |

'Production levies' will be known to US owners as "severance", "harvest" or "yield" taxes. The US Federal income tax system also provides 'personal allowances' called, in general terms, "exemptions" and "deductions" - and, more specifically, Form 1040 "personal exemptions" and "standard deductions" and Schedule A "itemised deductions". As used in the text, 'capital allowances' in the US are also called "depreciation". US practice limits depreciation to capital assets and uses the term "depletion" for the same concept when applied to natural resources (oil, gas, timber, minerals). Different procedures exist for calculating depletion depending on the type of resource.

Regarding the 'Tax on inflationary gains on assets', the US Federal income tax system also allows for a 'capital gains tax'. Distinction is made, however, between "long-term (LTCG)" and "short-term" capital gains with differences in how each is taxed. Long-term capital gain is generally the most advantageous. To qualify timber as a capital asset, four factors are evaluated: the (1) primary purpose for which the timber is held/owned, (2) length of time the timber was held prior to disposal, (3) form of disposal, and (4) nature of the timber product. Providing that all four provisions are satisfied and the timber sale is correctly structured, the sale income may qualify, either completely or partially, for the tax advantages of LTCG treatment. If not treated as LTCG, then timber sale income is either taxed completely as ordinary income or, with IRS Code Section 631(a) log sales (vs. selling standing trees as "stumpage"), the gain is partitioned between LTCG and ordinary income. For a comprehensive discussion of these details, readers should consult the Hoover (Hoover, 2000) and the USDA Forest Service (USDA Forest Service, 1995) references.

Finally, the US system also levies taxes on gifts and assets passed through inheritance. US owners may recognise these 'Inheritance taxes' by the terms "estate" or "death" taxes. Some states levy their own estate and gift taxes and others pass them through to the Federal level as "pick-up" or "piggyback" taxes. The text's statement that 'Because inheritance tax is levied on individuals it is not of direct relevance to the forest business, but the actions of the owner or major shareholder to reduce liability to this tax may have major effects on the business', while true, is too simplified for the US situation. The focus is not on whom the tax is levied, but on the effects of the tax on the business and the actions taken to limit the effects of the tax. An entire, specialised "industry" of tax and financial planning known as "estate planning" exists to provide such service. A vast array of financial, legal, and tax mechanisms exist to structure, guide, and administer the transfer of assets from the estate to heirs.

# Chapter 15: Computers and Forest Accounts

This short chapter is very important for all forest owners. As the world becomes smaller through electronic networking, forest owners will want to avail themselves of both the capacity to get/store information *and* to process it.

Increasingly, US forest owners are learning about, acquiring and using computers. This author agrees with this chapter's discussion and would add just one thought. Regarding computers becoming quickly outdated - while true in absolute terms - practically, a computer set-up only really outdates when it no longer meets the user's needs, when it fails to do what is needed. Staying abreast of the latest technology is an expensive undertaking both in time and money. Few forest owners will find it absolutely essential to always be on that cutting edge.

# Appendix B

# New Zealand/Australia Overview

Edward M. Bilek

*School of Forestry, University of Canterbury, Private Bag 4800, Christchurch, New Zealand*

I have been asked to discuss the book's topics from a New Zealand/Australian perspective.

To be consistent with Appendix A (which discusses the topics from a US perspective), I shall mirror the book's chapter sequence.

Any perspective will be biased by the author's background. To allow you to evaluate my perspective, you should know a bit about my background. My undergraduate and post-graduate education was in the United States. However, I have worked for 14 years in New Zealand in forestry economics, finance, management, and administration. I have done work in forest valuation and project valuation.

## Chapter 1: Introduction

Southern Hemisphere readers may think of forest management as a way of managing or manipulating forest yields (fibre, non-fibre, or cash) over time. The management definition given in Chapter 1 is a much broader one that encompasses the manipulation of forest yields. The planning sequence described is one with which Southern readers should be comfortable.

## Chapter 2: Budgeting - Step 1 - The Plan

Southern readers will be familiar with the steps outlined in the plan. Short-term, medium-term, and long-term planning is much the same. However, a difference is evident in the organisation plan. The book breaks the enterprise into cost centres. New Zealand and Australian organisations are more often broken into profit centres. Each sub-group is expected to provide a profit to the group rather than to provide a product or service at a cost.

The planning sequence should be similar, no matter where the organisation. However, in the production forecast, rather than using yield tables to determine recoverable volumes, more commonly computerised growth models are used. In addition, in working out total output for the total forested area, some form of estate model will be used. Such models are usually based on linear programming and are set to optimise something (usually net present value) subject to some constraints (usually wood flow).

In setting out a list of operating assets (Table 2.2), in New Zealand it would be considered important to separate the value of the growing crop from the land value. This is done both for practical management reasons and for tax reasons. Management will usually want to know about the changing value of the forest crop. For tax purposes, the income earned from sale of the trees is taxed as current income. However, gains in land value are usually taxed at a capital gains rate, currently 0%.

# Chapter 3: Budgeting - Step 2 - Profit Budget Based on Cost Centres

In this chapter, the management goal of producing a 'normal' forest is introduced. Southern foresters will be familiar with the term, but a 'normal' forest is rarely a deliberate objective of forest management. Changing markets or forest disturbance due to wind, fire, or disease usually ensure that a forest is only 'normal' in its physical structure by accident, and that a 'normal' forest will not stay that way for long.

Management plans are generally formulated to maximise net present value. Depending on the alternative returns available, dividends may be maximised and capital value maintained if a forest is partially liquidated and the resulting capital reinvested. This may be the best option, even allowing for the cost of protecting the land for 'environmental sensitivity' (one of Douglas's management objectives).

In the Southern Hemisphere, 'estate' refers to the forest estate. The forest estate is made up of many different stands of different ages and species. Readers will not be familiar with 'estate' referring to the entire forest enterprise.

The term, 'on costs' will be unfamiliar to Southern readers. Overheads are generally divided into fixed and variable. Occasionally in planning, semi-variable overhead costs may also be used.

# Chapter 4: Valuations

The valuations followed in this book are stand valuations. This is consistent with the author's focus on cost centres and his desire to get costings down to the compartment or sub-compartment level. Nonetheless, Southern readers will be more familiar with forest estate valuation, where the forest is valued as a whole. That means that stands may, for various reasons (e.g. wood flow or cash flow, product requirements, logistical considerations, etc.), not be felled at their target or optimum rotation ages. Such deviations result in a forest value being less than the sum of the stands' optimum values. A small-scale forest enterprise, such as Menzies', may be able to harvest its stands at close to their optimum ages. A large-scale forest enterprise will not, due to mill requirements, wood supply obligations, operational efficiencies, etc.

The valuation techniques discussed - market price, devastation value, accumulated net costs, and expectation value should all be familiar to Southern readers, although the terms would be a bit different. Devastation value would be known as liquidation value. Accumulated net costs would be compounded costs. And expectation value would normally be called the discounted cash flow (DCF) approach.

Regarding forestland valuation, values from Faustmann's land expectation value approach could be used in New Zealand or Australia. Alternatively, valuations from the land department or from a registered land valuer would be used, depending on the purpose of the valuation and the significance of the land value in the total value.

Comprehensive forest valuation procedures have been published by the New Zealand Institute of Forestry (1996).

# Chapter 5: Depreciation

Southern readers will be familiar with straight-line depreciation, although they may also see the term "cost price depreciation", which means the same thing. Declining balance depreciation is also known as diminishing value depreciation.

The Inland Revenue Department (IRD) controls depreciation in New Zealand tightly. The IRD publishes a booklet that sets out a table of almost every asset imaginable along with accompanying depreciation allowances (Inland Revenue Department, 1994). Most assets may be depreciated using either straight line or diminishing value depreciation, but the rates that may be used are determined by the IRD. The rates are given in percentages. For straight-line depreciation, the percentage is multiplied by the asset's historic cost. This results in a constant annual depreciation. Note that no deduction for an estimated salvage value is made. The IRD has incorporated estimated salvage values in its rate calculation. For diminishing value depreciation, the rate provided by the IRD is multiplied by the asset's closing balance each year, just as it is done in this book. The IRD rates are often quite conservative, leading to an asset having no economic value long before it is written off the books.

For example, contractors seem to agree that a skidder has an estimated useful life of about five years. Yet, the IRD specifies that a skidder must be depreciated at a straight-line rate of 10% or a diminishing value rate of 12.5%, based on an estimated useful life of 12.5 years (Inland Revenue Department, 1994 p. 45).

This raises issues regarding the usefulness of an accountant's depreciation for management purposes. If the asset actually wears out over five years, but is being depreciated as if it had a 12.5-year life, then too little depreciation is being taken. This will lead to overstating profits in the early years of the asset's life. If depreciation expense is being used as a guideline for reinvestment into capital assets, then too little will be reinvested and productivity will suffer.

Management needs to be aware that depreciation is not a cash expense. As such, it is subject to manipulation, both by creative accountants and by the tax department. The depreciation expense that is taken, may not match what is happening to the useful value of a firm's assets. If it does not, and if depreciation expense is a significant item in the profit and loss statement, then depreciation schedules need to be revised for management purposes.

## Chapter 6: Budgeting - Step 3 - Cash Flow Budget

Apart from perhaps the beginning, there is little in this chapter that would be considered differently in New Zealand.

The budgeting is done as a part of forest management planning. The budget usually begins with a forest plan. The plan dictates what physical inputs will be required as well as the outputs that are expected.

For larger forest estates, the plan is constructed as part of a strategic planning exercise, as illustrated below.

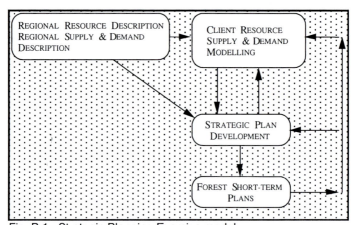

Fig. B.1  Strategic Planning Exercise model.

In a strategic plan, the firm's forest resources are considered in the context of the region's forest resources. Once the strategic plan is developed, short-term forest management plans are made. There are feedback loops to illustrate the interactions between the regional description, the modelling, the strategic plans, and the short-term plans. As in this chapter, the short-term forest plan provides the basis for next year's budget.

In New Zealand, the forest management software itself would usually provide many of the numbers needed in the cash flow budget, although it is certainly good in a textbook to go through a manual example to see how the software produces the numbers.

In New Zealand, after the budget is initially drawn up, there would usually be a check to see if the budgeted cash flows met the enterprise cash flow requirements. If it did not, then there would be revisions in the forest management plans. This would certainly be possible to do on the Menzies Estate, but perhaps due to brevity, it is not done in this example.

## Chapter 7: Budgeting Step 4 - Budgeted Profit and Loss Statement

Southern readers will be familiar with the profit and loss statement. They may also know of it as the earnings statement or as the income statement. Similarly, 'net profit' may be known of as "net income", or "net earnings".

In Appendix 7.3, the author recommends bringing changes in growing stock valuations directly to the profit and loss statement. This practice was once followed by one New Zealand company. However, now it is not followed - at least not in publicly presented statements. Instead, valuation changes are generally taken directly to the balance sheet, into a forest revaluation reserve, a sub-section of owners' equity. If the forest asset diminishes so much in value that the revaluation reserve is eliminated, then any further reductions in value are taken as losses on the profit and loss statement during the year in which they occur.

## Chapter 8: Budgeting Step 5 - Budgeted Balance Sheet

Southern readers will be familiar with the balance sheets as presented. It is common in New Zealand to subtract current liabilities from current assets to arrive at net current assets. The horizontal format presented in Appendix 8.1 is also common.

## Chapter 9:  Recording

New Zealand and Australian readers will know the value added tax (VAT) as the goods and services tax (GST). In either case, records need to be kept and taxes claimed or paid for goods that are bought or sold within the countries.

## Chapter 10:  Accounts - Construction

The term 'prime costs' will be unfamiliar to New Zealand readers. Otherwise, the chapter is a straightforward way to construct the accounts.

## Chapter 11:  Accounts - Analysis

Southern readers should have no problems with this section. The terms used are all common in New Zealand and Australia.

## Chapter 12:  Appraising Investments

Southern readers may know the term 'investment appraisal' as "investment evaluation" (as the author mentions) or "investment analysis".  In any case, the techniques used to determine whether or not an investment should be undertaken, are the same.

Southern readers may also know net present value (NPV) as net present worth (NPW), present net worth (PNW), or present net value (PNV). These are all different names for the result of the equation subtracting a project's discounted costs from its discounted benefits. They all mean the same thing.

The incremental returns, costs, profitability, IRR, etc. are the same as the marginal returns, costs, profitability, IRR, etc. Southern readers may be more familiar with the latter term. As the Author notes, incremental and marginal both mean the additional returns, costs, etc. that would result from undertaking the project.

## Chapter 13:  Finance

The organisational forms discussed are similar to those in New Zealand. The advantages and disadvantages are also the same. New Zealand has "special partnerships", similar to limited partnerships under English law. Special partnerships may be formed to transact business other than banking or insurance.

Special partners generally contribute specific sums of capital to the business, but beyond that contribution are not liable for debts the partnership incurs.

## Chapter 14: Taxation

Taxation in the Southern Hemisphere is different than taxation in the UK, although the general principals of taxation apply universally. It is a good thing to discuss general principals as the Author has done, because taxation specifics can change with the stroke of a legislator's pen. With changes in government administration, often come changes in tax policy and changes in the regulations affecting forestry taxation. Such changes may have significant effects on the profitability of forestry investments. For example, in New Zealand in 1983, a grants scheme subsidised forest planting. In 1984, this scheme was abolished, but growing costs were deductible in the year incurred. In 1987, government introduced a scheme whereby growing costs had to be capitalised and carried until harvest. In 1991, establishment and management costs again became deductible in the year of occurrence. That was four major policy changes in 8 years.

## Chapter 15:  Computers and Forest Accounts

Computers are as common as chainsaws and pruning shears as tools of forest managers in New Zealand and Australia. There are two additional factors, which come to mind, that a forest manager might consider.

- Portability

You can take it with you – but at a price. Laptop computers are increasingly common. Their capacity is approaching that of desktop machines. This means that you can use the same computer on your desk at work, for giving presentations, at home, and on the road. Some are even weather and knock-proof and are safe to use in the forest. The trade-offs for this flexibility are a price that is usually around double that of a comparable desktop machine, limited expansion and upgrade options, a cut-down and possibly cramped keyboard, with a finicky mouse, and a small monitor (although it is possible that an external keyboard, mouse, and monitor may be plugged into the laptop, giving the laptop the 'feel' of a desktop machine).

- Compatibility

Your computer can be used for far more than report generation and accounts management. It can also be used to assist general forest management operations. For this, there may be specialised forestry software packages that require a specific operating system. In New Zealand and Australia, such packages would commonly include a stand growth model, a geographic information systems (GIS) package to keep track of the forest areas and plan roading, planting, silviculture, and harvesting operations, and a forest simulator or optimiser to produce long-term forest management plans.

# References

Arnold, J., Hope, T. and Southward, A. (1985) *Financial Accounting* Prentice Hall, Englewood Cliffs, New Jersey.

Audsley, E. and Wheeler, J. (1978) The Annual Cost of Machinery Calculated Using Actual Cash Flows. *Journal of Agricultural Engineering Research*, 23, 189-201.

Bannock, G., Baxter, R.E. and Rees, R. (eds) (1978) *The Penguin Dictionary of Economics.* Second edition. Penguin Books.

Barnard, C.S. and Nix, J.S. (1979) *Farm Planning and Control.* Cambridge University Press, Cambridge, UK.

Brealey, R.A. and Myers, S.C. (1991) *Principles of Corporate Finance.* Fourth Edition. McGraw-Hill, New York.

Bright, G.A. (1986) The Current Economics of Machinery Leasing. *Farm Management*, 6, No. 3, 105-112.

Bright, G.A. (1992) Partial Budgeting: Inflation and Medium-Term Capital. *Farm, Management*, 8, No. 3, 141-148.

Bright, G.A. (1997) Return on Capital and Modest Inflation. *Journal of Agricultural Economics*, 48, No.3.

Bright, G. and Price, C. (2000) Valuing forest land under hazards to crop survival. *Forestry*, 73, 4, 361-370.

Chopping, D. and Skerratt, L. (1998) *Applying GAAP - A Practical Guide to Financial Reporting.* Accountancy Books.

CLUES (1997) *Budget Builder 2.1 – a computer assisted learning module for farm management.* Consortium for Courseware in Land Use and Environmental Sciences, University of Aberdeen, Aberdeen, UK.

Cunningham, S. and Turner, M.M. (1995) Actual Depreciation Rates of Farm Machinery. *Farm Management*, 6, No. 9, 381-387.

Davis, L.S. and Johnson, K.N. (1987) *Forest Management.* Third edition. McGraw-Hill, New York.

Dodge, R. (1993) *Foundations of Business Accounting.* Chapman and Hall, London.

Dunn and Bradstreet (1998) *Key Business Ratios.* Dunn and Bradstreet, High Wycombe, UK.

Duerr, W.A., Teeguarden, D.E., Christiansen, N.B. and Guttenberg, S. (1982) *Forest Resource Management: Decision-Making Principles and Cases.* O.S.U. Book Stores.

Edwards, J., Kay, J. and Mayer, C. (1987) *The Economic Analysis of Accounting Profitability.* Clarendon Press, Oxford, UK.

Elwood, N. (1998) personal communication.

Farley, S. (1993) *Depreciation and the Costing of Forest Harvesting Machinery.* BSc Dissertation, School of Agricultural and Forest Sciences, University of Wales, Bangor.

Forbes, R.D. (1976) *Woodlands For Profit and Pleasure.* American Forestry Association, Washington, DC.

Foster, B.B. and Brooks, G.N. (1983) Rates of Return: Internal or Composite. *Journal of Forestry*, 81, 669-670.

Gane, M. (1966) The Valuation of Growing Stock Changes. *Quarterly Journal of Forestry*, 60 (2), 110-120.

Glautier, M.W.E. and Underdown, B. (1986) *Accounting Theory and Practice.* Third Edition. Pitman Publishing, London.

Gregory, G.R. (1972) *Forest Resource Economics.* John Wiley & Sons, New York.

Gunter, J.E. and Haney, H.L. (1984) *Essentials of Forestry Investment Analysis.* O.S.U. Book Stores.

Haney, H.L. and Siegel, W.C. (1993) *Estate Planning for Forest Landowners.* GTR-SO-97. U.S.D.A. Forest Service. Southern Forest Experiment Station.

Hart, C. (1991) *Practical forestry for the Agent and Surveyor.* Third edition. Alan Sutton Publishing, Far Thrupp, Gloucestershire, UK.

Hill, G.P. (1984) Measuring Farm Income under Conditions of Inflation: the Gains from Borrowing. *Journal of Agricultural Economics*, 31 (1), 45-54.

Hoover, W.L. (2000) *Timber Tax Management for Tree Farmers*. FNR-80. Purdue University, Agriculture Communication Service Media Distribution Center, Lafayette, IN 47901-1232.

Hussey, R. (1995) (ed.) *Oxford Dictionary of Accounting*. Oxford University Press, Oxford, UK.

Inland Revenue Department (1994) *Depreciation Guide*. IR260. April. Wellington, New Zealand.

Investment Property Databank (1997) *IPD Forestry Index: A Technical Guide*. IPD, London.

Klemperer, W.D. (1996) *Forest Resource Economics and Finance*. McGraw-Hill, New York.

Lorraine-Smith, R. (1998) personal communication.

MAFF (1977) *Definition of Terms Used in Agricultural Business Management*. Booklet 2269 Ministry of Agriculture, Fisheries and Food, London.

Mayhead, G.J. (1990) Management Plans for Smaller Woods. *Quarterly Journal of Forestry*, 4, 313-318.

Nautiyal, J.C. (1988) *Forest Economics. Principles and Applications*. Canadian Scholars Press, Toronto.

New Zealand Institute of Forestry (1996) *Forest Valuation Guidelines*. Christchurch, New Zealand.

Openshaw, K. (1980) *Cost and Financial Accounting in Forestry*. Pergamon Press, Oxford.

Petrini, S. (1953) *Elements of Forest Economics*. Oliver and Boyd, Edinburgh.

Price, C. (1989) *The Theory and Application of Forest Economics*. Blackwell, Oxford, UK.

Price, C. (1993) *Time, Discounting and Value*. Blackwell, Oxford, UK.

Reed, W.J. (1984) The effects of the risk of fire on the optimal rotation of a forest. *Journal of Environmental Economics and Management*, 11, 180-190.

Schallau, C.H. and Wirth, M.E. (1980) Reinvestment Rate and the analysis of forestry enteprises. *Journal of Forestry*, 78, 740-742.

Scottish Woodland Owners Association (1978) *Forestry Management Accounting*. SWOA, Edinburgh.

Shukla, D.K. (1996) *Project Appraisal under Risk and Uncertainty: A Case Study of the Afforestation Project of Bihar, India*. PhD thesis. University of Wales, Bangor.

Turner, J. and Taylor, M. (1998) *Applied Farm Management*. Blackwell Science, Oxford, UK.

USDA Forest Service (1995) *Forest Owners' Guide to the Federal Income Tax*. Agriculture Handbook 708. US Department of Agriculture, Washington, DC.

Vause, B. (1997) *Guide to Analysing Companies*. Economist Books.

Warren, M.F. (1998) *Financial Management for Farmers and Rural Managers*. Fourth Edition. Blackwell Science, Oxford, UK.

Wenger, K.F. (ed.) (1984) *Forestry Handbook*. Second edition. John Wiley & Sons, New York.

Yule, I.J. (1995) Calculating Tractor Operating Costs. *Farm Management*, 9, No. 3, 133-148.

# Glossary of Terms

**Accounting**: the tabulated financial results of a business; the financial 'looking back'.

**Accounting packages**: packages of computer programs designed to carry out a range of accountancy tasks.

**Accruals**: a form of creditors, and are amounts owed by the business, but for which no invoice has yet been issued.

**Annual percentage rate** or **APR**: the true rate of interest on a loan or other finance calculated using DCF in the same way as the IRR, but as a rate paid instead of a rate earned.

**Assets**: anything of value in the possession of the business or claims on anything of value in the possession of others, or values of things **owned** by the business.

**Asset turnover ratio** (Utilisation ratio): sales ÷ net assets (or long-term capital).

**Balance sheet**: a statement of the assets and liabilities of a business at a point in time.

**Bank overdraft**: a negative bank current account balance.

**Bank term loans**: loans which are contractual arrangements with a set term and repayment schedule. They may have a fixed rate of interest or a rate which varies with the bank's base rate. They can have terms (lifetimes) of anything from three months to 20 years or more.

**Benefit:cost ratio**: like IRR and NPV, a discounted measure of profitability. It is measured as the ratio of the discounted benefits (DB) of the investment to the discounted costs (DC) and can be derived by dividing DB by DC.

**Benefits in kind** (perquisites or 'perks'): the value of produce or inputs taken by the owner for his or her personal use or given to employees.

**Brashing**: pruning

**Budget**: 'a detailed quantitative statement of a plan, or a change in a plan, and the forecast of its financial result' (Barnard and Nix, 1979). For the forest enterprise the budget is sometimes referred to as the **management scheme** which is set out in the form of a **working plan** (Hart, 1991) or **woodland management plan** (Mayhead, 1990).

**Business**: the organisation for which a separate set of accounts are provided and with the overall financial performance of which we are concerned.

**Capital cash flows**: cash flows which relate to purchases and sales of machinery, buildings and any other items which are normally depreciated, as well as receipts of loans and repayments of loan principal (the money borrowed, as opposed to the interest on the money borrowed).

**Capital gains tax**: a tax on gains made when the asset is sold or passed on to another individual.

*Ceteris paribus*: 'with other things being equal'.

**Company**: "an incorporated body recognised by law as having an existence entirely independent from that of its members and directors" (Hussey, 1995, p. 81). A company has **limited liability**.

**Co-operative**: although not a company, the co-operative is similar in certain respects: it is formed with a legally binding agreement, is a separate entity and conveys limited liability. The co-operative members contribute funds (in money or in kind), make decisions about its management and have voting powers, although each member has one vote rather than a number in proportion to their financial contribution.

**Corporation Tax**: a tax on the profits of companies or corporations.

**Cost centres**: separate production units or sections of the business to which costs and receipts can be allocated. In forestry these might be compartments and sub-compartments within forest blocks.

**Creditor payment period** (Creditor-days ratio; average credit taken): indicates the average length of time between purchases and payment of bills by the business. Measured by:

creditors ÷ purchases (trading payments) × 365 days (or × 12 months)

**Crossover discount rate**: occurs when, because of different cash flow patterns, the NPVs of the two investments cross over at a certain discount rate.

**Current assets** (short term or circulating capital): assets with lifetimes of less than one year to 18 months: cash, debtors and stocks. They can be split between **liquid assets**, and **physical working assets**.

**Current Cost Accounting**: an accounting method which is able to deal with inflation (as opposed to the normal Historic Cost Accounting).

**Current liabilities**: overdraft, short-term loans and trade creditors.

**Current ratio** = Current Assets ÷ Current Liabilities

**Database**: a program for storing, retrieving and analysing data and information in an ordered fashion.

**Debenture**: like a share, issued by a company, although it is not equity, but a form of debt. It is a type of long-term loan which, unlike shares, has to be repaid and usually obliges the company to pay a fixed rate of interest (Hussey, 1995).

**Debt profile**: shows the pattern of outstanding debt associated with a project over its lifetime. It can be measured as the closing bank balance at the end of each period.

**Debtor payment period** (Debtor collection period; average credit given): indicates the average length of time between sales and receipt from customers. Measured by: debtors ÷ sales × 365 days (or × 12 months).

**Depreciation**: an estimated cost of the loss in value of a machine, building or similar item through wear, tear and obsolescence.

**Devastation value** (actual, liquidation or stumpage value): for a stand of trees, it is the trees could be sold for as timber if they were to be felled today.

**Direct costs:** are those which are readily identified with the product and include raw materials and the wages of production workers.

**Dividends**: the profits distributed by a company to shareholders.

**Endowment mortgage** ('interest only' mortgage): a mortgage which involves only paying interest over its lifetime, but not paying back the capital or principal element until the end. In order to make this final payment, the borrower would normally take out an endowment assurance policy which would guarantee to pay off the principal should the borrower die before the end of the period, and otherwise to provide a lump sum at the end, which, hopefully will be sufficient to meet the amount owing.

**Enterprises**: those areas of the organisation which are involved in producing distinctly different products.

**Equity**: the value of shares issued, although, strictly speaking, it only refers to the value of the ordinary shares issued.

**Equivalent annual value (EAV)**: the NPV converted into an annuity or equal amount for every year of the lifetime of the investment. The formula is:

$$EAV = NPV \times \frac{(1+r)^t \times r}{(1+r)^t - 1}$$

**Equivalent annual value of an investment (EAVI)**: takes account of the initial cost and salvage value of an investment and converts this to a value occurring for each year of its life. It is measured by the formula:

$$EAVI = \left( Investment - \frac{Salvage}{(1+r)^t} \right) \times \left( \frac{(1+r)^t \times r}{(1+r)^t - 1} \right)$$

where Investment refers to the initial outlay; and Salvage means the extra benefit (or cost) at the end of the investment lifetime arising from the sale of assets involved in the project.

**Expectation value** (holding value): the value to the business today of growing a stand of trees on to maturity. For the land itself the expectation value is the value today of the stream of costs and benefits which are expected to arise from that land into perpetuity.

**Feasibility**: when referring to an investment, is the likelihood of the investment succeeding in the face of potential constraints.

**Finance**: the money to set up, run and expand the business.

**Finance lease**: like a loan to finance machinery or other assets, but it differs in that legal ownership of the assets never passes from the **lessor** (the financial institution) to the **lessee** (the borrower).

**Fixed assets**: or fixed capital. Assets tending to have lifetimes of greater than one year to 18 months.

**Fixed asset ratio**: fixed assets ÷ total assets. Shows the proportion of the assets tied up over the long term.

**Fixed costs**: costs which do not seem to vary with the size of compartment or cost centre or with the volume of production.

**Flat rate of interest**: the charging of interest, under certain forms of finance, based throughout on the initial amount borrowed. This is not equivalent to the APR.

**Gearing Ratio**: (capital gearing, debt ratio, debt:equity ratio, leverage): calculated here as:

long-term debt ÷ equity
where 'long-term debt' (loan capital) includes all liabilities which incur interest charges and which have lifetimes of more than a year or so.

**Grants and subsidies**: government or quasi-government organisations may provide grants for planting, maintenance and harvesting and, in agriculture, production subsidies may be claimed.

**Hardware**: the computer equipment: the keyboard, the screen or monitor, the mouse, and the box that contain the parts which do the work, such as the processor.

**Hire purchase (HP)**: a form of finance used for financing investment in machinery or other medium-term assets, similar to loan and leasing in many respects, but the details may be expressed in different terms and ownership does ultimately pass to the borrower.

**Historic cost accounting**: Accounts based on original values of assets without making any adjustment for inflation.

**Holding gain**: gain in value of a machine or building or similar asset occurring as a result of inflation.

**Income tax**: tax levied on incomes of individuals.

**Incremental internal rate of return (IRR)**: the break-even discount rate used to discount the extra costs and benefits arising from an investment. A more formal definition is:
"that rate of interest which, when used to discount the cash flows associated with an investment project, reduces its net present value to zero" (Bannock *et al.* 1978).

**Indicating percent**: the percentage change in net felling revenue from one year to the next (Price, 1989). A quick way of estimating the optimum rotation age is to calculate the point beyond which the indicating percentage is no longer greater than the discount rate (although the point of maximum LEV may be slightly earlier than this).

**Inflation adjusted profit (IAP)**: Profit before interest and tax with holding gain on machinery and buildings added back.

**Inheritance tax**: a tax on individuals who have received gifts from another individual at or within a few years of death of the latter.

**Internal rate of return (IRR, yield)**: in discounted cash flow, the discount rate which generates an NPV of zero. More formally defined as: "that rate of interest which, when used to discount the cash flows associated with an investment project, reduces its net present value to zero" (Bannock *et al.*, 1978).

**Investment appraisal**: the management activity involving the evaluation of alternative courses of action in which funds are invested and a stream of costs and benefits results from this.

**Land Expectation Value (LEV, soil expectation value)**: the present value of an infinite series of rotations. If all future rotations on the site are expected to be the same the formula is

$$LEV = PV \times \frac{(1 + \text{discount rate})^{\text{years}}}{(1 + \text{discount rate})^{\text{years}} - 1}$$

**Lease**: see **operating lease** and **finance lease**.

**Liabilities**: the total value of claims on the assets of a business by the various suppliers of funds to it (MAFF, 1978), or the values of things owed by the business.

**Lifetime** of an investment: the length of time for which the investment or project will last, or the period for which the effects of the investment will be felt.

**Limited liability**: exists for a company: if it is unable to pay its debts only the assets of the business can be seized; the shareholders' personal assets can not.

**Liquid assets**: cash and near cash items.

**Liquidity**: the availability of cash to the business to meet the day to day requirements.

**Liquidity Ratio** (Quick Ratio, Acid Test): measured as:

Liquidity Ratio = Liquid Assets ÷ Current Liabilities

where Liquid Assets includes only cash and debtors, although some would also include any items which are to be sold within a short period, perhaps one to two months.

**Long-term capital**: assets lasting for more than about 10 years.

**Management**: the dynamic activity of taking and carrying out decisions concerning the use of the scarce resources of land, labour and capital and the ensuing product, in the light of the objectives of the business.

**Market price** (comparable sales): the approach to the valuation of trees and land based on the price which could be expected if the complete forest enterprise was bought or sold today.

**Mortgage**: a form of long-term loan which is secured on title to land or property.

**Multiple roots**: the situation in investment appraisal in which there is more than one discount rate that makes the NPV equal to zero.

**Net current assets**: or working capital. The difference between current assets and current liabilities.

**Net present value (NPV)**: that rate of interest which, when used to discount the cash flows associated with an investment project, reduces its net present value to zero.

**Net profit ratio** (Net profit margin; net profit percentage, profitability ratio): net profit (before tax and interest) ÷ sales.

**Net realisable value (NRV)**: the amount the item could be sold for under normal trading conditions, net of selling expenses.

**Net worth**: the owner's share of the business, calculated by subtracting the value of all that is owed from the value of all that is owned. The value of the assets left over to the owners of a business after all other claims have been met.

**Nominal terms or nominal value (actual value)**: figures expressed in terms of price levels prevailing when they occur. In other words, without adjusting for, or taking out, the effects of inflation.

**On-costs**: costs which do not fit readily into direct costs, but which are nevertheless, closely associated with them particularly labour, and to some extent machinery. Slack or wet time, travel time, sickness and holiday pay, training, clothing, employers insurance contributions and machinery tax and insurance are considered as on-costs.

**Operating lease**: similar to **contract hire**, is a form of finance which covers the costs of the rental of machinery. Usually the costs of depreciation, repairs, maintenance, insurance and vehicle tax, are covered by the rental charge.

**Opportunity cost of capital**: what return or interest rate could be generated in the next best alternative use of the resource concerned.

**Optimum rotation age**: the age of maximum LEV.

**Ordinary shares**: company shares which confer the right of their holder to receive dividends, a pay-out from profits, if and when they are paid. Such shares also give voting rights.

**Output**: the value of the year's (or whatever period is being considered) production.

**Overheads**: those costs which are not directly related to the production activities of the business and cannot be allocated directly to cost centres.

**Overtrading**: a situation occurring when a business expands too fast, acquiring fixed assets, but not leaving sufficient liquid assets to spare.

**Partnership**: similar form of business organisation to the **sole trader** except that the business will have more than one owner. It is a legal entity and the partners will often share benefits in proportion to their financial contribution.

**Payback period**: the minimum length of time taken by an investment to generate sufficient funds to pay back the money borrowed.

**Percent Equity** = Equity ÷ Total Assets × 100%

**Personal cash flows**: in a sole trader or partnership situation, money taken out of the business for their owners' personal use or for paying tax on their personal income (income tax as opposed to company or corporation tax).

**Physical outline plan:** a plan of what is proposed for a specified period in terms of objectives and what and how much will be produced and what resources will be used.

**Physical working capital** (physical working assets): inputs, finished or harvested produce and work in progress which will be used up or sold within one year to 18 months.

**Plan of operations**: outline plan of what activities we aim to carry out over the short to medium term.

**Post-tax discount rate**: the discount rate adjusted for tax effects on interest. The formula, taking account of tax lags, is:

$$r^* = r \times (1 - \frac{t}{(1+r^*)^g})$$

where: r* is the lagged post-tax discount rate; r is the pre-tax discount rate; t is the tax rate; and g is the length of lag.

**Preference shares**: confer a right to receipt of dividends before ordinary shareholders, but do not give voting rights.

**Prepayments**: special kinds of debtors, referring to payments which have been made in advance of receipt of the good or service.

**Present Value (PV)**: the value of an asset based on the discounted stream of future costs and returns arising from its use.

**Private company**: a limited company with a limit to the number of shareholders it may have (in the UK the maximum is 50) and not allowed to appeal for funds on the stock exchange.

**Production forecast**: a forecast of volumes of timber to be produced over a number of years (20 years is common).

**Production levies**: are taxes on production, such as royalties payable for logging concessions.

**Profitability**: the measure of the financial worthwhileness of doing business over a period.

**Public company** (public limited company or plc): a limited company unlimited in the number of shares and shareholders and allowed to appeal for funds in the market known as the stock exchange.

**Real terms or real values**: figures expressed in terms of (constant) prices at one particular point in time, ie having adjusted for, or taken out, the effects of inflation.

**Repayment mortgage**: a mortgage, the payments of which will meet the full cost of principal (the amount borrowed) and interest by the end of the term.

**Replacement cost (RC)**: the current cost if the asset were to be replaced.

**Return on Capital Employed (ROCE)**:

Profit before interest and tax ÷ Opening Net Assets × 100%
where Net Assets = Total Assets - Current Liabilities
Other terms: return on assets (ROA), the primary ratio, accounting rate of return (ARR), accounting rate of profit (ARP), return on all capital (ROAC), return on investment and return on net assets mean more or less the same thing.

**Return on Equity (ROE**, return on owners' capital employed, shareholders' return and return on own capital): profit before tax, but not before interest, divided by 'equity' (total assets minus total liabilities) at the start of the accounting period.

**Sales**: the value of all produce, both major and subsidiary items.

**Sales and purchase taxes**: taxes, duties and levies which may be charged on items sold or inputs purchased (or both in the case of value added tax).

**Salvage value**: the extra benefit (or cost) at the end of the investment lifetime arising from the sale of the assets involved in the project.

**Sensitivity analysis**: measures how sensitive our financial projections are to changes in some of the variables. To assess sensitivity we simply need to vary different elements, financial and technical, *one at a time*, and measure the degree of change in the NPV, IRR or whatever profitability measure we are using.

**Shares**: entitlements issued when a company or corporation is set up or seeks further funds from those who have contributed the finance necessary for its establishment. They entitle the owner to a proportion of distributed profits and of the residual value if the company is liquidated (Bannock *et al.*, 1978).

**Software**: the programs and packages of programs which run on computers. The collection of software which runs the computers and determines what goes on the screen is known as the **operating system**. The types of software for typing letters and reports, for storing, retrieving and analysing data, for producing lectures and presentations, for teaching, and for many other purposes are known as **desktop applications**.

**Sole trader**: an unincorporated business owned by the proprietor alone. Such a business is not a company (Hussey, 1995) so the business is not deemed a separate entity from its owner and it does not have **limited liability**.

**Solvency Ratio** = Total Assets ÷ Total Liabilities

**Spreadsheets**: computer programs which are particularly useful for carrying out calculations and showing them in a 'transparent' way. Spreadsheets effectively provide a sheet, divided into boxes or pigeon holes and in these 'cells', text, numbers and calculations can be inserted.

**Stability**: the ability of the business to remain viable in the long term

**Standard costs**: published costs based on industry averages.

**Stock turnover period** (Stock turnover cycle, stock holding period): indicates the average length of time that stocks are on the premises before being sold as produce. Calculated by:

stock ÷ cost of sales × 365 days (or × 12 months)

It can indicate if stocks are being kept at too high a level, although for forestry the length of the production cycle may dictate a lengthy period. If the reciprocal is used this is termed **stock** or **inventory turnover** and is expressed as so many 'times', rather than 'days' or 'months'.

**Strategic objectives**: objectives for the whole business or organisation.

**Tactical objectives**: objectives relating to the daily, routine activities

**Tax lag**: the time delay between when profits are generated and when the resulting tax is paid.

**Terminal value**: the amount of money which would be built up in the bank by the end of the lifetime of an investment if all costs were paid from, and all revenues were paid into, the bank account.

**Times interest covered** (income gearing; interest cover ratio): similar to gearing, in that it shows how comfortably the profits of the business cover the interest charges. Calculated by:

profit (before tax and interest) ÷ interest (may include leasing and loan repayments)

Banks sometimes used related measures such as finance charges (rent and interest) ÷ gross output (sales).

**Total real return on capital (TRROC)**:

$$\text{TRROC} = \frac{(\text{TROC} - \text{f})}{1 + \text{f}}$$

where f = the general rate of inflation, expressed as a decimal.

**Total return on capital (TROC)**: Inflation adjusted profit divided by total asssets.

**Trade credit**: a liability which arises when the business purchases material inputs, but does not pay for them immediately.

**Trade creditors** (accounts payable): amounts owed by the business to other organisations or individuals.

**Trade debtors** (accounts receivable): amounts owed to the business by other organisations or individuals.

**Trading cash flows**: not very helpfully defined as 'those cash flows of a trading nature'; i.e. those cash flows which relate to the production and selling activities of the business (as well as the costs of securing the finance borrowed to run the business), which encompasses most items.

**Transfers**: value of goods and services moved between cost centres.

**Unlimited liability**: exists for an unincorporated business (**sole trader** or **partnership**): if it is unable to pay its debts, legal action may be taken to seize the owners' personal assets as well as the assets of the business.

**Variable costs**: costs which vary with size or volume.

**Wealth tax**: a tax levied on the *net worth* of the individual.

**Word processing package**: a set of computer programs used for writing letters and documents.

**World-Wide Web (www)**: the 'web' consists of millions of computers linked by communications systems, such as telephone lines, which allows users across the globe to browse through the information offered by millions of web site owners.

# Discount Tables

| time | 1% | 2% | 3% | 4% | 5% | 6% | 7% | 8% | 9% |
|---|---|---|---|---|---|---|---|---|---|
| | \multicolumn{9}{l}{discount rate} |
| 1 | 0.990 | 0.980 | 0.971 | 0.962 | 0.952 | 0.943 | 0.935 | 0.926 | 0.917 |
| 2 | 0.980 | 0.961 | 0.943 | 0.925 | 0.907 | 0.890 | 0.873 | 0.857 | 0.842 |
| 3 | 0.971 | 0.942 | 0.915 | 0.889 | 0.864 | 0.840 | 0.816 | 0.794 | 0.772 |
| 4 | 0.961 | 0.924 | 0.888 | 0.855 | 0.823 | 0.792 | 0.763 | 0.735 | 0.708 |
| 5 | 0.951 | 0.906 | 0.863 | 0.822 | 0.784 | 0.747 | 0.713 | 0.681 | 0.650 |
| 6 | 0.942 | 0.888 | 0.837 | 0.790 | 0.746 | 0.705 | 0.666 | 0.630 | 0.596 |
| 7 | 0.933 | 0.871 | 0.813 | 0.760 | 0.711 | 0.665 | 0.623 | 0.583 | 0.547 |
| 8 | 0.923 | 0.853 | 0.789 | 0.731 | 0.677 | 0.627 | 0.582 | 0.540 | 0.502 |
| 9 | 0.914 | 0.837 | 0.766 | 0.703 | 0.645 | 0.592 | 0.544 | 0.500 | 0.460 |
| 10 | 0.905 | 0.820 | 0.744 | 0.676 | 0.614 | 0.558 | 0.508 | 0.463 | 0.422 |
| 11 | 0.896 | 0.804 | 0.722 | 0.650 | 0.585 | 0.527 | 0.475 | 0.429 | 0.388 |
| 12 | 0.887 | 0.788 | 0.701 | 0.625 | 0.557 | 0.497 | 0.444 | 0.397 | 0.356 |
| 13 | 0.879 | 0.773 | 0.681 | 0.601 | 0.530 | 0.469 | 0.415 | 0.368 | 0.326 |
| 14 | 0.870 | 0.758 | 0.661 | 0.577 | 0.505 | 0.442 | 0.388 | 0.340 | 0.299 |
| 15 | 0.861 | 0.743 | 0.642 | 0.555 | 0.481 | 0.417 | 0.362 | 0.315 | 0.275 |
| 16 | 0.853 | 0.728 | 0.623 | 0.534 | 0.458 | 0.394 | 0.339 | 0.292 | 0.252 |
| 17 | 0.844 | 0.714 | 0.605 | 0.513 | 0.436 | 0.371 | 0.317 | 0.270 | 0.231 |
| 18 | 0.836 | 0.700 | 0.587 | 0.494 | 0.416 | 0.350 | 0.296 | 0.250 | 0.212 |
| 19 | 0.828 | 0.686 | 0.570 | 0.475 | 0.396 | 0.331 | 0.277 | 0.232 | 0.194 |
| 20 | 0.820 | 0.673 | 0.554 | 0.456 | 0.377 | 0.312 | 0.258 | 0.215 | 0.178 |
| 21 | 0.811 | 0.660 | 0.538 | 0.439 | 0.359 | 0.294 | 0.242 | 0.199 | 0.164 |
| 22 | 0.803 | 0.647 | 0.522 | 0.422 | 0.342 | 0.278 | 0.226 | 0.184 | 0.150 |
| 23 | 0.795 | 0.634 | 0.507 | 0.406 | 0.326 | 0.262 | 0.211 | 0.170 | 0.138 |
| 24 | 0.788 | 0.622 | 0.492 | 0.390 | 0.310 | 0.247 | 0.197 | 0.158 | 0.126 |
| 25 | 0.780 | 0.610 | 0.478 | 0.375 | 0.295 | 0.233 | 0.184 | 0.146 | 0.116 |
| 26 | 0.772 | 0.598 | 0.464 | 0.361 | 0.281 | 0.220 | 0.172 | 0.135 | 0.106 |
| 27 | 0.764 | 0.586 | 0.450 | 0.347 | 0.268 | 0.207 | 0.161 | 0.125 | 0.098 |
| 28 | 0.757 | 0.574 | 0.437 | 0.333 | 0.255 | 0.196 | 0.150 | 0.116 | 0.090 |
| 29 | 0.749 | 0.563 | 0.424 | 0.321 | 0.243 | 0.185 | 0.141 | 0.107 | 0.082 |
| 30 | 0.742 | 0.552 | 0.412 | 0.308 | 0.231 | 0.174 | 0.131 | 0.099 | 0.075 |
| 31 | 0.735 | 0.541 | 0.400 | 0.296 | 0.220 | 0.164 | 0.123 | 0.092 | 0.069 |
| 32 | 0.727 | 0.531 | 0.388 | 0.285 | 0.210 | 0.155 | 0.115 | 0.085 | 0.063 |
| 33 | 0.720 | 0.520 | 0.377 | 0.274 | 0.200 | 0.146 | 0.107 | 0.079 | 0.058 |
| 34 | 0.713 | 0.510 | 0.366 | 0.264 | 0.190 | 0.138 | 0.100 | 0.073 | 0.053 |
| 35 | 0.706 | 0.500 | 0.355 | 0.253 | 0.181 | 0.130 | 0.094 | 0.068 | 0.049 |
| 36 | 0.699 | 0.490 | 0.345 | 0.244 | 0.173 | 0.123 | 0.088 | 0.063 | 0.045 |
| 37 | 0.692 | 0.481 | 0.335 | 0.234 | 0.164 | 0.116 | 0.082 | 0.058 | 0.041 |

| time | discount rate | | | | | | | | |
|---|---|---|---|---|---|---|---|---|---|
| | 1% | 2% | 3% | 4% | 5% | 6% | 7% | 8% | 9% |
| 38 | 0.685 | 0.471 | 0.325 | 0.225 | 0.157 | 0.109 | 0.076 | 0.054 | 0.038 |
| 39 | 0.678 | 0.462 | 0.316 | 0.217 | 0.149 | 0.103 | 0.071 | 0.050 | 0.035 |
| 40 | 0.672 | 0.453 | 0.307 | 0.208 | 0.142 | 0.097 | 0.067 | 0.046 | 0.032 |
| 41 | 0.665 | 0.444 | 0.298 | 0.200 | 0.135 | 0.092 | 0.062 | 0.043 | 0.029 |
| 42 | 0.658 | 0.435 | 0.289 | 0.193 | 0.129 | 0.087 | 0.058 | 0.039 | 0.027 |
| 43 | 0.652 | 0.427 | 0.281 | 0.185 | 0.123 | 0.082 | 0.055 | 0.037 | 0.025 |
| 44 | 0.645 | 0.418 | 0.272 | 0.178 | 0.117 | 0.077 | 0.051 | 0.034 | 0.023 |
| 45 | 0.639 | 0.410 | 0.264 | 0.171 | 0.111 | 0.073 | 0.048 | 0.031 | 0.021 |
| 46 | 0.633 | 0.402 | 0.257 | 0.165 | 0.106 | 0.069 | 0.044 | 0.029 | 0.019 |
| 47 | 0.626 | 0.394 | 0.249 | 0.158 | 0.101 | 0.065 | 0.042 | 0.027 | 0.017 |
| 48 | 0.620 | 0.387 | 0.242 | 0.152 | 0.096 | 0.061 | 0.039 | 0.025 | 0.016 |
| 49 | 0.614 | 0.379 | 0.235 | 0.146 | 0.092 | 0.058 | 0.036 | 0.023 | 0.015 |
| 50 | 0.608 | 0.372 | 0.228 | 0.141 | 0.087 | 0.054 | 0.034 | 0.021 | 0.013 |
| 51 | 0.602 | 0.364 | 0.221 | 0.135 | 0.083 | 0.051 | 0.032 | 0.020 | 0.012 |
| 52 | 0.596 | 0.357 | 0.215 | 0.130 | 0.079 | 0.048 | 0.030 | 0.018 | 0.011 |
| 53 | 0.590 | 0.350 | 0.209 | 0.125 | 0.075 | 0.046 | 0.028 | 0.017 | 0.010 |
| 54 | 0.584 | 0.343 | 0.203 | 0.120 | 0.072 | 0.043 | 0.026 | 0.016 | 0.010 |
| 55 | 0.579 | 0.337 | 0.197 | 0.116 | 0.068 | 0.041 | 0.024 | 0.015 | 0.009 |
| 56 | 0.573 | 0.330 | 0.191 | 0.111 | 0.065 | 0.038 | 0.023 | 0.013 | 0.008 |
| 57 | 0.567 | 0.323 | 0.185 | 0.107 | 0.062 | 0.036 | 0.021 | 0.012 | 0.007 |
| 58 | 0.562 | 0.317 | 0.180 | 0.103 | 0.059 | 0.034 | 0.020 | 0.012 | 0.007 |
| 59 | 0.556 | 0.311 | 0.175 | 0.099 | 0.056 | 0.032 | 0.018 | 0.011 | 0.006 |
| 60 | 0.550 | 0.305 | 0.170 | 0.095 | 0.054 | 0.030 | 0.017 | 0.010 | 0.006 |
| 70 | 0.498 | 0.250 | 0.126 | 0.064 | 0.033 | 0.017 | 0.009 | 0.005 | 0.002 |
| 80 | 0.451 | 0.205 | 0.094 | 0.043 | 0.020 | 0.009 | 0.004 | 0.002 | 0.001 |
| 90 | 0.408 | 0.168 | 0.070 | 0.029 | 0.012 | 0.005 | 0.002 | 0.001 | 0.000 |
| 100 | 0.370 | 0.138 | 0.052 | 0.020 | 0.008 | 0.003 | 0.001 | 0.000 | 0.000 |
| 120 | 0.303 | 0.093 | 0.029 | 0.009 | 0.003 | 0.001 | 0.000 | 0.000 | 0.000 |
| 150 | 0.225 | 0.051 | 0.012 | 0.003 | 0.001 | 0.000 | 0.000 | 0.000 | 0.000 |

| time | discount rate | | | | | | | |
|------|-------|-------|-------|-------|-------|-------|-------|-------|
|      | 10%   | 12%   | 15%   | 20%   | 25%   | 30%   | 40%   | 50%   |
| 1    | 0.909 | 0.893 | 0.870 | 0.833 | 0.800 | 0.769 | 0.714 | 0.667 |
| 2    | 0.826 | 0.797 | 0.756 | 0.694 | 0.640 | 0.592 | 0.510 | 0.444 |
| 3    | 0.751 | 0.712 | 0.658 | 0.579 | 0.512 | 0.455 | 0.364 | 0.296 |
| 4    | 0.683 | 0.636 | 0.572 | 0.482 | 0.410 | 0.350 | 0.260 | 0.198 |
| 5    | 0.621 | 0.567 | 0.497 | 0.402 | 0.328 | 0.269 | 0.186 | 0.132 |
| 6    | 0.564 | 0.507 | 0.432 | 0.335 | 0.262 | 0.207 | 0.133 | 0.088 |
| 7    | 0.513 | 0.452 | 0.376 | 0.279 | 0.210 | 0.159 | 0.095 | 0.059 |
| 8    | 0.467 | 0.404 | 0.327 | 0.233 | 0.168 | 0.123 | 0.068 | 0.039 |
| 9    | 0.424 | 0.361 | 0.284 | 0.194 | 0.134 | 0.094 | 0.048 | 0.026 |
| 10   | 0.386 | 0.322 | 0.247 | 0.162 | 0.107 | 0.073 | 0.035 | 0.017 |
| 11   | 0.350 | 0.287 | 0.215 | 0.135 | 0.086 | 0.056 | 0.025 | 0.012 |
| 12   | 0.319 | 0.257 | 0.187 | 0.112 | 0.069 | 0.043 | 0.018 | 0.008 |
| 13   | 0.290 | 0.229 | 0.163 | 0.093 | 0.055 | 0.033 | 0.013 | 0.005 |
| 14   | 0.263 | 0.205 | 0.141 | 0.078 | 0.044 | 0.025 | 0.009 | 0.003 |
| 15   | 0.239 | 0.183 | 0.123 | 0.065 | 0.035 | 0.020 | 0.006 | 0.002 |
| 16   | 0.218 | 0.163 | 0.107 | 0.054 | 0.028 | 0.015 | 0.005 | 0.002 |
| 17   | 0.198 | 0.146 | 0.093 | 0.045 | 0.023 | 0.012 | 0.003 | 0.001 |
| 18   | 0.180 | 0.130 | 0.081 | 0.038 | 0.018 | 0.009 | 0.002 | 0.001 |
| 19   | 0.164 | 0.116 | 0.070 | 0.031 | 0.014 | 0.007 | 0.002 | 0.000 |
| 20   | 0.149 | 0.104 | 0.061 | 0.026 | 0.012 | 0.005 | 0.001 | 0.000 |
| 21   | 0.135 | 0.093 | 0.053 | 0.022 | 0.009 | 0.004 | 0.001 | 0.000 |
| 22   | 0.123 | 0.083 | 0.046 | 0.018 | 0.007 | 0.003 | 0.001 | 0.000 |
| 23   | 0.112 | 0.074 | 0.040 | 0.015 | 0.006 | 0.002 | 0.000 | 0.000 |
| 24   | 0.102 | 0.066 | 0.035 | 0.013 | 0.005 | 0.002 | 0.000 | 0.000 |
| 25   | 0.092 | 0.059 | 0.030 | 0.010 | 0.004 | 0.001 | 0.000 | 0.000 |
| 26   | 0.084 | 0.053 | 0.026 | 0.009 | 0.003 | 0.001 | 0.000 | 0.000 |
| 27   | 0.076 | 0.047 | 0.023 | 0.007 | 0.002 | 0.001 | 0.000 | 0.000 |
| 28   | 0.069 | 0.042 | 0.020 | 0.006 | 0.002 | 0.001 | 0.000 | 0.000 |
| 29   | 0.063 | 0.037 | 0.017 | 0.005 | 0.002 | 0.000 | 0.000 | 0.000 |
| 30   | 0.057 | 0.033 | 0.015 | 0.004 | 0.001 | 0.000 | 0.000 | 0.000 |
| 31   | 0.052 | 0.030 | 0.013 | 0.004 | 0.001 | 0.000 | 0.000 | 0.000 |
| 32   | 0.047 | 0.027 | 0.011 | 0.003 | 0.001 | 0.000 | 0.000 | 0.000 |
| 33   | 0.043 | 0.024 | 0.010 | 0.002 | 0.001 | 0.000 | 0.000 | 0.000 |
| 34   | 0.039 | 0.021 | 0.009 | 0.002 | 0.001 | 0.000 | 0.000 | 0.000 |
| 35   | 0.036 | 0.019 | 0.008 | 0.002 | 0.000 | 0.000 | 0.000 | 0.000 |
| 36   | 0.032 | 0.017 | 0.007 | 0.001 | 0.000 | 0.000 | 0.000 | 0.000 |
| 37   | 0.029 | 0.015 | 0.006 | 0.001 | 0.000 | 0.000 | 0.000 | 0.000 |

| time | discount rate | | | | | | | |
|---|---|---|---|---|---|---|---|---|
| | 10% | 12% | 15% | 20% | 25% | 30% | 40% | 50% |
| 38 | 0.027 | 0.013 | 0.005 | 0.001 | 0.000 | 0.000 | 0.000 | 0.000 |
| 39 | 0.024 | 0.012 | 0.004 | 0.001 | 0.000 | 0.000 | 0.000 | 0.000 |
| 40 | 0.022 | 0.011 | 0.004 | 0.001 | 0.000 | 0.000 | 0.000 | 0.000 |
| 41 | 0.020 | 0.010 | 0.003 | 0.001 | 0.000 | 0.000 | 0.000 | 0.000 |
| 42 | 0.018 | 0.009 | 0.003 | 0.000 | 0.000 | 0.000 | 0.000 | 0.000 |
| 43 | 0.017 | 0.008 | 0.002 | 0.000 | 0.000 | 0.000 | 0.000 | 0.000 |
| 44 | 0.015 | 0.007 | 0.002 | 0.000 | 0.000 | 0.000 | 0.000 | 0.000 |
| 45 | 0.014 | 0.006 | 0.002 | 0.000 | 0.000 | 0.000 | 0.000 | 0.000 |
| 46 | 0.012 | 0.005 | 0.002 | 0.000 | 0.000 | 0.000 | 0.000 | 0.000 |
| 47 | 0.011 | 0.005 | 0.001 | 0.000 | 0.000 | 0.000 | 0.000 | 0.000 |
| 48 | 0.010 | 0.004 | 0.001 | 0.000 | 0.000 | 0.000 | 0.000 | 0.000 |
| 49 | 0.009 | 0.004 | 0.001 | 0.000 | 0.000 | 0.000 | 0.000 | 0.000 |
| 50 | 0.009 | 0.003 | 0.001 | 0.000 | 0.000 | 0.000 | 0.000 | 0.000 |
| 51 | 0.008 | 0.003 | 0.001 | 0.000 | 0.000 | 0.000 | 0.000 | 0.000 |
| 52 | 0.007 | 0.003 | 0.001 | 0.000 | 0.000 | 0.000 | 0.000 | 0.000 |
| 53 | 0.006 | 0.002 | 0.001 | 0.000 | 0.000 | 0.000 | 0.000 | 0.000 |
| 54 | 0.006 | 0.002 | 0.001 | 0.000 | 0.000 | 0.000 | 0.000 | 0.000 |
| 55 | 0.005 | 0.002 | 0.000 | 0.000 | 0.000 | 0.000 | 0.000 | 0.000 |
| 56 | 0.005 | 0.002 | 0.000 | 0.000 | 0.000 | 0.000 | 0.000 | 0.000 |
| 57 | 0.004 | 0.002 | 0.000 | 0.000 | 0.000 | 0.000 | 0.000 | 0.000 |
| 58 | 0.004 | 0.001 | 0.000 | 0.000 | 0.000 | 0.000 | 0.000 | 0.000 |
| 59 | 0.004 | 0.001 | 0.000 | 0.000 | 0.000 | 0.000 | 0.000 | 0.000 |
| 60 | 0.003 | 0.001 | 0.000 | 0.000 | 0.000 | 0.000 | 0.000 | 0.000 |
| 70 | 0.001 | 0.000 | 0.000 | 0.000 | 0.000 | 0.000 | 0.000 | 0.000 |
| 80 | 0.000 | 0.000 | 0.000 | 0.000 | 0.000 | 0.000 | 0.000 | 0.000 |
| 90 | 0.000 | 0.000 | 0.000 | 0.000 | 0.000 | 0.000 | 0.000 | 0.000 |
| 100 | 0.000 | 0.000 | 0.000 | 0.000 | 0.000 | 0.000 | 0.000 | 0.000 |
| 120 | 0.000 | 0.000 | 0.000 | 0.000 | 0.000 | 0.000 | 0.000 | 0.000 |
| 150 | 0.000 | 0.000 | 0.000 | 0.000 | 0.000 | 0.000 | 0.000 | 0.000 |

Note: formula is

$$\frac{1}{(1 + r)^n}$$

where r is interest rate (expressed as decimal) and n is number of years.

# Index

Figures are noted in *italic* and tables in *bold* type